It was the
next morning
that it happened.
Katie woke up
at the sound
of voices
in the kitchen.
Daddy yelled,
and that scared
Katie.
Daddy never
yelled! . . .

Daddy jumped up
from the table
and ran outside.
"Dad!"
Brother called.

Daddy turned and
then trudged on
across the flat
without ever
looking back.

Katie

by
Margaret
Graham

LIVING BOOKS
Tyndale House
Publishers, Inc.
Wheaton, Illinois

First printing, September 1981.

Library of Congress Catalog Card Number 81-51465
ISBN 0-8423-2028-8, Living Books edition
Copyright © 1981 by Margaret Graham
All rights reserved.
Printed in the United States of America.

*To my brothers
and sisters,
who excel in
courage,
compassion,
    and
perseverance.*

CONTENTS

Introduction   9

The Early Years

1 *Twenty-nine   17*
2 *The Old
   Elmira Inn   22*
3 *Katie's Dream   39*
4 *The Carnival   51*

Bull Creek, Part I

5 *Let Me Call You
   Sweetheart   63*
6 *The Auction   75*
7 *Red Ants!   94*
8 *Maas's Map   105*
9 *Witch!   117*
10 *Daddy Never
   Sang Anymore   128*

Bull Creek, Part II

11 *The Norther   139*
12 *The Escapee   151*
13 *The Way to
   Be Brave   161*
14 *Mama's Dream   173*
15 *Johnson Hollow
   Treasure   190*
16 *The Feud Erupts   200*
17 *The Play Party   219*

Back in Carolina

18 *Nora*   233
19 *Sweet As Pie*   244
20 *The Tiff
   with Ethel*   258
21 *He Touched Me!*   274
22 *Sadie Allen,
   Resurrected*   288
23 *Archer Seeks
   His Fortune*   310

New York City

24 *Chris, Tony,
   and David*   329
25 *Moling in
   Manhattan*   346
26 *Brahms and
   Lilacs*   366
27 *Myths Must Die*   376

INTRODUCTION

Katie could not remember much about the morning that her father smashed his plate on the floor and left home for good.

They had been living in Texas, in a three-room house out from Austin. The place was across Bull Creek from Cat Mountain on a plateau the Texans call a flat. Katie and her younger brother, Timothy, were sick with measles that February day, lying in one bed in the middle room.

The rest of the family—their mother, Becky; the oldest child, Brother; the twins, Alice and Jane; Archer; and their father, Malcolm—all were at the breakfast table in the kitchen.

It was some time later that they told Katie about the day their Daddy left—later, when she was older than going on nine. They talked about it in front of her when they thought she was old enough to hear. It was frozen in their memories, like the last frame of a moving picture show, and they told the story over and over again, with little change in the words and with the same long pauses as their minds turned over every detail.

Katie could tell they were searching the past like detectives, looking for a clue, something that would explain what Daddy had done.

Every time they spoke of it, Becky MacLeod would punctuate the conversation with the declaration, "Your father would never desert his children." Katie took comfort in that.

Malcolm MacLeod was not a mean man. Katie never remembered him raising his voice or being angry. And he was the handsomest man she ever saw—tall, well-dressed, and well-mannered. Even in the Depression, which in 1933 had brought him down to rock bottom, he dressed in a pin-striped suit and wore a Stetson hat when he drove into town to his real estate office.

Getting to town wasn't easy. Often the old Cadillac wouldn't start. Even if the tires weren't flat, something was usually wrong with it. Often, it was stuck at the bottom of the hill, unable to make the steep climb up to the house. But Brother and Mama always got it going. Mama could do anything.

One morning when the car wouldn't start, Brother and Mama had gone down to Bull Creek to coax it out of the mud where it had stalled fording the creek. Mama was determined that the children would get to school.

Katie was standing in the doorway beside Daddy, looking across the flat, listening for the sound of the motor, when she heard Daddy mutter under his breath, "Witch." The word came out like a hiss, and Katie couldn't move she was so stunned.

On the way to school Katie was very quiet. There was a lump in her throat, and if she was not careful, tears would spill down her cheeks. The car roared through the wide creek, casting up water on both sides. Pulling out of the creek, the motor sputtered, revived, and bumped over the cattle guard onto the paved road.

Katie was sitting on the front seat between Daddy and Brother, who was a freshman at the university; the girls and Archer were in the back seat. Why would

Daddy call Mama a witch? In all fairness, maybe it had something to do with the fact that he slept late and Mama got up early. Mama was always "pitcher-pumping" him, to use her own words, about getting them to school on time. Daddy wanted to stay home and look for the treasure, although he didn't say so. Perhaps Mama should understand that since Daddy wasn't selling any real estate, it must be hard for him to get up, take them to school, then spend the whole day in his office waiting to bring them home again. As much as Katie hated to admit it, there were times when Mama seemed to want her own way.

Like when they were planning to move to Bull Creek; Katie remembered them talking about it. Daddy had acres and acres of property out there to divide into lots and sell. The property was poor ranch land full of cacti and cedar, with steep bluffs overlooking the creek and the Colorado River. The place sounded exciting to Katie and Archer.

Brother, who was eighteen and the oldest, had spent several weeks with the woodcutters living in tents on the land, and he told Katie and Archer wild stories about rattlesnakes as big as his leg and coyotes prowling about at night—how he hit a coyote with a hammer through the canvas.

Daddy said he had great plans for promoting Bull Creek as resort property and wanted to move the family there while the land was being cleared. Best of all, he wanted them to live in tents. Mama right away said no, that he would have to build them a house. Archer, who was three years older than Katie, stuck out his lips, pouting. That amused Mama, and she put her arms around him and petted him as she always did.

Daddy built the house, but there was no stove, and Mama didn't like that. "Malcolm, I don't see how I can make do with a cook tent and open fire," she said.

She did, of course, and cooked three meals a day for all of them and the men who were clearing the land.

But even Daddy seemed disappointed when they

11

drew water from the artesian well on the flat and the bucket came up with dead horned toads in it. That meant they couldn't drink from the well and would have to haul water from a spring at the foot of the cliff nearly a mile away. Going to the spring was Katie's greatest joy, what with the steep cliff to descend and climb up again, the cool shade of the cottonwoods along the creek bank, and the clear cold water of the spring.

The house Daddy had built was made of stained pine, three rooms in a row, a door at either end on the front side, and screen wire all the way around. That is, there were boards as high as Daddy's waist and screens from there to the roof. Long eaves protected the openings from rain which seldom fell.

"It's only for the summer," Daddy said, but Katie wished it would be forever. There had never been a more beautiful house.

"Where's the bathroom?" Alice wanted to know.

"Well, you use the woods," Daddy said.

The twins were horrified. "The *woods*?"

They didn't like the idea because they were very prissy. Katie didn't mind at all; having no bathroom was more like camping out.

"The girls will go back there," Daddy said, pointing back of the house. "And the boys will go over there." He pointed to his right. "Your mother will show you what to do."

Alice and Jane groaned.

"It's only for the summer," he repeated patiently.

"And, Daddy, there are no curtains to the screens," Alice complained. "People can see in."

Daddy laughed. "You needn't worry about that. The nearest neighbor is across the creek, miles away."

Mama didn't laugh. "I'll make curtains, Alice," she said, and she did. She made them out of sea island cotton with a needle and thread, curtains that hung on cords and went all the way around the house.

Even after Daddy had left home, Katie loved Bull Creek passionately. Brother called it a "God-forsaken place." More than once he said, "How could he leave us in such a God-forsaken place!"

"Shhh," Mama scolded. "He hasn't *left* us. Your father is looking for work."

As much as she loved Brother, Katie didn't like his calling Bull Creek "God-forsaken." From the first day she saw the flat—that broad expanse dancing with Mexican Hat flowers and grasshoppers bounding, singing as they sprang—she knew she was where she belonged. After Daddy was gone and the heaviness in her heart was more than she could bear, Katie clung to the flat, afraid ever to leave it in case he should return and find them gone. During the long nights when the moon over Cat Mountain made the road which stretched around it as bright as day, when she watched for the headlights of a car to round Lookout Point, when she listened for a motor to sound in the distance, praying to God her father would come home, Katie never wanted to leave the flat above Bull Creek.

THE EARLY YEARS

ONE
Twenty-nine

There were times when Katie thought of Aunt Ethel and Uncle Helmut back east in Charlotte, and she wished their funny little Studebaker would come around Lookout Point. It had been two years since Katie's family had lived in North Carolina, but she often thought of Aunt Ethel's pretty little stone house and the flowers she and her husband sold from their greenhouse. Katie was Aunt Ethel's favorite. That's why Katie had more clothes than Alice and Jane: Aunt Ethel sent her dresses.

The big rock and shingle house where Katie's family had lived in Charlotte was on the same street as Aunt Ethel's. The MacLeods called their Charlotte house "Twenty-nine" because that was its number on Laurel Lane.

The twins, who were five years older than Katie, were really responsible for getting Aunt Ethel and Uncle Helmut together—he a widower and she, Mama's single sister. When Daddy sold the house to the old gentleman, Mr. Helmut Schneider, he promised to get Helmut a wife. Alice and Jane took care of the details. On several occasions the two of them visited Mr. Schneider and told him their Aunt Ethel would be pleased to see him in the evening; then they informed Aunt Ethel that Mr. Schneider was coming to pay her a visit. A courtship was launched. In time Mr. Schneider asked Aunt Ethel to marry him. The wedding was in the parlor at Twenty-nine, and the twins served as flower girls, scattering rose petals before the bride.

Katie was a baby when they moved to Charlotte from South Carolina in 1924, but there was not much she did not remember about Twenty-nine. It was a spooky place, especially after ghost stories. A staircase ran cross-wise the house and at the top was a long hall leading to the bathroom where the light was. When Katie was the youngest child (before Timothy was born), her brothers and sisters would persuade her to climb the stairs first and turn on the light that dispelled all fears. Even Brother, who was eleven years older than Katie, would stand at the foot of the stairs and encourage her by saying, "Katie is the brave one. She isn't afraid to go upstairs and turn on the light for us."

Trembling from head to toe, Katie would ease up the dark stairs where, at times, a mouse had been spied scurrying about one of the top steps. She would race down the hall past all the scary doors, jump up on the commode and pull the string that flooded the hall with light. When she couldn't find the string she would almost panic. There was also the time when the lid was up and she jumped right in the water.

Twenty-nine saw a steady flow of aunts and uncles, Daddy's brothers and sisters, going to college or working for Daddy. Grandmother and Granddaddy MacLeod lived across town. They followed Daddy to Charlotte when he moved from South Carolina. Grandmother MacLeod was a tall lady who had an important way of talking as she looked over her pince-nez glasses. Granddaddy MacLeod looked like a spider. He made everybody laugh and was quite friendly, but he never seemed to remember Katie's name. Mama said he was a lawyer.

Daddy was happiest around his family of nine young er brothers and sisters and his parents. He wanted lots of food on the table when they came and he was always writing checks for them. Mama said Daddy's people were "aristocrats," but then Mama used many words Katie didn't understand. Mama was forever saying, "You need never be ashamed of your father's blood," and she said it with pride.

Katie didn't quite understand that either. It had something to do with being a "blue blood," but when Daddy cut himself shaving, his blood was red. Katie was sure Grandmother MacLeod's blood was blue—you could see it in the little veins on the backs of her hands. When Grandmother MacLeod came, Katie felt like going upstairs and hiding until she left.

When Grandmother MacLeod had a stroke, it was Mama who cared for her, not the aunts or uncles who lived with her. Aunt Claire, the youngest of Daddy's sisters, helped but she was in high school and did not have much time. Katie was glad when Mama came back home after Grandmother MacLeod died. The casket was carried into the big Presbyterian Church where Daddy took up the offering on Sundays. Katie loved the hollow sound of the old church and its cool stone walls. As Dr. Hyatt talked on and on in his church voice, Katie swung her legs and counted the organ pipes.

Perhaps with Grandmother MacLeod in heaven, Daddy would belong entirely to them. Often, when he promised to take the family for a ride on a Sunday afternoon, they'd wait all day on the porch only to have him explain suddenly that "Ma" needed him and all was off.

Still, Mama said Daddy was just crazy about chil-dren—that he wouldn't be satisfied until he had a house full. Sometimes Katie thought the house was, indeed, full. Yet there was no doubt that Daddy loved them all, especially the girls. He thought the twins were miracles and showed them off with great pride. Katie fancied herself as his favorite because he let her crawl up on his stomach when he lay on the sofa, and if she woke him up he only smiled and hugged her.

Of course, he loved Mama best. Sometimes he put his finger under Mama's chin—under that little soft curve—and turned up her face just to look in her eyes. Mama's eyes were wide and bluer than the sky. He teased Mama and she teased him back and they had great fun together.

But, somehow, all of them were not enough for Daddy. Not long after Grandmother MacLeod died, he began having lots of friends come to Twenty-nine. They were not like the important men he talked with at church—they smoked cigars and laughed so loud the dishes rattled. The ladies played cards and smoked cigarettes in long holders; ropes of long beads fell to their laps and they smelled like Aunt Ethel's gardenias.

Mama was always cross when they came, and when she caught Katie on the stairs gazing through the bannisters at them, she spanked her bottom and sent her to bed. Upstairs, lying on the big feather bed and sucking her thumb, Katie wondered why the women did not have children to keep them at home.

Alice and Jane were in the next bed whispering. "Mama won't have them coming here," Jane was saying. "They're common."

"Well," Alice said softly, "let's just say they're not our class."

Katie knew what that meant. It meant being proper the way the twins were. Alice liked to sit around the table after dinner pretending she was a fashionable lady having tea. She even got Archer to hold a cup with his little finger poking out the way "refined" people did. The twins were soft-spoken like Mama and sat still in church and never spoke unless they were spoken to. Katie sighed. It was awfully hard being a MacLeod.

For whatever reason, the *common* people did stop coming to Twenty-nine and then Daddy spent all his time at the office. One day he came home, scooped Katie up in his arms, kissed her over and over again, and tickled her mercilessly to her great delight. "Becky!" he called.

By the time Mama came downstairs, all the children had piled into the living room hoping to hear what he had to say. Daddy set Katie down and announced, "We're all going up to the mountains. I'm going to open up the scenic wonders of the Blue Ridge to the world!" He was smiling and pulling his ear the way he did when he was excited.

Brother scowled. "Aw, Daddy, what'll I do about baseball practice?" At sixteen, Brother had ambitions of becoming a professional pitcher.

"It will only be for a few weeks, Son." He stooped to look in the hall tree mirror, smoothing his sandy hair.

Brother slammed his mitt to the floor.

Mama spoke sharply. "Oliver O'Gilvie! Pick up that glove right now!"

Brother's face was flushed with anger. "It's not a glove—it's a mitt!"

"What did you say?" Daddy asked, frowning.

"Nothing," he answered.

"There will be no disrespect in this house," Daddy said.

Brother picked up the mitt, his face red and his lips pressed together. Katie knew he wanted to stomp across the floor; instead he went silently up to his room.

TWO
The Old Elmira Inn

For several days Mama was packing and telling the colored woman what to do. There was washing and ironing to be done, and the ice box had to be cleaned out. Mama wrote notes to the milkman and the ice man, and there were all kinds of instructions for Aunt Ethel, who was to look after Twenty-nine while they were away.

Daddy sold the touring car and traded some Blue Ridge lots for two Buicks. With Daddy driving one of the cars and Mama the other, they headed for the mountains. Brother had a stack of posters on his lap printed in red, white, and blue with Daddy's handsome face in the center. "They're to advertise the sales," Brother explained to Katie.

They rode for hours over bumpy roads but Katie and Archer were asleep most of the way. When Katie woke up, Daddy was carrying her up the steps of a big house.

"It's the Elmira Inn," Brother was telling the girls in his impatient way.

"I can read," Jane said sarcastically.

Katie opened her eyes, took her thumb out of her

mouth and sat up in her father's arms. There was a wide porch with rockers and a big burly dog barking.

"Oh, smell the honeysuckle," Mama said.

A thin, wiry man hurried to the door. "Come in, Colonel MacLeod, come in," he said, holding the screen door for them. A fat woman joined him, drying her hands on her apron. "Wife, this is Colonel MacLeod, the auctioneer with the development company."

"And this is Mrs. MacLeod," Daddy said proudly.

"These are our children," Mama said and introduced them in order by age, "Oliver O'Gilvie," which was Brother's real name, "Alice and Jane, who are ten, Archer, who is eight, and Katie, our five-year-old."

They filed into the living room and waited as the man continued talking excitedly. "We been looking for you all day, Colonel. Thought the road might be washed out someplace."

Katie was looking at the biggest fireplace she had ever seen, with long logs just lit and struggling to burn.

"The Elmira has fallen on hard times lately. Been here since before the turn of the century, you know. You don't know how glad we are to see a promoter come to these parts, Colonel MacLeod; yes, sir, we can't wait to get city folks coming up here."

The man's wife nodded in agreement, excused herself and went back to the kitchen.

There was a strong damp smell about the place that made Katie rub her nose. When her eyes grew accustomed to the dimly lit room, she gazed up the stairway, following the railings made of whole tree trunks, the limbs left on part way like hat racks. A narrow balcony went around the lobby and led to rooms on the second floor. When Mama and Daddy followed the innkeeper up the steps, Katie trailed behind them, looking back over her shoulder at all the interesting things in the big room: peacock feathers in the umbrella stand with walking canes; a slicker and bonnet hanging on a clothes tree; a dead hornets' nest clinging to a broken branch above the mantle.

"Come along, girls," Mama called.

Alice and Jane obeyed, taking each step in a ladylike manner, not minding at all that the banisters were not the kind you could slide down.

Archer pointed to a deer head on the wall. "Lookit, Brother, a twelve-point buck."

Brother grunted, uninterested.

"Brother, is Daddy a colonel?" Archer asked.

"Of course not. He was never in the army. It's for publicity."

"The bags, son," Daddy called from the balcony.

Brother made a face but obeyed.

Katie followed the others upstairs where the man showed them their rooms on the third floor and the bath at the head of the stairs. Daddy opened the blinds, felt the bed, and looked around. "Well, Becky, what do you think?"

"It's clean, Malcolm."

"And modern," he added, "with a sink in every room." He turned a spigot and a trickle of water poured into the basin. "Wish he would hurry up with the suitcases." He took off his coat, removed his pocket watch, then his vest and tie.

Katie heard Brother struggling up the steps with the bags bumping. She opened the door for him. He swung Daddy's big leather grip onto a chair and left to get the rest of the luggage.

Mama began unstrapping the bag. "Hand me my shaving case, please, Becky," Daddy asked, looking in the mirror above the sink. He rubbed his hand over his face and unfastened his collar.

"Thank you." He placed the mug on the shelf and fastened his razor strap to a hook. Stropping the razor, he looked at himself in the mirror.

"The walls are thin," Mama was saying as she held up a petticoat to make sure it was Katie's and not one of the twins'. "If one of the children cries in the night, I can hear them."

Brother arrived with more of the baggage. "Put that

one in the twins' room—the other one is yours and Archer's," Mama told him.

"Mama, you still have on your hat," Brother said.

She took off the hat and laid it on the dresser, careful not to harm the feathery plume when she stuck the pin in the crown. Little wisps of brown curls clung to her white neck as she tried to tuck them under the bun with hairpins.

Katie was taking off her dress. Mama helped her. "We'll change everything. Here—" she held out bloomers for Katie to step in, then pulled them up. She laughed. "You and your skinny MacLeod hips. No wonder you can't hold up your drawers."

Katie put on a petticoat stiff with starch, then stood with hands over her head while Mama matched her hands to the armholes and pulled the dress over her head. It was a hideous yellow dress with a sash that tied in back. Taking a brush from the bag, Mama said, "Here, Katie, I'll fix your hair."

The brush nearly pulled her hair out by the roots, and Mama would never stop until she got it perfect, absolutely perfect. Katie hated stovepipe curls.

"Stand still!" Mama would say a thousand times. If Katie moved the least bit, Mama would give her a yank. "I'm going to pop you if you don't stand still," she said, and she meant it. Each curl had to be measured and separated, then dampened, wrapped around her finger, and brushed. If it didn't look just right, it had to be done all over again. It took forever; usually Mama lost patience, and Katie wound up crying.

What Katie hated most was the big bow Mama tied on one side of her head. "Now look in the mirror. Don't you look pretty?"

Katie never thought she looked pretty. Her eyes seemed too big for her face. Ruffled dresses and wide sashes made her feel all tied up, and with her hair curled she had to walk just so and not get in the wind or it would get messed up.

But Katie did like her shoes that buttoned all the way

up the side. There were several straps across her foot with little round pearl buttons fastening them. Sometimes Katie was allowed to use the buttonhook, but usually Mama was in too big a hurry.

"Here, Katie, button your shoes." She handed Katie the buttonhook and went over to the bureau to let down her hair.

Katie was too busy buttoning her shoes to watch Mama. Daddy sat down on the bed beside her. Mama removed the hairpins from her bun, first the large, tortoise-shell pins, then the tiny wire ones hidden here and there. She laid them on the bureau carefully in order not to lose any and then she shook her head to make the hair fall down her back. How beautiful it was, shining in the late afternoon sun. She brushed it, pulling the brush through the hair, first on top, then underneath.

Using the comb for tangles and for dividing the hair into parts, Mama pulled each part over her shoulder and brushed some more.

Daddy didn't like marcel waves, so Mama wore it soft on top and swept up the long lengths in the bun. It was fun to watch her do it. The divided parts were plaited on the ends, then wound together expertly. Using one hand to twine the lengths together and the other to hold the bun securely, Mama held the pins in her mouth. She chose one pin at a time and placed it firmly to fasten the bun close to the head.

When she was done, she patted her hair and glanced at herself in the mirror. Then, hurriedly, she powdered her face.

Daddy got up abruptly, took the puff out of her hand and proceeded to dab her face with it. "Becky, you don't know how to powder your own face!"

When he was through, he stepped back to examine his handiwork. "There," he said, without seeing what was in Mama's eyes. He turned to shine his shoes.

Mama didn't say anything. She stood still, her face white, and the corner of her mouth quivered. When

Mama pressed her eyes shut and held them closed, Katie knew her feelings were hurt bad.

Mama took the buttonhook from Katie and fastened the last two buttons. Katie was ready to go on the porch where the twins were. Mama mumbled a warning about getting dirty and told her not to leave the porch.

Katie stood on the rockers of one of the chairs, and the three of them looked out over the lawn. Alice and Jane stood side by side in their dotted Swiss dresses with puffed sleeves and held their hands folded before them like angels were supposed to do. They had straight hair and bangs so they never had to have their hair curled unless they used the curling iron, which was fun. They were thin like Katie, but it wasn't because they ran hard and played a lot. They never got dirty. Jane liked to jump rope but because Alice didn't, they almost never jumped rope. They were like that—they wouldn't do anything unless they did it together. Sometimes they did backbends because Alice was double-jointed, and they made cartwheels, but mostly they played hopscotch. Jane liked to push a baby carriage, which Grandmother MacLeod used to call a perambulator, and long after Katie was too big to ride in the buggy, they carted her all over the neighborhood in it. But on the whole, Alice and Jane didn't need anyone else to play with, least of all Katie.

Katie noticed big buds on the shrubs around the porch. Mama would know the name of them. In the yard there was a rail fence covered with pink roses that trailed along the slope to the road. Beyond the road was a rushing stream pouring over and around huge rocks. Katie couldn't wait to climb out on the boulders and see if she and Archer could make it to the other side without falling in. Of course, Mama, if she knew about it, would never in a million years let them do that.

After a while Mama and Daddy joined them on the porch. Mama wore her blue "power puff muslin," as she called it, the one that clung to her shape and fell softly from her hips. There was a clean, fresh scent about Mama, as gentle as the fragrance of the pink roses.

Daddy slipped his gold watch from his vest pocket, the one that had belonged to his great grandfather. He snapped open the lid and looked at the time.

"Oh, Malcolm, what about snakes?" Mama wanted to know. "Look at all those rocks and that hemlock hedge."

Daddy laughed. "Don't worry, Becky, when this brood of children is turned loose the snakes will skid-daddle!"

Suddenly Katie's foot slipped from the rocker, the chair swung back and knocked her in the mouth. Stunned, she put her hand to her face, felt blood and screamed.

"Shhh, Katie, let me see." Mama took Katie's hand down from her face. "It's her tongue—she's cut her tongue. Malcolm, take the children to supper. I'll have to take her upstairs." Blood was staining the front of the yellow dress.

Daddy handed Mama his handkerchief. Blood kept wetting Katie's mouth, tasting terrible, oozing between her lips. Mama could not wipe it fast enough to keep it from trickling down Katie's neck. Drops fell on Mama's dress, and the floor, and wherever Katie put her hand she left a handprint. She was trying not to cry but the pain and fear were too much.

In the room, Mama quickly wet a towel and told Katie to hold it to her tongue. With a washcloth she bathed Katie's face and hands. Katie was sobbing.

"Here, let me see," Mama said, gently pulling Katie's hand that held the towel. "Let me see if you knocked any teeth loose."

Katie stood rigid, holding her breath for fear Mama would touch the wounded tongue.

Mama's forefinger reached behind every tooth and felt carefully. Satisfied, she withdrew it. "No, your teeth are all right. Now, if we can just stop this bleeding—if I had some ice." She washed her hands in the lavatory.

"This dress is ruined—even your stockings; there's blood on your stockings."

Katie peered over the towel to see if there was blood on her button-up shoes. There was!

A fresh flood of tears started.

"Crying won't help," Mama fumed. "I'll clean your shoes. Here, help me get the dress over your head."

Mama put the soiled clothes in the sink to soak and began looking for more towels. "Wrap up in your bathrobe while I run the water in the tub." She went down the hall to the bathroom.

When she came back, Mama opened the suitcase and took out Katie's favorite dress, a light green pongee with silk ribbons at the neck. Katie stopped crying.

Sitting in the warm tub, Katie felt better. Mama soaped the washcloth and bathed her carefully around the mouth. "Katie, you exasperate me! For the life of me, I don't see how you do it. How do you manage to get into all these scrapes?"

Katie didn't know what "exasperate" meant. It must be bad. She felt miserable.

"You give me more trouble than all the rest of the children put together."

Mama splashed water onto Katie's back to rinse away soapsuds. Maybe Daddy would notice her pongee dress and not be exasperated, Katie thought.

Mama pulled the plug and the water began swirling down the drain. Wrapping Katie in a big towel, she carried her back to the room.

When Katie was dressed again, Mama changed clothes, and together they went downstairs. Mama laid her hand on Katie's head and stroked her hair lovingly. The storm was over.

Mama and Daddy moved to the lobby to drink coffee by the fireplace. Brother joined Archer exploring the lobby and adjoining rooms, examining the player piano and records for the gramophone while the girls sat primly in chairs listening to the grown-ups talk.

"Colonel MacLeod, there are lotsa' purty places around here," the man began. His apple-cheeked wife bobbed her head in agreement. Katie wondered if she could talk.

"Any caves, waterfalls?" Daddy asked.

"You bet, eh, wife?"

The woman nodded, smiling her pasted-on smile.

"The widow Brewer's got a tract of land she wants to get shet of, and she's got a waterfall on it a mile high."

"She wants to sell?" Daddy leaned forward pulling his ear nervously.

"Yep. She's going to Tennessee to live with her daughter."

"I'd like to drive up there in the morning."

"Oh, ye cain't drive up there. There's a trail leads back of here." He thumbed over his shoulder. "I'll take ye up there."

"That's no problem. If we want the property we'll build a road." He turned to Mama. " Becky, help me think of a good name for that waterfall. Can't you see it now—a picture of that mile-high cataract right on the front of the brochure?"

Mama smiled, but said nothing. In the firelight her creamy cheeks were pink.

"You mentioned caves, Colonel MacLeod. Well, there's a cavern runs under this mountain with an underground river. I been in it many a time since I was a boy. There's pools there so deep you can drop a hammerhead on a string and it won't never hit bottom. It's the gospel truth!"

"Is that a fact?" Daddy shifted about in his chair too excited to sit still. "Well, I want to see that too." He turned to Mama. "Thought of a name yet?"

"For the waterfall?"

"The waterfall."

"Not yet," she said. Daddy didn't notice how quiet she was.

Archer was holding a record in his hands waiting for a break in the conversation. "May we play the gramophone?" he asked.

Mama looked at the innkeeper.

"Sure, son, go right ahead," he said.

Brother snatched the record out of Archer's hands. "Not 'Jessica Dragonette'!" He shuffled through the stack. "Here's 'Alabamy Bound.'"

Archer cranked up the gramophone and Brother carefully placed the shiny round arm with the needle on the record. Music poured out of the cabinet. Katie didn't understand how the banjo player got inside the box but she knew better than to ask. Once before she had asked how the singers got inside the speaker on top of the radio, and Archer had told her they were all midgets. Everybody laughed, so she knew that wasn't true.

Daddy stood up. "Let's dance, Becky."

She was slow to answer. "Well, get something decent to dance by."

The man helped Brother and Archer push back the horsehair furniture and clear a space while Daddy found music he liked. When he took Mama in his arms, they began to move across the floor, making quick little steps.

"That's a fox-trot," Brother told them.

"As if we didn't know," Jane retorted.

"Daddy's only dancing with Mama because there are no flappers up here." Brother was sitting on the step above the girls and Katie.

"That's not true!" Alice flared back. "Mama's beautiful."

"That has nothing to do with it."

Katie knew that Daddy, too, thought Mama was beautiful. Daddy would watch Mama walking across the floor, and you could tell he admired the way she moved—she moved like a willow did when a breeze was stirring.

The twins sat with their skinny legs extending to the floor. Alice fretted, "Our legs will never be pretty like Mama's."

"I think my left one will," Jane said. "See?"

Daddy changed the record and the music came out slower. Brother groaned so loud everybody could hear him. "Rudy Vallee!" When the man started singing, Archer groaned and the dog on the porch began howling.

Mama and Daddy were dancing close together and moving ever so slowly.

Brother leaned over and whispered to the twins. "I'll bet Katie doesn't sleep with Mama and Daddy tonight."

The girls swung around to glare at him. "What do you mean, smart aleck?" Jane demanded.

Brother wouldn't answer, just sat there leaning back on his elbows, looking smug.

"Ever since you outgrew knickers you've acted like you were grown. I'm going to tell Mama!" Jane threatened.

"What's he talking about?" Alice asked.

"Who cares? He thinks he's the cat's pajamas."

When the music ended, Mama said, "Now run along to bed, children."

Brother was going to stay up and play the player piano. Archer begged to stay up, too, and Mama let him because she always let Archer do what he wanted to.

Upstairs in the room, Daddy asked Mama, "Why don't you let Katie sleep with the girls tonight?"

"Not tonight, Malcolm, it's been a long day."

"Afraid of having another child, aren't you, Becky?"

"Shhh, you know she's precocious."

Mama moved across the room and started rinsing out the clothes in the sink. Daddy followed her. "Well?"

"She's cut her tongue and all—"

Daddy slipped his arms around Mama's waist. "Please?"

Mama smiled back at him in the mirror. He gave her a quick hug and let her go.

"Katie, let me look at your tongue," Mama said,

drying her hands on a towel. Katie held open her mouth, stuck out her sore tongue and Mama turned her to the light. "Split right down the middle, see?" she said to Daddy.

"It'll be all right," Daddy said. "Katie, get your nightgown out of the suitcase. You'll sleep with your sisters tonight."

Daddy led Katie to the door, his hand on her back. Opening the door for her, he said, "Go find your sisters—they're right down the hall." The door closed behind her.

Katie looked up the hall at all the doors, then down the hall where there were more doors. She didn't know which way to go. Slowly she walked toward the bathroom, listening at every door but all was silent. Then she heard Alice and Jane giggling. She stood before the bedroom door a while, making sure it was the right room, then she knocked.

The giggling stopped. "Who is it?" Jane asked.

"Me," Katie answered.

Jane flung open the door. "Well, you can't sleep with me. You kick!"

"I don't want her in my bed," Alice said. "She's sure to wet it."

Katie put her thumb in her mouth and moved it to the side of her tongue.

Alice relented. "All right, you can sleep with me but I warn you, you better not wet the bed!"

"Take that thumb out of your mouth!" Jane demanded. "You're five years old!"

By the time the buds burst open on the shrubs surrounding the porch of the inn and the lavender and pink blossoms hung heavy on their limbs, Katie had explored everything about the Elmira. Because Mama was busy helping Daddy—going to Charlotte to bring up prospective buyers—Katie and Archer, under Brother's supervision, were free to climb all over the rocks in the stream. Of course they fell in, but Brother helped them dry their clothes and clean up before Mama found out.

The boys caught mountain trout, and Archer got the lady in the kitchen to cook them for him. Archer was a good-looking boy; he had fat cheeks, yet was straight as an arrow and slender. That, along with a natural charm which he seemed able to turn on and off like a spigot, helped him get his way with nearly everybody. He was like Daddy.

Katie's knees were skinned, and there were black and blue places on her arms and legs, which made Mama fuss. When the boys found inner tubes to float in down the river, Mama wouldn't let Katie go with them.

People in all kinds of automobiles began coming to the inn for the auctions Daddy was holding. Because there were so many guests—ladies in leghorn hats and men who wore bow ties—Mama would not leave the children in Brother's care. During the afternoons she kept the girls on the porch with her as she talked with people. Gentlemen in straw hats and white linen suits seemed to flock around Mama, talking about the weather, the mountains, and the land business. The other women seemed cross as they rocked and fluttered silk fans. They couldn't talk and cheer people up the way Mama could. When Mama talked, everybody listened. There was music in her voice, and when she laughed it was as pleasant as the sound of the wind chimes hanging on the porch. Katie wondered if it was what she said, because she seemed to know something about everything, or if it was the way she said it. Folks were always asking Mama where she came from, and when she said, "Near Charleston—Hemingway," their faces lit up and they would say, "I thought so." Daddy said people from the "Low Country" had their own way of talking and they shouldn't change it.

In the late afternoon Mama would take all the children for a walk up the road. Often one or two of the men would stroll along. Mama knew the names of the trees and plants, and when they saw a bird, she knew whether it was a thrush or a wren, what it ate, how it built its nest, and what its eggs looked like.

One of the gentlemen kept saying, "Most extraordinary, Mrs. MacLeod, most extraordinary."

After that, Mama, in fun, referred to him as Mr. Extraordinary.

"I like Mr. Very Entertaining better," Brother said.

"Who is he?" Mama asked.

"Mr. Longchamp, the polo player. Every time he sees me he says, 'Your mother is very entertaining.'"

Mama laughed.

On the long walks, Archer chased butterflies. When he caught them he put pins through their poor bodies to stick to the wall. He had no feelings at all.

On the last day of July, Mama let Katie tear off the calendar page. Beneath that page were letters written in bold red print. "Katie," Daddy said, "that reads, 'August 1928' and this is, indeed, a red letter day for us." Spread on the bed before them were piles of checks, bills, and papers which he was sorting. As he counted the money he stuffed it into heavy canvas bags. The next day Mama would drive them home to Charlotte to get ready for the opening of school and she would put the money in the bank. Daddy would stay in the mountains until cold weather.

Before they went to bed, Mama took Katie out on the porch for the last time to watch for the first star to appear. They sat on the steps, Katie nestling in the curve of Mama's arm. The heavy fragrance of mountain spruce scented the air, and the sound of the stream across the road made Katie sleepy. Crickets were singing and the last of the birds were darting about. Mama pulled her close, tucking Katie's dress around her legs to keep her warm. Rubbing her cheek against Katie's hair, Mama whispered,

Twinkle, twinkle, little star,
How I wonder what you are,
Up above the world so high. . . .

They were all up early the next morning. Brother brought the bags down before breakfast. When they were ready to leave, they walked out to the car past all the people on the porch. Katie felt very proud trailing along behind them. Mama in the lead, holding her head erect, the plumed hat elegant in the morning sun; her father touching Mama's elbow and looking at her as if he could eat her. Brother was wearing a suit. The twins were carrying their parasols and Katie wished she had one. Archer was already in the Buick, sitting on the front seat. Between his legs was a fruit jar full of minnows which, he said, must be on the front seat so they would get plenty of air. Archer always knew how to get what he wanted.

Daddy wanted to kiss Mama at the car but she frowned. "Not in front of all the guests and the children."

"Oh, I almost forgot," Daddy said. "Please, I'll be right back." He went behind the inn; when he came back around the corner he was carrying a bucket with a plant in it. "It's a redbud tree," he explained. "Its leaves are heart-shaped and if it could, it would sing, 'Let Me Call You Sweetheart' the way you do, Becky. Plant it at Twenty-nine, honey, because that's where my heart is." He smiled his sweet-sad smile.

Then Mama smiled and turned her cheek for him to kiss her.

Right away she started the engine, let it roar a few minutes, and then the car rolled down the driveway. Katie pressed her nose against the window, waving to Daddy until they were out of sight. On the road the Buick rocked from side to side in the ruts as they went around one curve after another, around and around and around. Katie's stomach was churning.

It was a long time before they came to a level place in the road, and it was then that Katie remembered her shoes. "Mama! Mama!" she cried above the sound of the motor. "I left my shoes!"

"Your good ones?"

"My button-up shoes!"

"Well, we can't go back, it's almost ten miles."

Katie began crying. She couldn't help it. Mama stopped the car and waited for the dust to settle. "Stop blubbering," she said impatiently. "Your Sunday shoes?"

"Yes, ma'am."

"Well, we'll have to go back for them. I declare, Katie, you cause me more trouble than all the rest of the children put together."

"Mama, Alice is sick. She's nauseated. It's the road. We can't go back over that winding road," Jane argued.

"There's a place not too far from here where you can turn around," Brother said. It took a long time to find it. Mama stopped the car. "Alice, you sit up front with Archer and me. Keep the glass rolled down. Tell me if you need to stop." Alice got into the front seat and Mama started to turn the car around. She had a hard time turning the big wooden wheel, rolling the car forward and back until they were headed in the right direction. Mama fussed all the way back to the Elmira.

Katie thought they would never get there—back over all those winding curves. Alice's face was white as a sheet, but she didn't throw up. When they finally drove up in the drive, no one was on the porch.

"Mama, I know right where they are—under the dresser," Katie said.

"Then you hop out and get them."

Katie jumped out of the car and bounded onto the porch. All the people were in the dining room. She dashed through the lobby and up the steps, around the balcony and up another flight of steps to the third floor. Someone flushed the toilet in the bathroom. When she reached her parents' room, she knocked quickly.

A woman's voice answered, "Malcolm?" But Katie had opened the door and there, standing before her was a lady dressed only in a chemise, and it was halfway down.

The lady shrieked. "What are you doing here!"

Katie reached for her shoes, never taking her eyes off the angry woman scrambling for cover.

Katie ran from the room, closing the door behind her. She knew she had done something terribly wicked. Her heart pounded. No one must ever know.

As she darted past the bathroom door, she heard her father singing.

THREE
Katie's
Dream

Long after they were settled at Twenty-nine, long after
Mama had bought the cloth and cut out dresses to sew
for the girls to wear to school, Katie felt bad inside.
Sometimes she felt so ashamed she thought she must
whisper her terrible secret to Brother, but she never
did.

Every night it was Katie's habit to make sure someone listened to her prayers, "Now I lay me down to
sleep." But after returning to Twenty-nine Katie just
didn't feel like praying to God. She decided to pray like
Alice and Jane, who knelt beside their beds and didn't
say anything aloud. After a week, Jane looked at her
suspiciously and asked, "What did you ask God for?"

"Nothing."

"Nothing? You mean you don't say anything to
God?"

Katie shook her head. "Nothing. I just kneel like you
do."

"How long have you been doing this?"

"'Bout a week."

"Seven days?"

Katie nodded.

"All right, young lady, you get right down on your knees and let me hear you say 'Now I lay me down to sleep' seven times!"

Jane's voice struck fear in Katie's heart and she lost no time in obeying.

When Daddy finally came home from the mountains, Katie felt strange around him. He brought her a baseball cap and wanted her to go in the yard with him to have a picture made. Mama made her go. Mama said she should tell Daddy all about kindergarten, but Katie wouldn't tell him anything. When he said he was going away again, Katie did not mind at all, but Mama did. "How can you leave me at a time like this?" she asked.

"I'll be back in time for the new arrival," he promised.

Brother explained to Katie that Daddy was going to Texas to buy horses where he could get a good one for ten dollars and bring it back east and sell it for a hundred dollars.

After he was gone, Katie heard Aunt Ethel telling Mama what to do. "It isn't right, Becky. He'll use up all the money."

"That's none of your business, Ethel," Mama said. "Besides, it takes money to get started in another business." Mama poured more coffee. "Malcolm is a good provider—you know that."

"It's a good thing this house is nearly paid for."

"I can manage my own affairs, Ethel." She turned toward Katie. "Little pitchers have big ears. Run outside and play, Katie."

Archer had a new game for them to play—"Real Estate"—something he made up. Each child had a different "business" to operate. Besides a real estate dealer (who was *always* Archer), there was a nurseryman, a lumberman, and a stone mason. Together they "developed property," building houses and landscaping yards. They bought and sold land, building materials, and shrubs, keeping the game going for days. In the end Archer always won and the rest of them went bankrupt.

By the time it was too cold to play outside, there was Christmas to look forward to.

Mama sold her Buick to "catch up on some bills," she said, "and to buy a tree and a few gifts." Katie hoped Daddy would come home for Christmas, but Mama said no, he was coming in February.

Aunt Ethel and Uncle Helmut joined the MacLeods for Christmas dinner, and later in the afternoon, with Uncle Helmut snoozing in the living room, Mama and Aunt Ethel talked about old times.

Aunt Ethel liked to talk about illness and death: the smallpox epidemic that claimed the lives of Aunt Clara and others and almost claimed Becky; the 1918 influenza, the year the twins were born—so tiny they had to be carried about on pillows—and people were dying all around; the long months of colic before Little Malcolm died; how sick Katie was with spasmodic croup when she was a baby. "The doctor told you if Katie has croup again, she'll die, Becky. Remember that; she'll die."

"Ethel, why do you harp on the unpleasant?" Mama fussed. "Isn't there something better to talk about?"

Then their conversation turned to their dead father, Oliver O'Gilvie McIntosh, whom Mama adored. They spoke of his violent temper which he vented only on mules, Negroes, and Uncle Robert.

Uncle Robert was Becky's half-uncle on her mother's side, and he had succeeded in gobbling up all the money in the family. He had never married and had held only one real job in his life, that being with the railroad. After he gave up that job, he worked for Becky's Grandpa in the dry goods store. There was a great mystery about the money Grandpa was supposed to have stashed away somewhere. The night Grandpa died, Uncle Robert had slipped down to the store alone, and later, when the family looked for the cash, it was gone. The scandal was hushed up and now spoken of only in whispers.

After that, Uncle Robert spent all his time on the

porch reading Robbie Burns' poetry or standing in the cotton field dressed as for church, holding a parasol over his head, overseeing the Negroes working. He would live forever, holding on to the property and whatever cash there was on Mama's side of the family until doomsday.

"Ethel," Mama said, "If I were starving to death, I would not ask Uncle Robert for one red cent!"

"You're just like Papa, Becky. He never had any use for Uncle Robert."

The McIntoshes were not proud people, but they might have been. One of them had edited the *Charleston Courier*; and Oliver McIntosh was getting started in naval stores down in Georgia when he married the uncomplicated, genteel Kathryn Felps. Because Kathryn could not abide Georgia crackers and red clay, however, they left Valdosta to return to the Low Country. There, all Oliver McIntosh could find to do was farming, and Kathryn was no farm wife—she was reared to make lace and visit the aunts down the road. Fortunately, one of their daughters, Becky, took after her father and could "take hold and do." She managed the house, taught the Negroes, and still found time for lantern parties and lots of beaux.

When young Malcolm MacLeod drifted into town to open a furniture store, his eyes fell on Becky, and they had to have each other. By then Becky was eighteen and teaching school—but she chose Malcolm and let Ethel have the school.

Malcolm was too poor to buy a ring for Becky, so they used a wedding band she had inherited from Aunt Clara; instead of a ring, Malcolm brought home a brand new cedar chest from the store as a wedding present. There were five gifts of silver pieces from the family, and with that Becky and Malcolm began housekeeping.

Katie had heard the stories many times, but listening to grownups talking about the olden days was her favorite pastime. The twins listened, too. Katie looked at them sitting side by side on the settee, their elbows on their knees, their chins cupped in their hands, their delicate features soft in the afternoon light. Katie envied them. They went to regular school and knew how to read anything they wanted to. Katie was tired of cutting out fish and stars in kindergarten.

But in no time at all, Katie was reading. Of course, at first all she could read was printing, and when Daddy's letters came they were written in his large, elegant handwriting. Mama read only parts of the letters to the children.

"Your father is helping criminals," she told them.

"What do you mean, 'he's helping criminals'?" Brother asked.

"Well, if a man has enough money, Malcolm will take his case. He goes back to the convicting judge and pleads his cause—you know how clever he is with words—and Granddaddy MacLeod knows the law. I'm sure they confer. Nine times out of ten the judge will reduce the sentence or release the man."

Brother frowned. "We could sure use some of that money he's making."

"He sent a check," Mama said. "You can take it down to Mr. Alexander at the bakery; he'll cash it."

Katie was confused. Daddy went to Texas to buy horses; now he was helping criminals. To Mama that seemed perfectly sensible, but as if reading their minds, Mama explained, "Children, I've lived with your father eighteen years and he has had more business enterprises than I can count. Rest assured that there is nothing he cannot do when he sets that fine mind to do it! He can make money hand over fist."

A few days later Mama received a phone call that made her angry. As she hung up, she called for Brother in a tight, strained voice and began rummaging through her pocketbook. Emptying her purse, she counted the money quickly and stuffed it in Brother's hand. "Take this to Mr. Alexander right away. He'll give you your father's check."

Brother hesitated, looking puzzled.

"Do as I say. The check was worthless."

She followed him to the door and stood looking after him, her lips pursed, her eyes flashing with anger.

Finally, Katie moved beside her and leaned against her. When Mama noticed she was there, she reached down and stroked Katie's head.

One morning in February, Mama was not at breakfast. Aunt Ethel and the cook were taking care of things, and Alice and Jane were very excited about something.

"Mama got us a baby brother," Brother explained.

Archer pushed his oatmeal aside and stuck out his lips. "I don't want any old baby brother."

"Oh, yes you do," Jane said. "Babies come from heaven—they're the gift of God."

"I don't care!"

"Now you better mind your tongue. We already have one little brother in heaven and if you don't watch out, God will take this one, too."

Archer stormed out of the breakfast room.

"Where is the baby?" Katie asked, lifting the oatmeal with her spoon and letting it plop back in the dish.

"He's upstairs with Mama," Brother explained. "His name is Timothy. Eat your breakfast and I'll take you up to see him."

The room was dark and all Katie could see was the baby's round head. Mama was propped up on pillows with her arm cradling the bundle beside her. She was smiling and so were Aunt Ethel, Alice, Jane, and Brother. Katie climbed up on the stack of books beside the bed to get a closer view. He was a precious little red-faced baby, straight from heaven and the hand of God.

When Mama finally came downstairs again, the baby was always on her lap or close by. Worst of all, Katie sometimes saw Mama nursing Timothy, and that re-minded her of the lady in the chemise whose lungs were showing. That was something Katie did not like to remember.

Mama didn't have time for anything else but the

baby. Diapers were always hanging by the radiators, or Mama was folding them. The only way she could read the *Delineator* was to prop it up on the ironing board when she was ironing. At breakfast she never finished the crossword puzzle in the newspaper anymore, and most of the time she asked Brother to listen to Katie's lessons. That's when Katie learned to read the funny papers for herself; she knew Mama would never again have time to read them to her.

Katie had just finished reading "Little Orphan Annie" one morning and was sitting by the window looking down the driveway. Suddenly, a yellow car swung into the turn and came to a halt at the foot of the porch steps. A colored man stepped out, opened the back seat door, and out climbed Daddy! He leaped up the steps two at a time. Katie yelled, "It's Daddy! It's Daddy!"

He scooped Katie up and kissed her. "Where's your Mama?"

Katie slid out of his arms as Mama came into the room. "Becky!"

My! Did he kiss Mama! He was still hugging her when the twins, Archer, and Brother came clattering down the stairs. They stood shyly, waiting—that is, all except Archer who went right past Daddy out the front door to see the automobile. Katie followed. She heard Mama telling Daddy, "Come see the baby."

"It's a Packard!" Archer yelled. "Look at that chrome!" He ran his hand over the spare tire on the fender. Inside, the car had soft upholstery—"mohair," Archer said. "And jump seats!" He lifted a lid-like contraption that folded out. Katie sat on the seat holding onto the rope running across the back of the front seat.

"And lookit, Katie, there's a window between the driver and the back seat. See, you have to roll it down when you want to talk to him." He motioned toward the driver, who was stretching his legs in the backyard.

There were side straps as well as the rope to hold

onto, and little lamps on the posts between the windows. Archer sat in the driver's seat, pretending to let off the brake, and that was when Katie went back into the house.

Daddy stayed a week and said he had to be on his way to Washington, D.C. He would settle a mail fraud case there, then go back to Texas. He promised he would move them to Texas when school was out.

The day he left for Washington, Daddy took Granddaddy MacLeod with him and two of his brothers, Uncle Steve and Uncle Benjamin. From Washington they would return to Texas. "Dad can help me in legal matters and I can use the boys at auctions," he explained to Mama.

After he was gone, Brother was very disagreeable. "What did he come for—to give us another baby?"

Mama's face turned white and without saying a word, she shamed Brother.

Later, Mama put Timothy in the baby buggy and went down to Aunt Ethel's. Aunt Ethel was watering the century plant on the front porch, talking a mile a minute. "Becky, it's a disgrace—you struggling to make ends meet and him coming in that fine car with a chauffeur, no less!"

"He has to have an expensive car in his business, Ethel. Besides, you know he shouldn't drive; he can't see out of his right eye."

"Yes, and I know how you nursed him when he had that eye trouble—keeping him in a dark room and carrying trays up those steps for nine long months! What's more, he promised he'd be here when the baby was born but he wasn't. I told Mr. Schneider that he wouldn't."

"Ethel, I don't have to be told that Malcolm is a prevaricator, but I have six children to think about. Malcolm will take us to Texas when he gets established."

"What are you going to do in the meantime?"

"I'm going to take in boarders. I've emptied the north room and the spare bedroom, and I sent word to

Mr. Alexander that I would consider taking four nice young men who work at the bakery."

Aunt Ethel's mouth dropped open. "Boarders?! Have you had another bad check?"

"How did you know about that?" Mama was angry. "With this crash and the banks folding—"

"You didn't answer my question."

"And I'm not going to!" With that, Mama wheeled the carriage around and headed home.

Boarders were a nuisance. They stayed in the bathroom just when everybody needed to get ready for school; they grabbed the funny papers first; they thought nothing of dragging Grandmother MacLeod's platform rocker up to the card table to play casino or setback. Some of them worked at night and slept in the daytime so that everybody had to tiptoe on the stairs and not make noise. But Mr. Thomas, one of the really nice ones, brought home jelly rolls from the bakery, and when he bought a secondhand car he took the children to ride in it.

Brother took a paper route and got up before daylight to carry the papers. He slung them over his shoulder in a canvas bag and they were so heavy his back bent beneath the load. Mama worried about him. "Son, your back will be ruined for life."

"Why don't you get a bicycle?" Archer asked.

"Bicycles cost money," he said bitterly, running his fingers through his blond hair.

"Girls cost money, too," Jane said and Brother glared at her. Brother had a girl friend, a pretty brunette who played tennis with him and drank lemonade on the front porch. Mama didn't approve of her because she had an "afflicted" brother and Mama said that meant "bad blood." When Brother wanted to go to the beach with Thelma, Mama said no in a very positive manner, and Brother got so mad he slammed the door and kicked the rooster across the yard.

Back of Twenty-nine, beyond the chicken coop and the clotheslines, ran a high wooden fence which separated the white neighborhood from the Negroes. Archer was always throwing rocks over the fence to antagonize the colored boys. Because one day someone unexpectedly threw a rock back, he came home with his head split and bleeding. Archer claimed he was taking revenge for the chickens those people stole, but Mama said they wouldn't steal chickens if they weren't hungry. Many mornings the milk was stolen from the porch. But even when long lines of clothes were stolen from the backyard, Mama didn't get angry. "We'll make do," she said, and with Aunt Ethel's help they made more dresses and shirts.

But mail was a different matter—Mama took pains to meet the postman so nothing would happen to the mail. She would go through the stack, put the window envelopes in her pocket and if there was a letter from Daddy, she would read it first, then tell them what he said. She told them that Granddaddy MacLeod had set up a law office in Tyler and that the uncles had invested in a hotel there.

"What else did he say?" Brother asked.

"Oh, nothing much—more grandiose plans for making a fortune."

"What's 'grandiose'?" Katie asked.

"Hot air," Brother answered.

Bill collectors were coming regularly to the house, the same ones repeatedly, with their tight-lipped, narrow faces beneath hats that did not fit. Brother was usually sent to the door to tell them Mama wasn't home. His forehead wet with perspiration, he would stutter when he tried to say something. One day Brother wasn't home; only Katie was there, lying on the bed watching Mama lace her corselet. When the doorbell rang, Mama peeked out the curtain. "It's Judge Reynolds, about the house," she said, "Katie, go downstairs and tell him I'm not home."

Katie hesitated, but Mama nodded her head toward the door, urging her to go along. She made her way down the stairs very slowly. The bell rang the second time. By the time Katie opened the door, she knew what she must say.

The well-dressed man asked, "Is your mother at home?"

Katie didn't answer right away. Finally, she said, "She's putting on her corset."

The gentleman smiled. "Very well, I think I'll have a look around the place." He walked back down the steps and began examining the house—its windows, the roof, the gutters. When Mama finally came down, she invited him to sit on the porch.

"Mrs. MacLeod, I understand your situation. I suggest that you write Mr. MacLeod and tell him I can arrange to rent you the place by the month."

"I understand, Judge Reynolds. I will write Mr. MacLeod and let you know his decision." He stood to leave. "And thank you, Judge Reynolds, for your kind consideration. These are difficult days."

"Indeed they are, Mrs. MacLeod. I don't know what the country is coming to."

That night Katie lay in her bed sucking her thumb because her heart ached. It was wrong to disobey Mama but it would also be wrong to tell a story. A story was the same thing as a lie, only Mama didn't allow them to say that word. Katie fluffed her pillow and turned on her side.

While she slept, a strange and wonderful dream came to her. In her dream Katie saw some steps leading from the edge of a rushing stream to a platform which was heaven. She knew it was heaven because there were gallon jars all around the platform banister holding babies God had just made. Jesus was standing on the steps with one hand on the railing and the other hand reaching out to her. He wanted Katie to take his hand, swing onto the first step and come to him, but Katie hung back. She couldn't leave Mama.

The dream became another secret for Katie—it was not the kind of dream she could ever forget; it was a holy dream, and Katie knew Jesus meant it only for her.

Sitting on the porch steps, smelling the luscious aroma of fresh bread being baked at the bakery on Main Street, Katie would ponder her dream, but never did she want to tell anyone, not even Brother. The special sacredness would vanish if she told it. She kept all the mystery and wonder of it in her heart, not knowing if she would ever fully understand what he meant or if ever she might do what he wished.

FOUR
The Carnival

In June, Archer turned nine, school was out, and Katie was told she could skip first grade. Archer had won a lot of marbles, playing for keeps, and hid them in the basement so Mama wouldn't know. Marble season was over and there was nothing much to do but catch June bugs, tie strings on their legs, and pretend they were aeroplanes. Then one morning Katie awoke to find the carnival had come to town! Across Laurel Lane right in front of Twenty-nine, tents and rides were spread all over the meadow. It was like a miracle!

Unmindful of Mama's strict warning that carnival people were not to be trusted, Archer stood on the other side of the street, inching closer and closer to where the men were working. Most frightening of all, carnival people snatched little girls and they were never heard of again. Archer wasn't scared of anything. Before midmorning he was watering the horses for the carnival people.

When darkness fell, the lights were turned on and the music blared. The MacLeod children lay across the beds in the upstairs rooms, watching from their windows the blazing, swirling colored lights and listening to the noisy loudspeakers. Mama was downstairs sewing. When the fireworks started, the children were to call her. At ten o'clock the first Roman candle streaked across the night sky, its boom following its burst like an echo.

"Its sound travels around the earth," Brother explained, "so we see it before we hear it."

Mama came up for the show and they made room for her on the twins' bed. "Sit by me, Mama," Archer said, and she did. Excitedly, they crowded close together, craning their necks to see the wide arcs of missiles ending in showers of falling sparks—red, blue, yellow, green.

"Wow! That was a big one!" Archer yelled. "Lookit! Lookit! Here comes another whopper!"

"Oh, Mama, a blue one!" exclaimed Alice.

"Beautiful. Just beautiful!"

"Have you ever seen anything like it?"

"No, I haven't, Jane," Mama answered.

Archer was too excited to sit still. "Mama, why can't we go to the carnival? Please! Please!" he begged.

"Now, Archer, don't pitcher-pump me."

"Aw, come on, Mama. I've never been to a carnival."

"Well," she said cautiously, "go downstairs and bring me the octagon can."

Mama kept soap coupons and loose change in the octagon can. The can was eight-sided with designs enameled in blue and gold. Dumping the contents on the bed, Mama spread the paper coupons to find the nickels and dimes mixed in. "Let's see if we have enough to get you in the gate."

"I got a ticket to the big tent. Got it for watering the horses." Archer grabbed every coin as soon as he saw it and counted in his head. "Hot dog! It's more'n enough, Mama."

The next day, when Brother came home from delivering papers, the four of them were all bathed and sitting on the porch, ready to go to the carnival. Mama gave strict instructions. "Archer, remember, no gambling games and no side shows. Katie, you hold on to Brother's hand and, girls, stay close by Brother. If you get lost from each other, go to the ferris wheel and wait for Brother to come."

People were jamming the turnstile to get onto the midway. Brother forgot his manners and pushed Katie through the crowd, the others following. The noise was deafening—motorcycles roaring in the hippodrome, music sounding from the calliope, riders on the "Whip" squealing, the fast-moving cars rumbling on the track, slackening, slamming forward and back; men in checked suits droning, "Hurry, hurry, hur-ree! Get your tickets, one a nickel, three a dime. Hur-ree! Hur-ree! Hur-ree!"

Katie clenched Brother's hand so hard he swore. Pictures of freaks stared down at her, tattooed men in leopard skins, fat women, two-headed calves. On a platform were painted women in spangled tights, waving fans, lifting their legs in a row, garters showing, their faces hard, eyes unseeing. "Hootchie-gootchie girls," Brother explained.

Weight guessers, monkey acts, penny-pitching games all clamored for attention. Bored ticket takers wearily strapped people in seats for thrill rides, then jingled the change in their apron pockets, their hands greasy, their bodies smelling sour.

From the hot dog stand came steam smelling of onion and kraut, popcorn, and candy apples. Brother held Katie up so she could watch sugar being spun into a pink hornet's nest of cotton candy.

They spent considerable time looking at various amusements before they bought tickets, for fear they would waste their money.

"Brother, she's *got* to go on the ferris wheel," Jane said determinedly. "She's never been on one."

Reluctantly, Brother pried Katie's fingers from around his thumb so he could buy her ticket and the twins grabbed her hands to run up the ramp. They took their places in the swinging bench and the sunburned attendant clamped the bar across them. Katie was in the middle and as soon as the motor sounded louder and faster, she wanted to get off. It was too late—the wheel began to turn, pulling them backward and upward—at first slowly then swiftly. Katie's stomach lurched. The wheel jerked to a stop to take on passengers and the three of them rocked back and forth high above the ground. Katie was so scared her teeth chattered. The wheel turned again and this time they were on the very top.

"Look down there—there's Brother!" Jane exclaimed leaning over the side. "He looks like a midget." Katie couldn't look. Her eyes were squeezed shut, and she gripped the bar so tightly her hands were numb.

The ferris wheel went round and round, faster and faster, stopping, starting, until Katie knew she was going to throw up.

"Don't you *dare* get sick!" Jane shouted. "Hang on, it won't be long." But it was long. Katie leaned against Alice who was having trouble not getting sick, too.

Finally, they began letting off passengers. When their turn came and she stepped down, Katie was not sure she could walk; her legs were like rubber and everything was spinning.

Archer used his pass to get into the big tent, but he left before the show was over. As soon as all the clowns had climbed out of their little car and had thrown candy into the crowd, Archer came out. He didn't care for trapeze and animal acts.

"You mean you didn't see the man shot out of the cannon?" Brother asked.

"Naw. I can see that tonight from the upstairs window."

Archer spent his money on baseballs trying to knock down milk bottles. That was really what Katie wanted to do, but it was a sin. Archer didn't care about sin—he hammered on Sunday and everything. Katie spent most of her money on the merry-go-round, pretending to ride a real horse and ignoring the polished brass poles. She saved her last nickel for cotton candy.

After their money was gone, they wandered along the midway toward home. "Step right up to the free show!" some man was shouting. They moved toward a cluster of people around a platform. The barker was announcing a Charleston contest. Jane looked at Alice and before Katie and the boys knew what was happening, they were hustled inside the tent. The twins left the three of them in the audience and went backstage to present themselves as contestants.

Five dancers preceded Alice and Jane on stage, each one doing his best at switching hands and knees in time with the music; but when the twins came out, giggling and bowing, the audience whistled and cheered. As they danced, their stockings kept falling down and they kept grabbing at them, all the time wobbling their legs like rubber bands, doing the Charleston a mile a minute. People laughed uproariously. The longer the girls danced, pulling at their stockings, trying not to miss a beat, the more people laughed, doubling over, faces red and tears rolling down their cheeks. A fat man slapped his thigh and gasped, "Better'n any Punch and Judy show I ever seen!"

Brother was furious. When the music stopped, the girls ran offstage but were called back several times by the loud clapping. Of course, they won, but the prize was only a ticket to the next performance.

Brother was blazing mad. "You wait 'till you get home," he threatened. "Mama's going to hear about this!"

Mama and Timothy were waiting on the porch for them. When Brother blurted out the story, Mama threw back her head and laughed and laughed. Brother shook his finger at the girls. "You wait and see if I ever take you anyplace again!" He slammed the screen behind him and stormed through the house to the icebox.

Archer followed Brother to the kitchen and the girls

went upstairs to change their clothes.

"How did you like the carnival, Katie?" Mama asked.

Katie didn't know what to say.

"What was it like?" Mama coaxed.

Katie was studying the toe of her shoe. "Cotton candy, Mama," she said in a small voice. Then she looked up at Mama.

"Like cotton candy?" Mama repeated, her blue eyes serious. "How is that?"

"It melts in your mouth, sweet and sticky. It's like . . . like *nothing*."

Mama's voice was soft and knowing. "You are right, Katie. You have been to Vanity Fair."

As quickly as it had come, the carnival moved away; overnight it was gone like the thief that it was. In the months that followed there was nothing to look forward to but second grade at Sycamore school.

Unfortunately, school was boring. Katie looked out the window of the classroom and thought about many things. She remembered her dream and wondered if she should tell Mama. Mama did not take dreams lightly. "Alice, Jane," she had said one day, "I dreamed we moved to Texas. We were living in a small house when a flood came and we could not get away."

Going to Texas seemed to be impossible. Daddy came home twice but Katie saw so little of him she could scarcely remember what he looked like from one visit to the next. He had been gone more than a year.

In the spring of the year another big tent was pitched in the meadow. Brother said the man who put it there was from California and was going to preach in the tent every night. Mama said Archer, Katie, and the twins could go to the services, as she called them, if they did exactly what Brother told them to do and to come home if he said so. Mama couldn't go anywhere because she had to stay home with Timothy.

Katie felt excited as they entered the tent. The smell

of sawdust and pine benches, the reflection of lights on the big curved piano, the shiny brass trombone beside the pulpit made this quite different from church uptown.

People who came to the meetings were not dressed up. There were children there Katie was not allowed to associate with—which meant she couldn't play with them—and there were grownups who smelled of perspiration. Archer called it sweat. The men wore suspenders and the women had pale faces and no curl in their hair. Everybody carried a fan with a picture of the Good Shepherd and a songbook of revival hymns.

The preacher was a big, bald man with a gold tooth in the front of his mouth. The way he chuckled and saw humor in everything made people feel good. He reminded Katie of the friendly gypsy in the *Our Wonder World* book. The preacher's wife was much younger than he, and Brother said she had been an actress. In her long white dress and with her blonde hair and easy smile, she looked like an angel to Katie. Playing the piano, she used all the keys on the keyboard, and everybody sang "Love Lifted Me" as loud as they could, holding the notes as long as the preacher's son held up his arms for the count.

The son was taller and a year older than Brother. He was the spitting image of Tarzan, and his California way of talking was, as Alice said, "sophisticated." When he sang, he used a megaphone so everyone could hear his rich, tenor voice—at least they could hear when the megaphone was turned their way and if the trolley car was not clanging past on Main Street.

Brother reported to Mama that the tent people were holy rollers, but Alice and Jane said that they weren't, that they were Dr. and Mrs. Nelson and they had moved into a house on Laurel Lane.

"Sounds like Evangelist Scottie Trotter," Mama said. She seemed amused. "I've known your father to pledge large sums of money to Scottie Trotter." She and Timothy were in the porch swing and it was swaying back and forth. Katie nuzzled Timothy's cheek. His two-year-old legs were like plump sausages, dimpled and creased; he smelled of baby powder. Timothy was an adorable, contented boy, with blond ringlets and Mama's blue eyes.

"Well, the meetings are more fun than the Alhambra Theater on Saturday mornings," Brother said jokingly.

In fact, instead of taking Katie to the picture show, Alice and Jane began taking her to the Saturday morning children's hour to hear the evangelist's wife teach Bible stories and songs. The child who sang best was given a nickel, and Katie always won the nickel. That pleased Katie more than it did Mama, who said, "Money prizes in church? Disgraceful."

Alice and Jane won a Bible story book and in the evenings they would sit on the settee looking at the pictures and reading it. Brother, who sat in Grandmother MacLeod's platform rocker and read the sports page, was curious about the book and from time to time he would take Katie on his lap and they would look at it together.

They were reading the Bible story book when the doorbell rang. A Western Union boy stood holding a telegram in his cap. "Telegram for Mrs. Malcolm MacLeod." Mama signed for the telegram and opened it as the boy swung onto his bicycle and coasted down the driveway.

"It's from your father." She brushed a hair from her face and smiled. "He has found a house and wants us to move to Austin."

"Whoop-de-do!" Archer shouted, throwing his notebook in the air. Everyone else was happy, but Katie wasn't sure she was.

"Are we going, Mama?" Alice asked.

"Of course," Mama answered.

As soon as Aunt Ethel heard the news, she brought Uncle Helmut to try to dissuade Mama. "Becky, it's a mistake going way out there. Malcolm should come home and live with you and the children—rent this house."

"Malcolm would never live in a rented house, Ethel. You know that."

"Tell her, Mr. Schneider, tell her she's making a mistake."

The old man stroked his white mustache. "No, Ethel, Becky should be where Malcolm is. A man should have his family with him."

Aunt Ethel clutched Katie. "You aren't going to take my dear little Katie, are you?"

Mama ignored her question. "Uncle Helmut, I will have to store some of our things. Do you think you can find room for a few things in your basement?"

"How will you get to Texas?" Aunt Ethel asked.

"Mr. Thomas, one of the boarders, has a Willys and he will drive us."

"What about all your things?" Her eyes were red-rimmed and Katie stared at her; she had never seen Aunt Ethel or Mama cry.

"Ethel, I will have to sell most of the things. I plan to ship the wedding silver, the cedar chest, the little green rocker, the sewing machine, and the radio. But the chairs—Grandmother MacLeod's platform rocker and the companion chair—I'd like for you to keep for me. We'll send for them later. You never know, Malcolm may come east again in another year. Then again we may not."

By the time school was out and Brother was graduated from high school, the arrangements were completed. Mama loaded the children into the little sedan, a few of the *Our Wonder World* books tucked here and there. Mama thought they should not be without books for even one day.

They kissed Aunt Ethel and Uncle Helmut good-bye and left them standing in the driveway as the car backed down the hill. The girls were crying and Archer sounded as if his voice might quiver when he asked, "Will we ever be coming back to Twenty-nine?"

"No," Mama answered softly. "The house doesn't belong to us any more."

Katie took one long last look as the car made its turn and pulled away. The redbud tree was as tall as the porch.

BULL CREEK, PART I

FIVE
Let Me
Call You
Sweetheart

Katie sat on Brother's lap all the way to Texas. When the car would hit a dip in the road, Brother's head would bounce against the ceiling, which made everybody laugh except Brother. He swore softly, so Mama wouldn't hear him.

Mama held Timothy on the front seat. On the back seat the rest of them played games and sang every song they knew. Archer cheated Katie in cow poker all the way across the country, all the time making fun of her. Katie trusted Archer, which was a big mistake, and she wished she weren't so stupid. Like when they were passing a field where a lot of trees had been cut down, Archer told her that it was a stump farm where they raised stumps, and Katie believed him until Brother told her differently.

Staying overnight in tourist cabins and picnicking along the way was fun, but crossing the Mississippi River on the ferry was the most exciting part of the trip. The Willys rolled right onto the boat. They got out of the car and went up on the front deck where they could lean over the railing, wind whipping their hair and spray wetting their faces.

After the ferry ride, Katie fell asleep and took

little notice of anything until they reached Austin.

In Austin they washed up in a gas station and Mama combed Katie's hair. Now that she was seven, her hair was bobbed like the twins', with bangs and straight to the ears. The twins were behaving like grownups, and Archer was cross because he had to wear a necktie.

The street in Austin wasn't hard to find but the number was. The automobile crept along as they leaned out the windows, trying to find number "1222."

"We must be on the wrong street," Brother said. "These houses look like mansions."

"Your father likes a big house," Mama said.

Archer saw the number first, naturally; it was a fine house so far removed from the street the lawn looked like a park. The little Willys turned into the long drive-way lined with trees and Katie gazed at the gabled roof, its slates reflecting the afternoon sun. There was a wide, wide porch upstairs as well as downstairs and the porches ran around three sides of the house.

"There he is!" Alice exclaimed, pointing excitedly.

Daddy was pacing up and down the porch, looking at his watch and pulling his ear. Yes, Katie thought, that is Daddy. I remember him pulling his ear, and I remember the gold watch and the fancy chain threaded through the buttonhole of his vest.

When he saw them he looked very excited, waving both hands and running to the coachway. As soon as the car stopped, he flung open the door, kissed Mama again and again, then the baby. Timothy started crying and pulled away from him, burying his face in Mama's shoulder. Katie did not want to kiss Daddy either, but she lined up with the others, stiff and strange, waiting her turn.

Inside the house, the front room was very long with a high ceiling. The children stood without moving, afraid to touch anything. There were divans, tables, chairs, mirrors—everything. Daddy was talking fast, pulling his ear and using his handkerchief to wipe his forehead.

"Now, Becky, this house is not far from the governor's mansion."

"Very nice, Malcolm," Mama said. "Where's the kitchen?"

Daddy slid open the wide mahogany doors that separated the living room from the library. Archer scooted down the hall, and he and Katie found the kitchen right away. In the wall of the pantry was a dumbwaiter that Archer made go up and down. He said food could be sent upstairs that way, but Katie didn't know whether or not to believe him. In the pantry were cases of oranges, eggs, sacks of flour, sugar, potatoes, cane syrup, fresh pineapples, and watermelons.

Archer and Katie tore up the stairs two at a time, Mama calling after them, "Children, don't race through the house." She sent Brother to quiet them down.

"There's *three* bathrooms!" Archer hollered, "with fancy fixtures!"

"Not so loud!" Brother shouted.

"And what's this?" Katie asked, stepping onto the second floor porch which was screened all around and had folding cots set up.

"It's a sleeping porch," Brother explained.

The best discovery of all was the tiny "studio," as Brother called it, a room under the attic roof with a skylight and secret stairway.

"Come on, quit gawking," Archer ordered as he led the way down the narrow, twisting steps.

Outside there was a garden with a few gaillardias blooming, a fountain, bird bath, and sundial. In the back lay a deep lot with an old-timey carriage house, stables and servants' quarters, a woodpile, a grape arbor, and a thicket of trees.

"The Colorado River runs back there somewhere," Brother told them.

All the family loved the house. When Mama was making beds or working in the kitchen, she was always singing, "Let Me Call You Sweetheart," "My Blue

Heaven," or "Little Sweetheart of the Rockies." When she wasn't singing sweetheart songs, she was singing, "When They Ring Those Golden Bells," and to Katie, Mama's voice was like a golden bell.

Summer in Texas was hot—dry and hot. Mama ordered naps for Katie as well as for Timothy. Katie was lying on her father's bed pretending to be asleep on a Sunday afternoon. Alice and Jane, who were nearly twelve and never took naps, came in looking for a dime to buy ice cream. Mama must have told them they could look in Daddy's pockets because they were going through his trousers, vest, and coat. Jane yanked an envelope from the inside coat pocket; they looked at each other. "Go ahead, open it," Alice said.

As they read, their faces looked scared. Jane whispered, "It's a love letter!" With that she stuffed the letter back in a pocket. As the two of them dashed out of the room, Katie saw the letter fall to the floor.

When Daddy came in to get his coat, he found the letter lying on the floor and picked it up. "How did this get on the floor?" he asked Katie.

"Jane dropped it."

Clenching his jaw, his face twitched. He left the room in a hurry but came right back. "Here's a quarter, Katie," Daddy said, pressing the coin in her palm and closing her fingers over it. "Don't tell anyone about this, hear?"

Katie didn't tell anyone. She waited to see what Daddy would do to the twins, but he never did anything. In fact, the very next day he hired an art teacher to give Alice and Jane lessons in oil painting. With paints, easels, and canvases, they withdrew to the studio and spent hours there practicing what they learned in the lessons. Katie couldn't even watch them. Daddy told Katie she wasn't allowed to bother their things and that he didn't want to hear any squabbling about it.

Daddy was hard to understand. He was like Archer—he could be very nice when he wanted something. Mama was different; sometimes Katie wondered if Mama loved her at all when she fussed, but Mama still found time to show Katie things and talk to her. There was nobody who understood Katie the way Mama did— Katie didn't have to say anything for Mama to know exactly what she was thinking.

Mama was making biscuits the day she told Katie about Mr. O. Henry. She was adding spoonfuls of creamy lard to flour in a bowl. "O. Henry was a writer and he lived in a small cabin by the river right in back of this house. Up on the street in one of these big homes lived a girl whose father was wealthy. This young girl liked O. Henry and would walk down to the river every day to see him."

Mama filled a crater in the flour with buttermilk and began stirring the mixture. "But she knew O. Henry would not ask her to marry him if he knew she was well-to-do, so she wore plain housedresses when she went walking by the river, and he never guessed."

Mama sprinkled flour on the board and dumped the dough from the bowl. Cupping the dough in her hands, Mama cuffed and patted it into a soft round mound. The gold band on her left hand was all floured over, but the ring was like a part of her. Alice said that ring had never been off Mama's hand since the day Daddy put it on her finger.

"Sure enough," Mama continued, "they fell in love." She was poking the dough with her knuckles and kneading it with the heel of her hand. "One day they walked up to a minister's house next door and asked him to marry them." Mama pinched off a piece of dough for Katie, then began rolling the biscuits with the rolling pin.

Katie was thinking about Mr. O. Henry when she found the tiles in the shed out back. They were large square tiles in different colors—blue, cream, red, yellow—and Katie was told she could play with them.

After some experimenting she knew exactly what she would do with them; she would make a walkway from the side porch to the sundial for Daddy. He would certainly like that.

In laying the tiles, Katie was careful to keep them straight, four to a step and a few inches apart, about the size of Daddy's long foot. As she worked, she realized that what she wanted to be was a writer like Mr. O. Henry. She thought: *I probably thought of that before; it seems like way back I did, but I never said I wanted to be a writer. Like these tiles—I will write about them. I'll write about beautiful ladies in organdy dresses strolling along this walk with their gentlemen friends dressed in riding breeches and polished boots.*

Making the walk took all afternoon, and when she was finished Katie took a bath and dressed in clean clothes from top to bottom. Waiting in the coachway for Daddy to come home, she sighed a hundred times. It took him forever, she thought, and he was always late when you most wanted him to come home early. At last, the Cadillac turned in the driveway. Daddy honked the horn, but when the car came to a stop he got out without looking her way, went to the trunk, and reached down for a box. "Look, I brought Timothy a puppy." Lifting the box, he was smiling, pleased with himself, and his mind was only on the puppy.

Katie tried to tell him about the walk. "Daddy, I have a surprise for you." But he did not hear her.

"His name is True Luck," Daddy was saying, motioning her to open the screen door. "Becky," he called, "I'm home. Bring Tim."

The other children heard him and came from all directions, crowding to see the dog, which to Katie was a strange looking creature with big ears and a tail too long for its body.

Daddy lifted the puppy out of the box and held it for all to see. Mama laughed. "Why, Malcolm, I do believe you have discovered an exotic species. Children, have any of you ever seen an animal like this?"

Suddenly the dog let loose a stream of water that poured down the front of Daddy's shirt. He thrust the puppy at arm's length, looking frantically for a place to put him. "In the box, Malcolm, in the box!" Everybody was laughing except poor Daddy. He dropped True Luck in the box disgustedly and went upstairs to wash. Brother went for the mop.

No one could coax Timothy to touch the puppy; he drew back and clung to Mama. Alice turned up her nose. "That dog has fleas—he's bound to!"

Archer was not afraid of fleas and took True Luck, wriggling in his arms, to find a doghouse out back. "Mind you," Mama called after him, "Kipling says, 'Brothers and sisters, I bid you beware, Of giving your heart to a dog to tear.'"

No one ever looked at the walk except Archer, and he said it was silly. Maybe it was. Katie decided not to show it to anyone. After supper, Daddy went walking in the yard, and although he walked over the tiles to the sundial, he didn't say anything about the little walkway.

When Mama came out on the porch, Daddy sat with her on the swing, his arm around her. "I've got to go to Tyler tomorrow," he said. "It's about the hotel. There's trouble there. I'll be gone about a week. If you need me, Dad will know where I am."

"What kind of trouble, Malcolm?"

"Nothing important."

While he was gone, two Mexicans came to see him. They were ex-convicts. Daddy had told them to come there until they could find jobs and a place to stay. When Mama told them they could not stay in her house, they became angry and started jabbering in Spanish. Mama reached for the pistol, pointed it at the men, and told them to leave.

The rest of the week Mama kept the doors locked and she slept downstairs with the gun under her pillow.

When Daddy returned, Mama was telling him about the men as she unpacked his suitcase. "Malcolm, you can't have ex-convicts coming to the house, that is all there is to it!"

He laughed. "Arturo and Martinez are harmless. I thought you could use them as house servants for a while."

"Malcolm, you must be out of your mind!" She stopped in the middle of the conversation, her hand touching a small round object in the corner of the bag. She straightened and said, "Malcolm, what is this rouge doing in your bag?"

"What rouge?" he asked. "Let me see that." He took it from her hand, glanced at it, and threw the rouge in the wastebasket. Mama followed him out of the room, and Katie knew she was furious.

Poor Daddy, thought Katie. *Why does Mama get upset about every little thing?*

After supper, when Daddy put on his slippers, Katie took his shoes and polished them until they shone like satin, then placed them beside his bed where he would be sure to see them. But when bedtime came, Daddy went to another room to sleep and did not notice the shoes.

Life in the big house was short-lived. In six months they moved into a smaller house on Guadalupe, a winding street, and the children had to change schools.

"Why do we have to move?" Archer asked.

"Daddy lost money on a deal that fell through," Brother told him.

"Shoot!"

"There's no place here to set up our easels," Alice complained.

The only thing that interested Katie about the new house was the French telephone, a phone made all in one piece. Every time it rang, one of the twins rushed to it first. When it rang one morning, Jane answered and hung up.

"Who was it?" Mama asked, putting down the paper.

"Some lady wanting Daddy."

Mama frowned. "Well, don't answer it next time. If it rings, I'll answer it." She began sprinkling clothes to iron, and Katie could tell by the way she was rolling them up and stacking them so firmly that she was getting angrier by the minute.

In the afternoon the phone rang again and Mama reached for it. Cupping her hand over the mouthpiece she said, "Children, find something outside to do."

Katie had not left the kitchen when Mama spoke into the receiver. Without saying more than a few words she slammed down the phone. "That hussy!" she muttered.

In a few months, the MacLeods moved again, this time to San Gabriel beyond the insane asylum—a scary place to live. All the men there wore white pants and shirts and stayed behind fences, sitting on benches and ambling about. Mama cautioned the girls about going on the grounds, although a lot of people who weren't patients strolled the paths and crossed bridges over the winding canals.

Katie associated life in the asylum with Tchaikovsky's symphonies because it was while they lived in San Gabriel that Mama insisted that they listen to Walter Damrosch on the radio to learn about music. Some of the dreary music seemed to say what those men in white must be feeling. Katie and Alice loved the program but the boys made every excuse not to listen. When Walter Damrosch came on the radio, True Luck would tuck his tail between his legs and howl like a hound, which he was not, and the boys would whoop with delight. "Make them stop!" Alice would beg, but Mama couldn't because she would be laughing too.

Katie shared the twins' room on San Gabriel, they in one double bed and she in another. It must have been very late one night when a light from the living room shined in her face and woke her up. Alice and Jane were not awakened because the light didn't shine on them.

Brother was coming out of the boys' room. "What is it, Mama?"

"Malcolm isn't home yet."

"Call the hotel; that's where he is!"

"When they hear my voice they won't ring his room. They'll make some excuse."

"Then I'll call him," Brother said angrily.

He looked up the number and dialed it. Katie heard him say, "Mr. MacLeod's room." There was a pause. "Daddy, this is Brother." Silence. "I'm your son, Oliver O'Gilvie MacLeod." He raised his voice. "Oh, yes, you do have a son! You know good and well who I am and you better get home!"

Brother put down the phone and came back to the living room. Katie could see his face, white with anger. Mama laid her hand on his shoulder.

Brother spoke and his voice cracked, "I'd like to ram my fist in his face."

"Shhh, you'll wake the children."

He wheeled around. "Mama, you ought to leave him!"

"I can't do that, Son."

"*Leave* him, Mama! *Leave* him!" he pleaded.

"Brother, he's been a philanderer most of our married life." The words were hard for Mama to say. "But I can't leave him—he's the father of these six children."

Brother crossed his arms on his knees and buried his head. Mama stroked his hair lovingly and laid her hand on his shoulder. "You are too young for all this, Son. All your life you've borne responsibility that was not yours to bear. If there was some other way—" She sighed. "Turn out the lights, Brother, he'll be home soon. Leave the porch light burning." She turned and went in her room.

In the darkness Katie lay in the double bed listening. Before long she heard an automobile round the corner and saw the headlights coming down the street. The car eased into the driveway. Daddy let himself in quietly, turned off the porch light, but instead of going to Mama's room he slipped into the girls' room. Katie could see him undressing by the light of the street lamp. As he eased into Katie's bed, he pushed her toward the wall and turned his back to her.

Katie did not see Daddy until the next afternoon when he came home from the office. Mama was not speaking to him, so he told Katie and the girls to get in the car, that they were going to the street market. Then he went in the kitchen and somehow persuaded Mama to go along. Archer came out with them but Brother wouldn't go.

The street market was wonderful—vegetable stands lined the plaza, people played guitars and sang in the street, pushcarts steamed with hot treats, women argued over prices.

"Just like the carnival," Jane said.

Mama bought fresh fruit and vegetables; Daddy bought each of them a hot tamale from a fat brown woman who spoke only Spanish.

The next morning, Daddy sat at the kitchen table with Brother after everyone had eaten breakfast and left. Everyone except Katie, that is. She was spooning oatmeal out of the three-cornered pot that rested in the deep well of the electric range.

"Son, I want you to go to the university in the fall. I gave your mother the money for the tuition. It'll be there when you need it."

Brother looked very sour. "Where'd you get it?"

"That's the best part of all. It's an advance. I'm going to develop property on Bull Creek, make it into a resort. Got the contract yesterday."

Brother kept his eyes on the saltshaker as he rolled it on its bottom.

"You can work for me through the summer, survey-ing the property." Brother still said nothing. "That's pretty land out there—all the natural formations and water necessary for a real resort."

Finally Brother spoke. There was an edge to his voice and he did not smile. "When do we start?"

Daddy smiled. "Tomorrow morning."

That was the first Katie had heard of Bull Creek. As soon as school was out they moved there.

SIX
The Auction

On Bull Creek everyone had something to do every
waking minute to get ready for the sale to be held in late
summer. Daddy was supervising a crew of men building
a boardwalk on the edge of the south cliff where the
view was spectacular. Brother was surveying the land;
men were chopping trees; Mama said even the girls
must do their part. Alice and Jane helped with the
cooking and serving of meals on tables under the live
oaks in back of the house. Archer helped Brother and
carried water to the workmen. If Daddy did not bring
enough water in the car, some of them would have to
walk to the spring and haul water up the cliff in
buckets.

Katie did not understand how her assignment helped
the effort. Her work was to empty and clean the
chamber pots and slop jars every morning.

"Katie, I know this is a disagreeable task," Mama
said, "but you do understand that we are all too busy to
do it and this is very important." They were carrying
the enamelware pots to the woods in back of the house.
"You must always go a great distance from the house,

Katie, because we don't want flies. Bury it well—I know the ground is hard. If you can't dig a hole, cover the excrement with dirt."

They emptied the vessels, and Mama piled dirt and cedar needles on the remains. "Do it the same way you do when you go to the bathroom. Don't leave any toilet tissue to be seen. Then you must wash the pots, scrub them with sand, and set them in the sun before you put them back under the beds."

Katie would do anything for Mama. Never in a million years would Alice touch a pee pot, which is what Archer called a chamber, and although Jane might, she wouldn't do it without a great big fuss. "We must never look down on work that is honest, Katie," Mama said, and often Mama cleaned the pots for her.

Of them all, Mama worked the hardest, standing over the open fire lifting heavy kettles, calling for more firewood, stirring, seasoning—the heat shimmering above the blaze and Mama's hair flying loose beneath her straw hat. In defiance of the merciless sun, she would take off the hat and throw it aside if it got in her way. Like Archer, she was not afraid of anything, not even the sun that could cook your brains. She kept the shotgun propped against a tree, ready if a snake should come near, and sometimes threatening True Luck with it when he came too close to the stew. Katie felt perfectly safe in her care.

Daddy would watch Mama work, and he'd smile with admiration. Every day that he went into town he brought home supplies—canned milk, sugar, beans, flour, rice, lard, and kerosene for the lamps. They stacked it on shelves in the cook tent secured against varmints. But Mama wanted live chickens on the place, so Daddy brought home barred rock pullets, biddies, silverlace Wyandotte hens, and a red rooster.

Mama was sitting at the picnic table, fanning with the big hat, when Daddy came up the mountain with provisions. "Did you bring the paper?" Mama asked.

Daddy never forgot the paper because if he did Mama

would be disappointed. She opened his jug of mineral water and poured him a glassful. He drank it every day for his health. No one else liked it. Archer said it smelled like vomit, but he didn't say that in front of Mama.

Daddy waved the paper at Mama, but folded it and tucked it under his arm. Plainly, he wanted to talk.

"Becky, I figure on two hundred lots all tol'. That doesn't include waterfront property. There's no telling what we'll make on this sale!" Katie could see him getting excited, his eyes sort of unseeing as ideas exploded in his head. "If land on the flat goes well, we'll make a fortune on the creek lots."

"I don't think we should count our chickens before they hatch, Malcolm. There's no water up here."

"There will be as soon as we get the money to clean the well. That's a fine artesian well."

"Malcolm, people don't have money to buy bread, much less land."

Katie rubbed her finger between her toes to get out the dirt. Mama never looked dirty and she never looked tired, no matter how hard she worked. It was as if work nourished her: she was soft and round in places and her skin was smooth as silk. Sometimes Katie wondered if Mama was real or if she would turn out to be something more than Mama, an important angel maybe or a champion like Joan of Arc, or a beautiful singer on a stage.

"Becky, you'd be surprised how much capital people have," Daddy was saying "Brother Tom is doing well in insurance out east; Steve and Benjamin in Tyler are making a mint in mortgages."

"Foreclosures?"

Daddy nodded. "Steve says he would give half his life to be a millionaire."

"What an awful thing to say!"

"This is an ideal time to buy real estate. Why a man can buy property now for a fraction of the price he'll pay five years from now."

"With Roosevelt?"

"With or without Roosevelt." Daddy was positive.

"I wish we had another Teddy Roosevelt."

"You'd probably like Calvin Coolidge."

"Maybe."

"Becky, after this sale you won't ever have to work like this again. After the sale you and I will take a nice long vacation. We'll take the children to Hot Springs and enjoy the baths."

"That would be nice. Now will you give me the paper?" He handed it to her and she headed for the house.

Katie leaned on the table, watching Daddy as he jotted down figures on the back of an envelope. She studied his hands, his face. There was a carefulness in the way he wrote as if he took pride in the big, bold handwriting full of sharp strokes and firm decimals. His hands were those of a gentleman, strong but gentle, with manicured nails and small blond hairs about the knuckles. The ruby ring on his right hand was just the right size to be gentlemanly.

In his face there was a special light when he was happy, but usually there was light and shadow as in a portrait. His brow was broad and high, his nose long and straight. It was in his eyes that Katie saw pain and sadness or laughter and joy. The mouth he kept composed, even as he controlled the sound of his gentleman's voice.

"Daddy," she asked, "what's a philanderer?"

He didn't hear her.

Katie spread her elbows on the table and rested her chin. Somewhere behind his dear face lay the reason for the shadows. He was not a mean man, not a bad man. Somewhere within him was a weakness.

Daddy kept pulling his ear and smiling. He was dreaming again.

There wasn't much time for anyone to dream. Katie got up and went down to the house to sit on the doorstep and look out across the flat. *All this work is only so they can sell the flat,* Katie thought. *Sell the flat so they can go back to life as it used to be. Why would anyone want that? I like Bull Creek. A person has everything he needs or wants right here.*

The flat was covered with Mexican Hat flowers bending with the wind away from the cliff, and massive clumps of cacti stood at different angles against the wind, unyielding and strong. Chunks of limestone, jagged forms riddled through with holes—honeycomb rocks—were strewn about as if some angry Providence had claimed the place and defied man to tame it. Only the pecan trees rimming the flat seemed tame and graceful.

Katie knew that over her head in the oak tree limbs, deadly centipedes crawled about, and under the house near where she sat, tarantulas and scorpions had been seen. Yet she loved this place with a passion such as she had never known before.

There was only one way to get to this Paradise. Brother and the other men had cut a crude road down the bluff to the place where the car could ford the creek. Coming from town on the paved road, the car was driven through the shallow water along Brother's road up to the flat. The road was passable, but Brother and the men were still working on it, digging out the bigger rocks and snaking logs up the mountain by horses to fill in low places.

As he worked, Brother was always hollering or yodeling for water. When Archer and Katie would reach him, he would be panting. A heat rash covered his fair skin, sweat drenched his pants, dripped off his nose. He could drink half a bucket of water.

Katie drew up her knees beneath her chin, listening to the sounds of hammers, axes chopping, and to the lazy clunking of a cowbell. Steers, standing in the shade of the lone oak in the middle of the flat, were waiting for the sun to lower and lengthen the shadows before making their way down to the creek to drink. They would wade the wide creek to get to the mineral spring on the other side. Horses, belonging to the cedar cutters, stood motionless beneath the pecan trees, drowsing.

Every morning Katie was awakened by the sound of horse hooves clip-clopping outside. Workmen would be dismounting and milling about, unfastening cinch belts and swinging down heavy saddles. The horses would graze all day while the men worked; then, at sundown each man would rope his mount and saddle up for the ride home. A few of the horses had to be hobbled to keep them from wandering away. Mama hated hobbling and Katie did too.

The smell of bacon and coffee drifting from the cook tent got everybody out of bed. Tin plates stacked with flapjacks were served. Katie would eat and watch the horses stamping their hooves, swishing their tails against the flies. Nibbling at weeds, they would raise their heads, blow through their nostrils, and take a few clomping strides, their heads tossing this way and that.

Sometimes Maas would let Katie ride his big bay, Sam. Maas, a bachelor, lived on the ranch across the creek and worked for Daddy. Hanging on to the saddle horn, her skinny legs askew, Katie was in her glory riding Sam. The creaking saddle, the smell of leather and sweat, the ground so far below, swaying with the powerful animal as it moved from side to side—all made Katie giddy with delight.

"Katie!" It was Archer in back of the house. "Come help me carry this water!"

It was easier when two of them carried a bucket because they could put a stick through the handle and distribute the load. Each of them held one end of the stick, and this meant they had to stay together or water would slosh out of the bucket. Katie helped Archer dodge cacti and cow droppings, but if the danger was on her side he did not cooperate; the best Katie could do was tiptoe through cow manure and pray it wasn't fresh.

The cedar cutters, stripped to the waist, were lean and hard, their ribs standing out like washboards. Their skin was leathery from the Texas sun, their hands horny from hard labor. Sweat stained the bands of their wide-brimmed hats, leaving permanent high water marks, thin brown lines where sweat had soaked the felt.

The men handled axes with expert skill, the rhythm of their strokes measured as if they were keeping time to music. Each stroke landed the blade in precisely the same angle as the one before so that the cut was clean, accurate to the hair, exposing the red wood. Large trees were felled by two men chopping one on either side of the tree, slashing with alternate strokes to bring the tree down. Working with double-bladed axes, they stripped limbs and branches from the trunks, leaving straight poles for building the boardwalk and road.

Water was always welcome. Maas held the dipper high, his neck stretched backward like a chicken's gullet, his Adam's apple bobbing up and down as he drank.

As a way of saying thank you, Maas handed Archer his Winchester. "Go ahead, take a shot."

Archer raised the gun, took aim and knocked a branch off a tree.

"Goldurnit, you're a good shot, Archie. How long you been in Texas?"

"More'n a year."

"City don't count." Maas put a piece of tobacco in his jaw. "How old are ye?"

"Eleven this month."

"Archie, boy, by the time I was your age I had done been bit two times by rattlers. I was cuttin' cedar by time I was nine year old and my pappy showed me how to slice a snake bite and suck out the poison. An' he taught me how to shoot. What's your pappy taught you?" When Archer didn't answer, he continued. "I been bit nine times all tol' by rattlers and I can't count the snakes I kilt."

They heard the dinner bell ringing. The men put on their shirts, shouldered their axes, and headed for the house.

The MacLeods ate at one table, the men at another. Like Joseph and his brothers in Egypt, Katie thought. Large pots of chicken and dumplings, rice, blackeye peas, and dried apples were on the tables, and tin plates were set for the men.

Mama tried to "maintain a semblance of gentility," as she called it, by using silver on the family table, but it was difficult; everybody was so hungry and so busy they came to the table ravenous and rude. Because there was an unwritten rule that when prayer was being offered everyone was to freeze in whatever position the plea to the Almighty caught him, Mama asked the blessing at the most strategic moment. To check the assault on the food, she would begin praying just as the boys were stepping over the benches to take their places. The brief halt in the action did little to slow the attack, but it helped.

In the Texas heat the men were obliged to rest after dinner, squatting on their spurs in the shade. The cedar cutters said a man never wasted time if he was sharpening his axe. Each man rubbed his blade with pumice until the steel glistened and then held it up to eye the edge. Maas beckoned to Archer as he leaned his axe blade at an angle to the sun and watched as nearly invisible red bugs crawled on the shiny surface. Maas grinned. "See them little devils? They's the ones bite the tar outta' you!"

Axes sharpened, the men pulled out tobacco pouches to roll cigarettes. Daddy tried to engage them in conversation. "Do you think the veterans will get their bonus?" he asked of no one in particular.

There was silence all around as stiff-jointed fingers handled cigarette papers.

"They're really raising a ruckus in Washington, not willing to wait until nineteen forty-five when it's promised to them," Daddy continued.

Still no response as the men clumsily formed cradles with the papers and sprinkled loose tobacco in them.

"Of course," Daddy said, shifting his position, trying

to hunker down the way they did, "if we go off the gold standard there's no telling what the country will come to. Probably be bankrupt by nineteen forty-five."

Maas spread the tobacco evenly in the paper trough, pulled the string of the pouch with his teeth and dropped the bag in his shirt pocket. Moistening the edge of the paper, he rolled it, pressed the ends closed, and drawled, "Worse thing they can do to folks in these parts is to do away with Prohibition." His leathery face creased into a grin. Holding a match head against his thigh, Maas raked it across his pants to strike it. Sheltering the flame with the palm of his hand, he brought the light to the cigarette and puffed twice. Then Maas took a long draw, savoring the smoke. "Wal," he continued, "there ain't nuthin' I ain't lived through. I seen drought come through here that only the goats lived through and I seen wind come barrellin' outa' the panhandle that froze cattle in their tracks—a norther that stretched ice all acrost these mountains. An' I seen flash floods fill Bull Creek so full o' water she spilled into the river clean over the mud bog. Right now, today, I know people on Prairie Dog Mount'in to git so hongry they eat prairie dogs—claim the young'uns is tender if'n they ain't tasty."

After that, Daddy gave up trying to talk with the men and went up to the tables where Mama was.

The days and weeks flew past. Daddy had taken Archer all over the country nailing up advertising posters. The boardwalk was completed, ready for city people to promenade along its planks and swoon over the breathtaking view. The road was in good enough condition for Daddy to begin bringing prospective buyers for a look at the land.

Brother was painting the last of the road signs to direct traffic to Bull Creek and place signs for the property's attractions. The pointers, painted white, were lettered with great care. Brother drew the narrow brush down and around, the gleaming black paint flowing smoothly, forming the letters for "Lakewood Hills," "Goats' Cave," "Mineral Spring," "Johnson Hollow," "Boardwalk," and names of streets still in the imagination.

Since there was absolutely no one else available, Daddy rolled up his sleeves and called Katie to help him stake the lots. Katie cut red sailcloth into narrow strips, making a little red flag for each of the stakes.

"Katie," he said, "never do anything that you can pay someone else to do." She handed him a stake. "If you can hire someone to do something, that frees you to think of other ideas. You can make more money with your head than with your hands."

Katie felt very important holding the stakes while he tacked the flags to them. She loved being with Daddy, but his attention was short-lived. He continued talking, but more to himself than to Katie.

"I have to get someone to start whitewashing the trees tomorrow. We don't have much time. And I've got to go into town to order the beef for the barbecue."

He sounded as if he was worrying but he wasn't—he was happy. When he wasn't talking out loud to himself, he was whistling. It was the same song he sang when he shaved, "Will There Be Any Stars in My Crown?" He had sung it so much Katie had learned all the words. The song reminded her of the tent meetings in the meadow across from Twenty-nine.

At the end of the day, Daddy would join the men at the picnic tables under the oaks and share a drink from their jug. Mama didn't like that—men swinging a jug onto their shoulder and taking a swig directly from its mouth. Daddy used a tin cup, but Mama didn't like that either. After a few swigs, Maas would mount Sam and ride across the flat, singing at the top of his voice, "Come ti yi youpy, youpy yea, youpy yea, Come ti yi youpy, youpy yea."

Katie was standing in the yard, watching Maas crossing the flat, when she heard Archer yodeling from the boardwalk. He beckoned her to come. She jumped up and ran across the flat, grasshoppers in flight hitting her legs. She leaped cacti and honeycomb rocks, True Luck hard on her heels.

Archer had disappeared into Goats' Cave and Katie scrambled down the trail to find him.

Goats' Cave ran along under the cliff beneath the boardwalk, one side open to the deep, wide chasm above the creek. Lower than the roof of the cave was a limestone shelf where, in the powdery dust or adobe, were the prints of goats' hooves. At one end of Goats' Cave was a wall of stone, pocked and seamed. "Rattlesnake den," Archer warned, as if Katie didn't know. High-stepping around the den, Katie kept her eye on the crevices, sure that a diamondback would strike out at her, but none did. Only a dry skin shed by a snake lay in the dust at her feet as evidence, and if the thin trails marking the floor of the cave were snake trails, then there was that too. True Luck, his ears laid back, was raising sand, barking and jumping about, his flanks trembling.

Archer was out of sight, thrashing through the brush. "Over here, Katie. Bandit Cave!" he yelled.

Katie crawled through the brush to get to him. Bandit Cave's narrow opening on the face of the cliff belied the deep black hole that reached the bowels of the earth.

"Daddy said they found the skeleton of a man in here, a bandit who robbed banks and hid out here. Lookit the bullet holes!" He pressed his finger in one hole after another. "Come on, let's see what's inside." Crouching down, he entered. "Maas swears there's bank loot in these hills." Archer's voice resounded in the hollow cavern. "He says it's in Johnson Hollow but I say it might be right here in this cave!"

Katie held onto Archer's shirt as they groped in the pitch black dark. Her heart was thumping in her chest. Stepping on what she thought must be a branch—it was underneath her instep—Katie felt it move! "Snake!" she screamed. "It's a snake!"

"Stand still!" Archer ordered as she clutched him frantically. The snake was not coiling; big and heavy, it was moving sluggishly across the floor of the cave. "Let's get outta' here," Archer said, and they made a dash for it.

Katie was shaking all over.

"Aw, it didn't hurt ya," he scoffed. "And you better not tell Mama or you'll never get to come here again."

Archer stood at the edge of the cliff looking straight down the steep drop. How much like an Indian, he was, thought Katie. He could stand motionless, like a part of the scene, fearless, defiant—his hair laid back by the wind. If he chose, he could break into a run, his lithe body slipping through the brush noiselessly. Already he had dismissed the snake from his mind and was seeing what he could see.

Below the bluff, hidden from view by the cottonwoods, was Bull Creek meandering all the way around the mountain. To the right was the Colorado River. "Over there," Archer said, sweeping his arm in a wide arc, "where the creek looks like it runs into the river, there's a mud bog. If you ever try to walk across that bog, you'll sink in over your head and get buried alive in no time. Nobody—*nobody* can pull you out unless there's somebody right there with a horse and a lasso. There's a bunch o' cows gone down in that bog."

He waited for the full effect to register with Katie.

Below them, between the creek and the Colorado, lay Maas's ranch, its pastures laid out with fences. If Maas was in a hurry to get to the flat, he would take a shortcut. He would cross the creek in his boat and climb the cliff but usually he went around by the road on horseback.

From where they stood they could hear a horse whinnying on Maas's place. The sound, traveling across the vast, open space, marked the limitless freedom Katie felt and gloried in.

A scuttling in the brush startled her; something was

scurrying in the undergrowth, kicking up rocks and dirt.

"Armadillos," Archer said calmly. "They're harmless. Come on, let's go. I'm hungry."

Before the day of the sale, Daddy brought two men from Round Rock to look over the property. Katie was in the yard, sitting on the ground, washing lamp chimneys. She had trimmed the wicks and filled the bases with oil. Washing chimneys was fun, but when the men in their city suits stood watching her, she felt embarrassed. The smut on her arms and hands must have been on her face as well because Daddy told her to find Mama and get cleaned up.

If Daddy was embarrassed, he forgot about it. The men bid on thirteen lots and said they would be back for the sale and raise their bids if necessary.

Daddy was happier than Katie had ever seen him—humming his favorite hymn, "Will There Be Any Stars in My Crown?" He laughed and joked at supper and drove twice to the spring for water so they could all take baths. Katie preferred the creek with its sun-warmed water, but the girls and Mama always used the galvanized tub. They bathed in Mama and Daddy's room with the curtains pulled, but when Katie and Timothy bathed, the tub was put outside on the picnic tables so water wouldn't splash all over the floor.

Alice and Jane were particular—they wouldn't wash their hair in anything but rainwater, but before the sale the rain barrels were dry. The girls were worrying about what they would do.

Two days before the sale, a barbecue pit was dug and Mama insisted that it be screened and a roof built overhead. Archer put up a cold drink stand under the oaks. Daddy and Brother sat at the picnic table with maps spread out, deciding where to put the bandstand, where to set up tables, where to start the auction, and who would be responsible for what.

"Son, you and Maas will be in the crowd to raise the

bids. Be sure you follow my signals. We don't want you buying any lots!"

Brother smiled.

Katie's heart was heavy as the day of the sale drew nearer. *Soon Bull Creek will be gone,* she thought, *and we'll be back in some house in town with cement sidewalks.*

Mama must have sensed how she felt because for dinner she made a big macaroni-and-cheese pie. "Katie, I made your favorite dish," Mama said.

The next morning, Mama woke Katie out of a sound sleep whispering, "Katie, come see—"

They slipped outside without a sound. Light was beginning to show over Cat Mountain. At first, Katie thought Mama wanted to show her a herd of jackrabbits heading for the creek, but then Mama stooped down and pointed toward the boardwalk. "Over there—" In the grayness it was hard to see, but then Katie caught sight of a deer, then another and another—three of them! A buck with a high crown of antlers, a doe, and a fawn were feeding on the edge of the flat. Katie did not budge as the deer moved cautiously across the flat. Then the buck was startled, snapped his head erect, and the three of them bounded into the cedar brake.

"Oh, Mama!"

That night all the workmen stayed to tend the barbecue. They were drinking and laughing. Some of them strummed guitars and sang.

As Katie lay on her cot, she saw heavy clouds rolling in over Cat Mountain with flashes of lightning. Brother came inside for his slicker. "Lord knows we need rain," he said. "Probably won't be enough to settle the dust, though."

Big drops began to splatter the ground. Katie pulled back the curtain and pressed against the screen. Then it began raining hard. Gusts of wind threw spray against her cheek; it felt cool on her face. Rain rolled off the roof in streams of water from the eaves. A bucket rolled in the yard. In the flash of lightning that crackled and split the sky, Katie could see broad sheets of water sweeping across the flat. Rain was thundering on the roof like cattle stampeding. It didn't last long. As it slackened, there was a rising and falling, a swelling sound, like heavy sighing.

The torrent was over but sometime in the night, Katie woke up and again rain was falling with a steady drumming on the roof.

Listening in the darkness, the many different sounds reminded Katie of the Walter Damrosch music. Above the drumming on the roof there was a rapid, "ting, ting, ting" as raindrops hit against tin. Another note, all out of harmony, kept up a dull, thudding sound against a screen. It was like fast and slow music; like joy and like sorrow.

Katie fell asleep again, and when she awoke in the night there was no more downpour, only water gushing, gurgling, running in rivulets on the ground. Pressing her head against the screen, she heard a drizzling rain whispering through the leaves; the wind blew a sweeping patter across the roof. Katie lay back. The rain barrels will be full, she thought. Alice and Jane could wash their hair.

The sale was only hours away. The thought of it made Katie's heart ache. She sat up, pulled back the curtain to see the men at the barbecue pit. Huddled under ponchos, silhouetted against the fires of the pit, they looked like vultures at vigil.

When day finally dawned, the flat was flooded with sunshine. The cook tent was down, collapsed under the weight of water and wind. A sack of flour was ruined and dry wood was hard to find, but Mama cooked oatmeal and coffee for everyone.

"That thar musta' been the end of a gulf storm," Maas said as he struggled to prop up the tent. "If the river rises I could lose my lower pasture."

People from the hills began arriving on horseback and in wagons, coming up the old abandoned wagon road back of the schoolhouse. Children and dogs swarmed around the barbecue pit, eyeing the succulent meat, drippings hissing in the fire as the spits were turned and the meat swabbed with sauce. Archer counted three cars on Lookout Point coming down Cat Mountain to the sale.

One of the mountain men remarked. "Creek's up."

Mama asked, "How high?"

"Just a tad."

They could hear a car's motor straining to climb the bluff up from the creek. "Somebody's coming," Brother said and began walking out to meet them. A Ford truck nosed through the cedar brake and battled its way across the flat.

"That's the band," Daddy said. On the side of the truck was lettered, "Luke Tomlinson's String Band." Daddy and Brother met the truck at the well. They talked, then Brother struck out running toward the creek.

Daddy came back to Mama, his face pale. "They say a car can't ford the creek, it's rising by the minute."

"Oh, Malcolm!"

He eased onto the bench, too weak to stand.

More and more hillbillies arrived, all in a holiday spirit, but no townspeople, nobody with money.

Brother came running back. "They can't get across the creek—" He was breathless. "They're turning back."

"Get Maas's boat. We can row them across!"

"That's too dangerous, Dad. We thought about it, but the current is swift. Somebody could drown."

"Lookit the cars going back to town," Archer said, pointing to Lookout Point. Katie had never seen two cars on the road at one time.

"There was lots more rain up the creek," Brother explained. "All the water from all those little hollows ran down and filled the creek. What're we going to do, Dad?"

"We'll have to go ahead with the sale. I'm under contract." There was no color in his face. "Get the band and take them to the boardwalk, we'll start there."

Katie and Archer ran ahead, True Luck loping alongside. Like a flock of birds migrating, the people followed.

The fiddler and banjo player took the lead and struck up spirited music, Luke Tomlinson singing at the top of his lungs, his jugular standing out like a cord against his red neck. "She'll Be Comin' Round the Mountain" brought on foot-patting and clapping with endless verses. Then Luke fiddled "Turkey in the Straw" sawing up and down, his fingers flying. Daddy stepped on the box and told one Will Rogers joke after another until the crowd was guffawing and slapping their thighs. Then Daddy talked fast about the property's great value and the scenic wonders of Bull Creek, which the people thought was funnier still. "What am I bid for this choice lot?" he began. "Let's start the bidding at twenty dollars. Do I hear twenty dollars?"

Nobody said anything, but quickly the rapid-fire language Daddy used when he auctioneered rolled off his tongue as fast as greased lightning, and the mountain people were thoroughly entertained. It was a good show, something they had never heard before. Daddy's mouth kept spilling out the sing-song rhythm with quick changes and shifts until the gavel came down. "Sold! To the gentleman in the bottle-green coat."

Katie looked around; the only person wearing a green coat was Brother.

The music, the auctioneering, and eating went on until dark with the crowd milling about between the barbecue pit, the drink stand, and the lots being auctioned.

After dark, when the food was all eaten and the band had left, the mountain people began loading their wagons and moving out. Some of them lingered for hours, lolling under the live oaks, talking and smoking. Finally, when Maas began saddling up, they knew it was time to go.

The sounds of the creaking wagons, the plodding hooves, the clanking traces, the muffled voices sounded a sadness. Katie watched the lanterns bobbing in the darkness until they were out of sight. It was midnight before the MacLeods were left alone around the picnic tables.

Katie leaned on the table, staring at the Milky Way; a shooting star fell across the sky. The pungent smell of meat lingered in the air and the sound of an owl came from the boys' woods—"tu-whit-tu-who, tu-whit-tu-who." The dark trees with their whitewashed trunks looked ghostly in the night.

In the lantern light, Daddy seemed old for his thirty-nine years. Mama stood beside him, facing the wind, tucking hairpins in place. No one spoke. Jane and Alice stood with their arms around each other's waist looking very sad, and Brother looked as if he would cry. Archer carefully emptied his bag of nickels and dimes onto the table, his profits from the drink stand, and proceeded to count them.

Brother blew his nose. He was trying to smile when he spoke. "Well, Maas and I each bought a couple of lots."

"We sold thirteen lots," Mama said. "Thirteen lots to those men from Round Rock and for a good price."

Daddy was staring into space.

"Can't we have another sale?" Jane asked.

Mama laid her hand on Daddy's shoulder and he looked up. "Another sale, can't we have another sale?" Jane repeated.

Daddy shook his head, unable to speak.

"There's no one to put up money for another sale now," Brother explained. "The band, the barbecue—it all costs money."

They fell silent for a long time, listening to the owl, watching Archer counting his money.

"Children, you must go to bed now," Mama said gently. Archer scooped up the coins, poured them back in the bag, and went over to kiss Mama goodnight. The twins and Brother followed him, but Katie waited; she wanted to kiss Daddy too. But Daddy didn't look up, so Mama leaned down, Katie put her arms around her neck and kissed her. "Goodnight, Mama." Mama hugged her and motioned her to run along to bed.

Katie sauntered toward the house, glancing back over her shoulder. She heard Mama speaking softly.

"Come to bed, Malcolm." He turned to Mama and she took him in her arms.

Daddy was crying.

SEVEN
Red
Ants!

After the sale, Daddy stayed in bed three days. Mama carried food to him but it was not touched. He looked as if he had not slept and lay all day staring at the ceiling or the wall. Everyone moved about quietly, speaking softly as they took down tables and the drink stand.

Only Archer seemed able to look straight ahead, forgetting what went before. To Katie, the little red flags drooping in the still air were painful to see.

After everything was dismantled, Brother and Archer went fishing, the twins played dominoes, and Katie lay on her cot to read the Bible story book to Timothy.

"That one," he said, pressing his brown thumb on the picture of the Good Samaritan.

Mama was sitting on Daddy's bed reading the newspaper aloud—all the articles that might interest him— the Washington news; Walter Lippman, who made him mad; and Will Rogers, who made him smile. But Daddy's expression did not change.

Mama worked the crossword puzzle and, still sitting on his bed, mended a shirt, turning the collar so the frayed side wouldn't show. "Malcolm, you cannot blame yourself." Her voice was gentle but strong and clear the way she spoke when someone was sick or scared. "It was an act of God that the creek rose. You could not help that."

Daddy turned his gray eyes toward her, his poor face as grave as death. His voice was hoarse. "What are we going to do, Becky?"

Mama dropped the shirt in her lap as if she had been waiting for him to ask that very question.

"Malcolm, your fee for the auction and the commission on those thirteen lots is due. We're going to take that money, buy a cook stove, move our bed in the girls' room, and make a kitchen out of this room. We'll buy some pigs and corn and we will live here until we can do better."

Daddy was about to roll over again, his face to the wall.

"Wait." There was the promise of surprise in her voice. "We're going to build another road, one that leads up the hill from Pleasant Valley School." Mama paused long enough for him to think through the idea. "Don't you see, if we join the paved road there, it will be above the highway bridge and we won't have to ford the creek. Next summer, if the owners want another sale, we'll be prepared."

Daddy raised his limp hand to his face. "My stars, why didn't I think of that?"

"Another thing. We still have the money for Brother's education. If you need it, it's in the octagon can in the cedar chest."

Daddy shook his head. "No. The boy must go to school."

Mama smiled. "Don't you think you'd better get up and put on your clothes?"

As she started to stand up, he pulled her back down. "Becky—" His face was troubled. As if he couldn't say it, he fell back on the pillow, covering his eyes with his arm.

"What is it, Malcolm?"

"There's one thing more . . . I didn't want to worry you with it."

"Go ahead."

With his arm still over his eyes, he continued. "When I was in Tyler, there was . . . trouble, Becky."

Mama waited. He took a deep breath before he could go on. "A drunk and disorderly woman came to the hotel . . . tried to force her way in. I had to remove her from the premises. She claims I shoved her down a flight of stairs. I say she fell."

Mama sat still, waiting for the rest.

"Claims she hurt her hip . . . Dad is taking care of it for me, but . . . she's threatening to sue for damages."

In the silence that followed, Mama slipped the thimble onto her finger and started working on the shirt again, frowning and pulling the thread slowly, thoughtfully. "Right away?" she asked.

"No. If she brings suit, Dad will put off the case as long as he can."

"If you need the college money to pay her off—"

"We don't have enough money to buy her," he said grimly.

Mama was whipping the collar carefully, giving herself time to think. Eventually, she bit the thread, smoothed the knot with her thumb and examined both sides of the collar. "Well, Malcolm, we will cross that bridge when we come to it." She stood up and crossed the room to where his clothes hung on the wall. "You should have this trench coat cleaned. You'll need it if winter ever comes." Mama put a pair of trousers over her arm. "I'll press these." She was not looking at him but his eyes followed her as she went outside. She called back to him. "Now get up, Malcolm. You need to be in your office."

After a while Daddy put his feet over the side of the bed. He sat in one position for some time, both hands on the edge of the bed, his arms straight, propping up his drooping shoulders.

When he was dressed, he and Mama walked toward

the boardwalk to look at the cows. There was nothing Daddy liked better than a good herd of cattle.

But that night, he was better. He called the family together for prayers. They gathered in their parents' room, Mama and Timothy in the green rocker, the rest of them on the bed. In Daddy's hand was Mama's Bible. They waited respectfully until he spoke.

"Each night one of us will read a chapter," Daddy said, "then we'll pray as we are led." It was a simple formula and it worked. In the evenings that followed, each child took his turn reading a chapter and Mama or Daddy prayed. Daddy never failed to ask the Lord, "May this family circle be unbroken." It was a lovely phrase and Katie thought of it often.

It reminded her of Mama's gold wedding band. Like the ring, the family was a circle—from Mama and Daddy, to Brother, the twins, Archer, and dear, sweet Timothy—without any one of them there would be no circle.

One morning, Katie lay on her stomach watching Daddy getting ready to go to town. As he was shaving, he did not sing as he once did. He wasn't really a good singer but his favorite hymn sounded very fine when he was happy. He would fill the house with "Will There Be Any Stars in My Crown?" and that amused Brother.

Daddy polished his shoes, combed his sandy hair with a fine-toothed comb, and put things back in his pockets with care—his pearl-handled knife, the gold watch, his wallet, and a clean linen handkerchief.

Katie admired his pride. He was like Alice, who as Mama said, "Always puts the best foot forward." *That's what makes us a circle*, Katie thought. *There are threads running through us from one to another. Like Mama's courage and Archer's courage; like Brother's determination and Jane's determination; like Alice's gentleness and Timothy's gentleness. I wonder where I fit in? I wonder if I'm a part of them and if they are a part of me? Could they do without me and the circle not be broken?*

As Daddy was going outside, he pinched Katie's

cheek. "You be a good girl, Cinderella, and help your mother."

Katie followed him into the yard, turning the name over in her mind. *Cinderella?*

Brother was already in the car, ready to go to town to buy the stove. The Cadillac churned up dust crossing the flat, and Katie waved them out of sight.

Katie thought about the Cinderella story with its wicked stepmother, stepsisters, and handsome prince. Nothing in the story really fit Katie except the Cinderella part, the part about Cinderella doing the dirty work. But, if Katie didn't wash the chamber pots and lamp chimneys, who would? Certainly not Alice and Jane who were too frail and pretty for work like that. Katie was not frail. She had almost as many scrapes and bruises as Archer and had survived them all. She didn't brag about the scars and tell all the gruesome details of their history the way Archer did, but she could not hide them, as they were white against her suntanned skin.

Katie decided she would never be pretty. She had too many freckles, and ears that would not lie close to her head.

The hens were singing, a sign they had laid their eggs. Katie would gather the eggs as soon as she saw the Cadillac on Cat Mountain. She sat down to wait.

The mountain was across the creek and although it was not a sharp peak, it was rugged and dominated everything in view. The sun rose over Cat Mountain and, when it was due, the moon. Named for its mountain lions and bobcats, but feared for its moonshiners wary of revenuers, there were legends galore to support its reputation for being a dangerous place. Next to Johnson Hollow, which lay behind the house, Cat Mountain was most feared.

Katie gazed at the mountain, studying the bare rock faces that jutted out, and the tiny trails threading through the brush. At night she could see the fires of the whiskey stills and coal kilns. Two slashes in the mountainside marked the paved road that wound around it. There was a lower cut not far up from the ford; another up the mountain on the right called Lookout Point. From the vantage of Lookout Point they could see the flat and all the hazy view between the creek and the Colorado. That's where Maas's ranch lay, between the creek and the river.

When they were coming from town, Daddy would blow the horn on Lookout Point and Mama would know they would be home in twenty minutes, more or less.

Katie looked up at the sky with its thin layer of buttermilk clouds. A hawk sailed lazily against the morning sun, its wings tipping this way and that to catch the flow of air; its roving eye relentlessly searching the flat for prey. Katie jumped up, waving her hat and hollering, to frighten the hawk away. It was one of her responsibilities. They had no chickens to give to hawks, or foxes, or polecats.

When the hawk flapped its wings and flew over the cedar brake, Katie sat down again. Soon the Cadillac appeared, first at the lower cut, dark against the adobe bank, then, with its motor straining, it climbed the grade to Lookout Point. Reappearing from behind the trees, the car crawled across the stretch of road that led around the shoulder of Cat Mountain, then disappeared from view.

The same road going the other way, followed the foot of the mountain beyond the ford. It ran along level ground beside the creek until it crossed the highway bridge where the spring was; it passed the schoolhouse and wound through the Texas hills to who knows where. Beyond the highway bridge, where the schoolyard led to the foot of their mountain, Mama said that was where they would build the new road. It would be a steep climb, but if Mama said they could do it, they would.

All day long, Mama, Jane, and Alice rearranged furniture, calling Katie to come help lift the cedar chest or to mind Timothy. In the afternoon the wood range was delivered on an open bed truck with Brother riding in the cab beside the driver. The driver climbed down from behind the wheel. "How in tarnation did you ever find this place, lady?"

Mama ignored his rudeness. "It is beautiful here, isn't it?"

Maas was riding up on Sam, his big bay, just in time to help Brother unload the iron stove.

The men cut a hole for the stovepipe to pass through the kitchen to the outside. They assembled the pipe, fitted the joints together, then extended the pipe beyond the eaves.

The men took turns examining their handiwork, looking inside the oven, checking the damper, opening the firebox—like children with a new plaything. Mama simply laid her hand on the brass handle of a lid litter and with a kind of caress, said, "Thank you, Lord."

School would start in two weeks, and that gave Brother precious little time to do all he had to do. Maas and Archer helped him cut the cottonwoods and haul them to the house. When the pigpen was finished, Daddy brought the shoats, and one of the hill men, Mr. Taylor, delivered a wagonload of corn.

"Wal, I reckon we kin ease up a bit," Maas said, spitting a stream of brown juice at a tree. "We'll git the smokehouse built direckly."

Archer and Katie were allowed to feed the pigs as long as they didn't argue. Standing with their feet stuck through the cracks between the logs, rubbing ears of corn together, shelling kernels into the trough, was a special delight. The squealing pigs, slurping and grunting in the mud provided a noisy show.

Mama, Archer, and Brother surveyed the route for the road, tagging trees where the cut should be made, and Maas said he could handle the work single-handedly. The familiar sound of wood-chopping was heard again and by the time school started, Maas was working his way well down the mountainside.

Katie didn't like going to school in town; she would much rather go to Pleasant Valley, the one-room school, but Daddy said Pleasant Valley was for hillbillies. Going to town meant wearing shoes and socks and making sure your hair stayed combed. She did not feel comfortable among city children and grown-ups, all crowded together within walls. Walls and bells interfered with thinking and doing—how could she ever learn anything in a school where penmanship was everything, where they had her doing push-pulls and ovals all the time?

The most painful part was the waiting after school to ride home with Daddy. After everyone except the janitor had left, Archer and Katie had to stay on the playground because no children were permitted in the building after hours. As they sat on the steps waiting, Katie felt like an orphan.

Alice and Jane, who went to another school, walked to Daddy's office and stayed there until he was ready to leave. Brother studied in the library at the university until they came for him.

Riding home in the old Cadillac was fun. Daddy let the automobile coast as far as it could to save gas; then he measured the distance coasted. Katie rode in the back seat but leaned over Daddy's shoulder to see the speedometer. His knuckles on the wheel reminded Katie of Brother's—the tiny blond hairs stood out against the light the way Brother's did, only Daddy had a ruby ring and Brother didn't. Daddy's breath had a pleasant scent, not of medicine but something Katie had smelled before, perhaps Maas's jug.

Rounding Lookout Point, Daddy blew the horn so Mama would know they were coming. "I see Mama and Timothy by the live oaks," Jane said. Mama would allow time for them to get water from the spring, drive back to the ford, cross the creek, and come up the bluff.

The spring was in a rock grotto, a pool several feet deep, clear as summer air and cold. Water spiders floated on the surface, breaking the surface with faint circles. Often, Mama and the children would do the laundry at the spring. There the creek was shallow, running over a flat rock bottom, and the clothes were washed in tubs, rinsed in the stream and spread on bushes to dry. Since school had started, they could wash only on Saturdays.

It was on a Saturday, that glorious day of freedom from school, when Katie was told to take care of Timothy. "I want to play with the tumbleweed," he said, and Katie put him in a safe place and went off by herself to enjoy the flat. She ran all the way to the boardwalk and stood feasting her eyes on the view, looking all the way to the bend of the Colorado. She could hear the cattle lowing at Maas's place. The humming of a motor boat came from the river. Revenuers, Katie thought. Maas says they're revenuers.

Katie held onto the boardwalk rail, giddy with the height. A lizard skirted her foot and darted up a post, stopped, and looked back at her the way lizards do, its sides pulsating. Against the cedar bark, he was hardly distinguishable.

The droning of the motor faded away, the boat lost to view behind the hollow. Katie turned to go back to the house and faintly heard Maas chopping trees on the new road. Wind blowing against her face brought up the dry smell of grass and the rich full odor of cedar. Katie drew in her breath and held it for the sheer ecstasy she felt.

Suddenly, Timothy was screaming! Katie ran as hard as she could across the flat. Mama was flinging off his clothes right and left. "Ants! I told you to watch him! Archer, run—get some tobacco!"

Archer raced for Maas.

Timothy was holding his breath, his face blood-red. "Katie MacLeod! Why can't you do one thing I tell you? Where were you?" Mama demanded.

Timothy stripped, she rushed him to the rain barrel and lowered him in the water. "I ought to give you a good thrashing, Katie!" Mama soothed Timothy, laving water onto his back. "Poor baby, welts all over him."

By the time Archer came running back with the tobacco, Timothy was calmer, sniffing and sobbing but not as scared. "Archer, cut a piece from the plug, moisten it and let me have it."

"Wouldn't it be better if I chewed it?"

One look from Mama answered that question and he cut the plug. "I only *asked*," he said.

Every sting had to be treated with the juice. Archer and Katie leaned their heads close to peer at Timothy, helping to find all the angry red bumps. "Look at them," Mama fumed, "He'll have fever." She felt his forehead. "I don't understand you, Katie. Why would you leave him and go traipsing about?"

Katie felt miserable.

"Good night, Mama, Katie's only eight years old," Archer argued. "She forgot, that's all."

"That will be enough out of you, young man." But as Mama took Timothy inside, she spoke more kindly. "Katie, you can go back to the boardwalk now; the damage is done."

The storm had passed, but Katie could not enjoy the rest of the day. That night, Timothy slept in the bed with Mama and Daddy. During the night, Katie could hear him whimpering in his sleep. Mama was up and down taking care of him, bathing his face, arms, and body; applying the juice. When he became fretful, she took him up and rocked him, singing softly.

Alice and Jane stirred in their bed, turned over and resumed the heavy breathing of sound sleep. Daddy lit the lamp, turned the wick low and sat on the side of the bed to smoke a cigarette. Nervously, he pulled at the ring on his finger, twisting it, turning it around and around.

"What are you thinking, Malcolm?" Mama asked softly.

"The same thing you are."

The chair creaked pleasantly as Mama rocked back and forth. "Little Malcolm?"

Daddy nodded and lay back to gaze at the light and shadows playing on their faces. Mama's hair fell loose about her shoulders, soft and lovely in the light.

"He was about the same age, wasn't he?" Daddy asked.

"Two and a half. Timothy is three and a half."

"You rocked Little Malcolm in that same green chair and sang that same lullabye."

Mama stroked Timothy's head and pressed her lips against his cheek. Timothy's blond curls were damp against his forehead; his face flushed. With eyes closed, his lashes lay dark against his skin.

Daddy snuffed out the cigarette and wiped tears from his eyes. Mama stopped rocking, waited to make sure Timothy would not be roused, then laid him in the bed beside Daddy. Lightly touching Timothy, settling him in the bed, Mama kissed him and hovered over him attentively. Then Mama leaned toward Daddy, took him in her arms and laid his head on her bosom. Daddy turned out the lamp.

As Katie lay in the darkness, tears slid from the corners of her eyes onto the pillow. "Please God, don't let Timothy die." With her eyes open or shut, Katie could see the little grave in the McIntosh cemetery, the one with the marble lamb on the headstone, the coping around the little plot and the words carved in the stone—something about a lamb in God's bosom; Little Malcolm's grave.

The hounds were baying on Cat Mountain—men were hunting something to kill—and somewhere an owl was shivering eerily.

EIGHT
Maas's Map

After two days of fever and three days of being kept quiet, Timothy was better, although Mama said it would be five more days before he would be well.

Mama was not cross with Katie, but she was cross. Perhaps she was worried about the car. Nearly every day Maas and Brother had to work on it to get it started. Katie and Archer were often late to school.

Or maybe Mama worried about money.

Daddy was sitting on the doorstep while Mama was darning socks. He had asked her to go look at the cows with him, but she said no, she had work to do. He was drinking mineral water and examining the glass as he spoke. "Becky, what would you think of our bottling the mineral water on this place and selling it as a medicinal aid?"

"Not much." Mama was in no mood for big ideas.

"You'll see the day when somebody gets rich off mineral water." He poured himself another glassful. "I know a full-blooded Sioux Indian who is willing to travel with me to promote it."

Mama stopped threading the needle, looked at him, and frowned. "You're not serious."

But he was.

"Medicine shows are very popular, Becky. With a full-blooded Sioux endorsing the product, we couldn't fail. Back East they'd flock to see a real live Indian."

"And who is this Sioux?"

Daddy smiled mischievously. "Maas."

"Maas?! He's as German as the Kaiser!"

"We'll change his name. With a headdress, deerskins, and moccasins, he'll make a fine Sioux."

"Malcolm, you are an unmitigated rogue!" She stretched the sock over the light bulb and started weaving the thread back and forth. "You better not let me hear another word about such nonsense. We don't have money to invest in bottles and Indian costumes."

"It wouldn't take much money."

"A bird in hand is worth two in the bush."

Daddy got up, brushed off the seat of his pants and walked toward the pigpen. "How long will it be before we can butcher hogs?"

"Not until cold weather. Your guess is as good as mine."

"Well, maybe we can make charcoal like the hillbillies," he said sarcastically, and he walked out to the cows alone.

When the darning was done, Mama filled her apron with chicken feed and went out to scatter it. "Beat the bucket, Katie—we need to kill a hen for Sunday dinner." Beating on the bucket made the chickens come running pell mell from the brush. They flew to the grain, flocking around Mama's feet, pecking excitedly. "Catch that Barred Rock, Katie."

Katie shied away from the red rooster, which delighted in attacking her, gouging her with his spurs. The Barred Rock took flight and Katie ran after her, the hen squawking for dear life. With a flying tackle, Katie grabbed the chicken by one leg and held on.

She did not relish killing chickens, but Katie's reputation for bravery made it necessary. Holding the chicken by its feet, Katie laid its head on the ground. Placing a stick across the hen's neck and planting her feet firmly on both ends of it, she pulled with all her might, determined to yank off the head cleanly with one try. Throwing the headless chicken onto the ground, Katie turned her face so as not to see the bird flopping about, splattering blood.

When at last the poor thing lay motionless, Mama doused it in hot water. The water loosened the feathers but made them give off a sickening smell. Katie plucked the hen, putting handfuls of feathers on newspaper; but some feathers stuck to her arms or flew about the yard. Jane came out and helped until Alice called her to come take a bath.

When the chicken was denuded of feathers, Mama took over, singeing the pin feathers left on the bird. She slit the chicken to remove the entrails, cleaned the craw, and washed the hen thoroughly. She would parboil it, stuff it with cornmeal dressing and bake it.

Katie cleaned up the feathers, burning them in the woods, then sat on the doorstep waiting her turn for a bath. She smelled of wet chicken feathers and there were beads of dirt around her neck. The tantalizing smell of apples bubbling on the stove drifted through the screen door. Cooking smells would bring True Luck home soon, no matter how much luck he and Archer were having hunting. Before long, Brother and Maas would call it a day and come up from the road. The twins, who had turned fourteen in October and thought they were grown, would soon be through with their baths. Chances were, Alice was using an eyebrow pencil to draw a beauty mark on her cheek, which Katie thought was wrong no matter which way you looked at it. If you weren't born with a mole on your cheek, you shouldn't put one there.

Katie heard someone talking and looked up to see three city people almost in the yard. Brother was with them, looking embarrassed. With him was a red-haired girl, a young man with eyeglasses, and another with freckled skin. Brother introduced them to Mama—they were students from the university—and Mama invited them inside.

Alice and Jane came out of the bedroom looking spic and span. Katie refused to go inside. Even when the girls served fried apple pies, she wouldn't go inside. She felt filthy.

The visitors outlined their plans for a Sunday school at Pleasant Valley schoolhouse. After they left, Daddy objected. "Becky, we can't have the children associate with hillbillies."

Mama argued. "Malcolm, it *is* Sunday school. It won't hurt the children to associate with mountain people one hour a week. I'll go with them."

And she did. The very next day, after dinner, they went down the hill. Although Katie was clean and wore a new dress Aunt Ethel had sent, she felt so mortified from the day before, she wouldn't talk.

"Katie," the red-haired girl said, "your hem is turned up. Kiss it and make a wish. Whatever you wish will come true."

But Katie wouldn't do it.

Halfway through the class, Sophie Roper appeared in the doorway. Sophie was fifteen, the oldest of twelve children. Alice and Jane had met her at the spring, and they said she was smart. Sophie always carried the baby, Lester, on her hip, and most of the other Roper children tagged along. Sophie's dress was ripped at the waist; she kept her hand over it so her flesh wouldn't show. Katie knew how she felt.

The only other children who came were the Taylors— Sybil, who was twelve and wanted to get married; Zelphi, who was still sucking a pacifier even though she went to school; and a boy of thirteen everyone called Rambler because he ran away so often.

After Sunday school, Mama invited the university students to come home with them. Katie straggled behind the others; the twins, Brother, Archer, Mama, and the others walked along ahead, chatting. Katie heard Archer speak up, saying, "Maas said the Taylor children have the itch."

"Nonsense!"

"There's something between their fingers. Besides, Maas said all those Taylors have pellagra and every disease you can name.'

Brother blushed as he spoke. "Archer, Maas just tells you those things because he doesn't like the Taylors. The Maas and Taylor families have feuded for generations."

"What do they feud over?" the freckled man asked.

"Everything they can think of. Since Maas is the last man left in his family, the Taylors would like nothing better than to see him die. They carry knives and guns for each other."

"What are they feuding about now?" Archer asked.

"Well, right now it's over some money bandits were supposed to have buried in Johnson Hollow. The Taylors swear it was one of their kin that buried it, but they don't know where it is. Maas's father somehow found a map showing where the loot is buried, but the old man died before he found it, and Maas doesn't know where the map is."

They were coming in sight of the house. The redhead made sure she walked beside Brother; it was plain to see she liked him. She was pretty but not pretty enough for Brother. The two fellows lined up alongside Alice and Jane, but they pretended not to notice.

Maas's horse was tied on the other side of the barbecue pit, and Maas and Daddy were at a table under the oaks, a roll of toilet paper blowing in the wind.

"What in the world are they doing?" Mama asked.

Coming nearer they could see Maas's jug between his legs. He had not shaved in days and there was tobacco stain on the stubble of his chin. He was loud, and Daddy was happier than usual. "Come see the new invention,"

Daddy called. His shirt collar was open and his sleeves rolled up; his vest didn't match his pants and he didn't have on socks. He looked awful!

Brother stormed into the house and the twins marched after him.

Daddy was experimenting with a cigarette machine— a little metal box in which they poured loose tobacco then cranked the paper through to make a cigarette— but it wasn't working. "Guess it's the toilet paper," he said and laughed.

Mama did not show her feelings but Katie knew what she was thinking when she turned to the guests and said, "I don't want to keep you too long. Come inside, we'll have refreshments, then you can be on your way."

The three ate apple pies and left. After they were gone, Mama fussed at Daddy. "Malcolm! You embarrassed the children!"

"Aw, Becky, they've seen toilet paper before."

"Maas, get this contraption out of my sight right now!"

"Becky, lemme' show you something. Maas, show the Missus—"

Maas scooped up a handful of pecans from a barrel beside the table.

"While you were in Sunday school, we picked up all these nuts."

"So?"

"Do you know what we're going to do?" There was something funny about the way Daddy was talking, the way he looked out of his eyes.

"I haven't the slightest idea, Malcolm."

"We're goin' to sell 'em. First, we shell 'em, then we sell 'em."

And shell nuts they did—dishpans full—every night. Daddy did not shell pecans because he could not see well. Unstrapping his briefcase, he would sort out papers on the bed, look worried, and smoke a lot.

Daddy could sell all the pecans they could shell.

Mama said he could sell ice boxes to Eskimos. People did not always pay in cash; they traded corn or groceries or gasoline. Once Daddy came home with hundred-pound bags of buckwheat and wholewheat flour.

But Daddy didn't seem satisfied. Even when Maas took Mama and Timothy fishing and they caught a string of bream, he didn't say anything. "She's a goldurn good fisherman, Mr. MacLeod. Put them grasshoppers on them hooks same as me. Ye orta' git a trotline, then all you'd have to do is bait the hooks and go back later and git yer supper."

Daddy looked as if he didn't even hear Maas. In fact, it had been a long time since he'd smiled. When he stood before the mirror in the mornings, stropping the razor and singing, the words came out sad and heavy. Before the sale, he had sung "Will There Be Any Stars in My Crown?" in a lively way; now it sounded like a funeral song.

When I wake with the blest
In the mansions of rest
Will there be any stars in my crown?

His singing was interrupted every time he was peeling off a strip of lather with the straight edge. With every interruption, Katie waited, wondering if he would start up again or if he would stop singing altogether.

Christmas was just around the corner and some days the weather was cool enough for Daddy to wear his trench coat. They had shaken almost all the pecans off the trees, and with the last batch Daddy brought home in exchange a milk can full of clabber. "We'll make cheese," Mama said.

She poured the clabber in a cotton sack and hung it in the kitchen with a pan beneath. "When all the whey seeps out, we'll have cheese."

Sure enough, in a few days they opened the sack and scooped out curds of crumbly white cheese. It was a welcome change from beans and salt pork and the game

Archer shot. Of course, Mama could make jackrabbit taste like chicken, and with a thick brown gravy, squirrel was not bad. Dried apples and eggs supplemented their diet and on Sunday there was chicken. There would be baked hen and extras for Christmas.

Before the holidays, Katie had a cold and Mama kept her home from school. Everyone else was in the car waiting for Daddy when Mama opened the cedar chest and took out the red sailcloth.

"Katie, do you remember what we used this for?"

"Yes, ma'am. For flags on the stakes."

"That's right." Mama sat on the bed with the bolt of cloth on her lap, smoothing it, feeling its quality the way she always did dress fabrics. "Malcolm, do you mind if I make something for the girls out of this material?"

"No, I'll never need it again."

After Daddy was gone, Mama spread the cloth on the kitchen table, making sure of the selvage and the folded side, smoothing it and laying the pattern carefully. "I'm going to make Alice and Jane some of those new-styled pajamas for Christmas—not to sleep in—they're worn in the daytime. Very stylish." She showed Katie the picture on front of the pattern—skinny women with long necks, dressed in big-legged trousers.

A spool of thread, a folded measuring tape, and a thimble all served as weights to keep the tissue pattern straight. "Don't lean on the table."

Katie took her elbow off the table. Sewing was serious business; things could go wrong even with an expert like Mama handling the scissors.

The wedding ring on Mama's hand reminded Katie again of the family circle. "Cinderella was a stepchild, wasn't she, Mama?"

"Hmm-n."

Katie thought about this. Cinderella did all the dirty work and she wasn't really a part of the family circle. Is that what Daddy meant? Katie knew she wasn't as pretty as Jane or Alice and she did things they wouldn't, like killing a chicken or helping Archer skin a rabbit, but Mama never acted as if this made her a Cinderella.

"Mama, am I as smart as Archer?"

"Well, he's very smart." She cut some more. "Oh, I wish I had a sewing machine."

Mama's machine sat on the closet floor. It was electric and useless.

Late that afternoon Katie and Timothy stood outside waiting for the Cadillac. Daddy had honked the horn as he crossed Lookout Point and the lower cut on Cat Mountain. They finally heard the car chugging up the hill. After a while it came into view, the brakes squealing and the motor wheezing as if it had the croup.

Timothy pointed toward the boardwalk. "There comes Maas."

Daddy waved to Katie as the Cadillac pulled in. "I brought you something."

"It's bantam chickens," Archer said bluntly. "The rooster's mine and the hen's yours." Dumping the box in her arms, he went inside. "What's for supper?"

The blue-green sheen of the rooster's tail feathers shone like ribbons and his comb was red, but Katie right away fell in love with the little copper-colored hen. The poor creature was so scared and wild-eyed, and Katie held her close, smoothing her wings and talking softly to her. Katie felt her craw and the prickled skin. "Thank you, Daddy, I'm going to name her after Aunt Ethel."

Mama opened the door. "Bantams? Malcolm, we can't eat bantams." She held open the door. "Supper's ready."

Daddy turned to Maas. "Can it wait, Maas?"

"No, sir, it cain't." Daddy turned and the two men walked toward the picnic table. Archer came bounding out the door to follow them. Katie tagged along.

As the men sat down, Maas looked at Katie and Archer sternly. "Not a word of this to nobody, you hear?"

They nodded their heads.

Maas turned to Daddy. "Mr. MacLeod, ye remember I told ye a while back 'bout them bandits buryin' some loot up here?"

Daddy nodded.

"Wal, my pappy said they buried what they got some whar in Johnson Hollow." He spit away from the table. "Them fellers musta' been plumb loco awanderin' aroun' in Johnson Hollow. Myself, I'd druther take a bullet as be tore in pieces by panthers."

He rolled the wad around in his jaw. "My pappy told me about a feller went into Johnson Hollow one time and when he come out his hair had turned snow white."

Archer couldn't stand the suspense. "How much money did they have?"

"The bandits?"

Archer nodded.

"Thousands and thousands of dollars." He wiped his mouth with the back of his hand. "Cleaned out the biggest bank in the state. They wuz smart fellers," he said with admiration. "My pappy said they holed up in these hills for pert nigh a year. Pappy give 'em likker an' vittles and when there was a shootout, Pappy came up here lookin' fer 'em in case they wuz shot an' needed help. As luck would have it, one was left for daid, and the dogs sniffed him out. Pappy found him near the mud bog. He warn't daid, but he was dyin' and he knowed it. He tol' my pappy them others wiz kilt 'cept one young feller. He got scairt and give himelf up; got drug off to jail." Maas paused, savoring the moment of climax. "Before the feller died, he give my pappy a map." Maas took off his ten gallon hat and reached in the crown for a dirty piece of paper.

Archer's eyes were wide with excitement.

"He ast my pappy to find the loot, keep half of it fer hisself, and take the rest to his young 'uns in the Panhandle."

"Is that the map?" Archer asked anxiously.

Maas nodded, fingering the folded paper, looking at it

on one side then the other but not opening it.

Mama called from the kitchen.

"Go tell your mother we can't come right now," Daddy said. He was pulling his ear, waiting nervously for Maas to continue.

Archer didn't go. He yelled, "We can't come now! Go ahead and eat!"

Daddy nodded to Maas. "Go ahead, Maas."

"Pappy took the map and when the feller died he give him a nice buryin', words and everything. Buried him deep in the bog. So no dawg nor varmint would worry him out. But Pappy had a feelin' about Johnson Hollow. He feared to go deep in the Hollow, whar the money's buried, him bein' a old man an' everythin'. He hid the map and wouldn't even tell me whar it was. Them Taylors was so hot and heavy to git the map, Pappy said they'd kill me fer hit. Said he'd tell me 'fore he died, but then he wuz kilt sudden when his hoss th'owed him."

Archer was getting very impatient.

"Where'd you find it?" Daddy asked.

"Whar you reckon?"

Daddy shook his head.

"All kinds o' people tore up Pappy's place lookin' fer hit, and they been to my place since he died. Lawd knows I looked fer hit. But you wanna' know whar I found hit?"

Daddy nodded.

Maas leaned across the table confidentially and spoke in a low voice. "In his gun stock!" He laid his Winchester on the table, pulled out his jackknife and pried open the end of the stock. A small hollowed-out place, the size of Maas's thumb, was secreted inside. "Right thar," he said, feeling the place with his finger. "I shoulda' knowed hit wuz thar—he carried this gun everywhar he went, same as me."

"Well?" Daddy asked, anxious to move ahead.

"Mr. MacLeod, I got a hankerin' to find thet money and I needs a pawdner. My Pappy made me swear never to go near Johnson Hollow without a pawdner. Since there ain't no other Maas left but me, an' I don't trust another man in these hills, how'd you like to spend a few days pokin' aroun' back thar?"

"I'd like that, Maas," Daddy said.

"Course, we might not find hit, but if we do, how does fifty-fifty sound to you?"

"Sounds just fine."

"Then put 'er thar," he said, sticking out his big horny hand.

Only then did Maas unfold the map. Squatting down, he spread the paper between his feet. Daddy was pulling his ear and shifting about on his haunches uncomfortably.

"See this here circle and thet thar circle? Them's rocks, big slab-like rocks, and they's propped up. You can still make it out—on one o' them is a hoss haid carved or drawed right on the rock, ye understan'?" Daddy nodded. "Now th' other one is a deer haid. What you do is pace off twelve paces thet-a-way and eighteen paces th' other way from them rocks to a cedar tree standin' between, like so." He traced the angles carefully with his finger. "Whar them two lines crosses is whar the loot is buried."

"When do we start?" Daddy asked.

Maas glanced at the sky. Dusk was falling on the flat. "Tomorrow's Saturday. I'll be here by sunup with Sam an' the pinto. We'll leave pronto."

"I'll be ready."

Maas turned to Katie and Archer. "Now you young 'uns is swore to secrecy. Them Taylors'll cut yer throat to git at that money."

Supper was in the oven keeping warm when they went into the house. They were too excited to eat, but nothing they told Mama made her excited. "Eat your supper," she said, and that was that.

NINE
Witch!

True to his word, Maas was in the yard by sunup, the saddled pinto in tow. He and Daddy were gone all day. Darkness was falling when Katie and Archer heard the horses trotting out of the cedar brake. They ran to meet them.

"Did you find it?" Archer asked.

Maas shook his head. "No, but we seen the biggest ma cat I ever seen in these parts." He reached down and swung Archer onto the back of Sam.

"Did ya kill it?" Archer asked.

"Naw. Figgered she had some cubs someplace. Got no mind to cause critters to suffer."

Katie ran alongside the horses.

"First we got to find them slabs with the pictures," Maas said. "Once we find them the rest is easy."

"Maybe in all these years they got blown down," Archer suggested.

"Mebbe."

The men went again the next day, and though they didn't find anything they were not discouraged. "Christmas holidays are coming up," Daddy said. "We'll find it during the holidays."

But before the holidays, during those few days in between, Katie knew Daddy wanted to stay home from the office and look for the treasure, but he knew Mama wouldn't hear of it.

On one of those mornings—the car wasn't working, it was stuck in the mud down at the creek—Mama woke everybody early. But Daddy refused to get up.

"Malcolm, how can you lie there in bed knowing these children must be in school in less than two hours? Get up, now, and help me!"

That was the morning, after Mama and Brother had left the house to work on the car, after Daddy had shaved in silence, that Katie stood with him in the doorway listening for the sound of the car starting. Katie was idly wishing it wouldn't start so they could stay home. Then it happened. They heard the car crank, and when it did, Daddy hissed, "Witch!"

Katie did not move. The sound of the word whipped around and around in her head like a lariat twirling: *Witch! Witch! Witch!* By force she held herself still, her head reeling. *How could he! How could he!* she screamed inside. She wanted to kick and claw and scream at him, but he didn't even know she had heard him.

Archer came running onto the flat, yelling for them to come. Daddy began slowly to put on his trench coat, staring blankly ahead. When he picked up his briefcase and started walking across the flat, Katie followed him.

Katie did not try to keep up with him as they followed the road through the cedars. When the Cadillac came into view, there was Mama, smiling triumphantly, her hands on her hips, the car motor running and backfiring. Daddy climbed behind the wheel wordlessly.

Mama took one look at Katie and the smile left her face. "Katie, are you all right?"

Katie nodded, afraid to speak.

Mama kissed her and helped her in the car. She stood

118

on the creek bank waving them good-bye as the Cadillac roared through the water to the other side.

All day long, Katie struggled to understand why he'd said it. On the way home in the car, she sat in a corner of the back seat paying no attention to how far they coasted and not hearing a word the others were talking about.

In the end, she wasn't sure she could understand, but one thing was certain, she would never tell anyone. Never in a million years. It wasn't like him. No one need ever know he said it. She would keep it to herself the way she kept her dream and a lot of other things.

When the holidays finally came, things seemed better. Daddy and Maas had plenty of time to look for the treasure. Katie had plenty of time to play with Ethel, who roosted in the trees and kept completely away from the other chickens, particularly the red rooster.

Katie heard Archer yodeling and turned to see him beckoning to her from the far side of the flat. "Come, help me hunt!"

They were scarcely out of the range of the house when Katie shook a brush pile and out darted a big rabbit. Archer threw up the shotgun. The rabbit's hind legs were pumping him forward in great bounding leaps, this way and that—no easy target. The gun boomed out its shot, and the rabbit was flung jerking into the air. True Luck raced to find the shot-ridden creature, twitching in the grass.

Before the day was over, they had four rabbits, their feet tied together and slung on a pole over Archer's shoulder.

Every day, when Maas and Daddy returned from the Hollow, Daddy seemed more desperate to find the treasure.

"If only we could find the two stones," he told Mama. "I never saw so many rocks in my entire life— there are outcroppings, ledges, boulders—all kinds but no two flat stones side by side, engraved by an outlaw."

As Christmas Day drew nearer, Mama insisted that Daddy take one day off from treasure hunting to drive Alice and Jane to town.

On the same day, before sundown, Brother took Timothy, Katie and Archer to find a Christmas tree. They spent a long time making the selection even after they heard the Cadillac returning, honking on Lookout Point. By the time they cut down the tree and were dragging it home, the car was parked in the yard.

Brother was nailing two boards crosswise for a tree stand when Alice and Jane came outside, looking secretive and pleased.

"Get everything?" Brother asked.

"Yes," Jane answered.

"What did you use for money?"

"Daddy sold the typewriter from his office."

"Where are we going to put the tree?" he asked.

"In the middle room at the foot of Katie's cot." Jane was like Mama—she always knew exactly what to do.

After they set up the tree, Mama brought out colored balls and tinsel from the cedar chest. "Here's all this paraphernalia." She held up a tiny bell, then an angel. "Come on, Katie, don't you want to help decorate?"

Brother answered for her. "No, Mama. You know Katie likes trees the way they're born—green and smelling good."

Katie grinned. It was the truth.

After the tree was decorated, they sat in a circle on the floor while Alice and Jane told exciting Santa Claus stories. Then Mama talked about how they used real candles on the tree when she was a child and how they had oranges only at Christmas time.

No one spoke of presents, and it had not occurred to Katie to think of them. Then in the middle of the night the moonlight flooding the flat awakened her. In the pale light the Christmas tree was cast in silhouette, and beneath the tree Katie saw the round curve of a ball. It was a total surprise. There were other packages, and maybe the ball was not for her, but no matter whose it was, she would get to play with it. She could hardly wait until morning!

Before breakfast, as soon as Timothy was awake, Mama called to the boys, "Come, boys. Time for the Christmas tree!"

Daddy handed the packages out, one for each of them. A dictionary for Brother, red pajamas for the twins, shotgun shells for Archer, a doll for Katie and a teddy bear for Timothy.

Katie tried not to show her disappointment with the doll.

"Who gets the ball?" Archer asked.

"You and Katie," Mama said.

He held it in his hands, a rubber ball just the right size to play "Annie Over." He tossed it to Katie.

"Go outside to play," Mama said, and they did. With one of them on each side of the house, one player would holler, "Annie Over," throw the ball, then try to run around the house to tag the other player.

It was a very happy Christmas Day, Katie thought, but Daddy never smiled. When Maas came for dinner, the two of them went out under the live oaks to drink from the jug. By the time they were called to dinner, Daddy seemed to be in better spirits.

Maas propped his gun beside the kitchen door and eased his rangey frame onto the bench.

He leaned back, cocked his head to one side and looked at Archer. "Son, you ever been on a polecat hunt?"

Archer shook his head.

"Then I aim to take ye this very night. That is, if'n it's all right with yer ma. I'll take alla' ye young 'uns if she says ye can go."

"Mama, can we?" Archer begged.

"It's my Christmas present to ye," Maas said. Mama looked inclined to say yes. "What do you think, Malcolm?"

He didn't answer.

"Will you go with them?"

He looked up, surprised.

"They've shelled a lot of nuts, Malcolm. It's something you can do for the children."

They were all looking at him, faces pleading. "How can I refuse?" he asked helplessly.

Archer jumped up from the table. "Gotta clean my gun!"

Maas swung his long legs over the bench. "I'll go git the dogs. Be back by dark."

"You be careful," Brother said.

By sundown Maas was back with half a dozen mountain men and a pack of ugly dogs. True Luck welcomed them with yapping and jumping about, but the dogs were tired. They had run alongside the horses for miles and were ready for a nap. They lay around the yard sleeping.

"Do they really eat polecats?" Archer asked Brother.

"No. They get paid fifty cents by the government for every cat they kill."

"Why?"

Brother shrugged his shoulders. "They're varmints."

While the men built a fire, Maas made torches by filling Nehi bottles with kerosene and stuffing a sock in the neck for a wick. "Maas, be careful," Brother cautioned, "you might blow us to kingdom come."

Maas didn't pretend to move away from the fire.

"What are the croaker sacks for?" Katie asked.

"For the bounty, Katie, for the bounty," Maas answered.

As the men cleaned their guns by the fire, they smoked and talked in throaty voices about dogs and mountain lions and revenuers, but Daddy did not enter in. In the firelight, his handsome face seemed as lined as theirs.

The moon back of Cat Mountain was beginning to brighten the sky as one by one the men finished their work and laid down their guns. The tethered horses snorted and stomped for attention. The men decided to unhitch them for grazing through the night.

Maas picked up a guitar one of them had brought and handed it to its owner. "Play 'Red Wing.'"

"Red Wing" was one of their better songs. Their ballads were usually much sadder, telling stories about lovers being killed or children dying. The strumming of the guitar, the country tenor voice, and the campfire with its capricious smoke, attracted Alice and Jane who came out of the house dressed for the hunt.

The moon tipped the mountain and rose steadily above the crest. Moonlight spilled over Cat Mountain, spreading light and shadow down its side, and marbling the ground. "Ye ort to have a play party up here, Mr. MacLeod," Maas said. "This here flat would be a ideal spot."

Daddy didn't respond one way or the other.

Maas stood up. "Time to go," he announced, and the men began stomping out the fire. The dogs roused, stretched themselves—the liver-colored hound, the old white dog, the black-and-tan mixed with blue tick, the terrier—they were ready to go. True Luck cocked his ears and turned his head to one side. "Yes, True Luck," Brother said, "you can go, too."

The dogs trotted ahead of them, sniffing the ground. "Go, White Man," Maas yelled. "Get on, Old Timer!" Men holding torches took the lead, Archer following close on their heels. Daddy and the girls were strung along single file with Brother bringing up the rear. Black smoke from the flaming bottles made Katie's eyes smart and her face feel greasy but keeping up with the others was her main concern. They crossed the flat, stumbling over honeycomb rocks and cactus, but the cedar brake was worse. Branches swung back, stinging Katie's face. If there was a trail, she could not see it. As they descended the bluff, it was every man for himself— a mad, mad scramble—with loose dirt sliding underfoot. When Katie slipped, Brother grabbed her to keep her from rolling headlong to the bottom.

The dogs were far ahead, yelping and yowling; the

men, shouting and whistling, urging them on. Maas followed hard after the dogs, plunging pell mell down the cliff—thrashing wildly with the torch. Katie tried to shut out of her mind the thought of rattlesnakes, but it wasn't easy.

Finally Maas called a halt. Katie fell to the ground trying to catch her breath. Even Brother sat down breathing hard. Maas put his hand over his ear, listening. "They got one on the run! Yipee!" He was off again, barreling through the brush.

Suddenly there was a loud bang and an exploding torch skyrocketed through the trees. Alice screamed. But the men whooped with delight and were spurred on by the excitement. Daddy stopped to make sure they were all right. "No time to waste!" Maas shouted, "They's bayin'—they got hit treed!"

Alice and Jane had fallen behind, and Katie followed in their wake, limbs and vines springing back, stinging across her face and arms. Then they were sliding on their bottoms, ruining their drawers, scraping elbows and backsides. The noise of the dogs drew nearer and then they were aware of a revolting, sweetish, sickening odor.

"Phewee!" Jane exclaimed and poor Alice held her nose.

The pack of dogs was all in a frenzy beneath a tree. The black-and-tan hound was leaping half way up the trunk making savage attempts to get at the polecat. Light from the torches reflected in the poor creature's eyes as it cringed in terror.

"This un's your'n, Archie," Maas said.

Archer raised his gun and took careful aim. Katie wouldn't look. The crack of the gun, and then the body thrashed through the limbs, hitting the ground with a thud. When Katie opened her eyes, the dogs were all over the polecat, yelping and tearing at it as the men kicked them back. Maas poked the poor thing with his gun butt, made sure it was dead, then stooped down to pick it up. Katie quickly shut her eyes.

"'At's a big un, Archie boy, granddaddy of 'em all," Maas boasted. "'At's it, drap that bugger right in this croaker sack."

Katie opened her eyes. Maas was counting heads. Satisfied, he beckoned for them to follow and struck out again. The lead man carried the bag, the horrible odor of polecat following in his wake. The stench was unbearable. Daddy tied a handkerchief around his nose and mouth.

"*Please*, Lord," Alice prayed aloud, "make the wind blow the other way!" The wind didn't change and she kept gagging.

There were other kills as brutal as the first; the sacks were filling up with dead victims. Jane kept saying "Phewee!" and Alice kept spitting, on the verge of vomiting. Clothing, hair, skin—everything smelled of polecat.

Finally the wind changed, or they changed their direction, and the scent was lessened. The moon was sinking behind Johnson Hollow when they made the last chase. They scrambled up the cliff to follow the dogs, and when they found them, they were baying outside a narrow slit in the rock face. True Luck growled deep in his throat, his ears laid back, his flanks trembling. The bigger dogs kept up the noise, baring their teeth, agitated.

"What kind o' critter might thet be?" asked one of the men.

"Ain't no polecat, I guarantee ye. Most likely a bob cat," Maas answered.

The twins clutched at Daddy's arms. Katie's heart was pounding in her chest.

"We'll build a fire an' smoke him out."

"That'll bring him out."

Some of the smaller dogs were nervously nosing inside the den. True Luck darted all the way in but landed right back outside, his face scratched and bleeding. A scrappy little dog, he went in again and again until Brother called him off and held him.

Katie kept close to Brother. If the bobcat leaped out, there would be no place to go on the narrow ledge. Katie was cold and shaking all over, despite the fire. One little dog after another kept going in and coming out, sprawling and rolling part way down the bluff, their heads raked by the cat's claws.

"I ain't gonna stand by an' see them pups cut to ribbons," Maas said. "Call 'em off, men."

The men whistled and hollered and the dogs gave up. "Prob'ly a old cat," Maas said, "a young'n woulda' been scairt and come high tailin' hit outta' there."

Wearily, they filed up the trail, leaving Brother and Katie to kick out the fire. Just as Brother was kicking at the last spark, Katie heard a hissing sound, wheeled around, and there was the bobcat, its teeth bared, snarling, spitting! Katie gasped, clutching Brother. The cat quickly slipped out of the hole and slunk into the brush, its narrow grayish body disappearing quickly.

"Did you see that!"

"Oh, Brother, I'm scared!" Her teeth were chattering.

They fled up the cliff, hollering to the others trying to catch up—the torches were bobbing far ahead of them on the trail. When Daddy heard them, he stopped and waited. Brother and Katie were breathing so hard they could hardly talk. "Dad, its ears were tufted like this," Brother explained, using his hands. "And its tail was about this long." He measured the length on his hand.

"Well, don't tell your mother," Daddy said. "We better get home."

When they reached the top of the cliff, the mountain men and Archer were not even breathing hard. Guns on their shoulders, dogs still frisky and flouncing about, they grinned at the bedraggled MacLeods. True Luck stood with his tongue hanging out. "That thar is a goldurned game little dawg," Maas said, rubbing his ears. Archer took True Luck in his arms to carry him the rest of the way.

Daylight peeked over Cat Mountain and the reflected

streaks of dawn showed in the sky over the house. Cattle grazed sleepily; a cowbell clunked. Smoke was rising from the stovepipe, and Katie was glad to be nearly home.

TEN
Daddy Never Sang Anymore

For many days after the hunt, the very sight of Maas revived the scent of polecat to Katie. The day after Christmas the weather turned cold and Maas came to take the pigs to the abattoir. The next day Daddy brought the butchered meat home and Maas was ready to go to work on it—two roaring fires were blazing in the yard and pots of water were boiling. "Gimme them innards," Maas told Archer as the packages of meat were unloaded. Maas examined the intestines and a wave of nausea came over Katie. "Good," he said, "They done been cleaned." He held them up to slide in the pot.

"What're they for?" Archer asked.

"Them's the casings for sausage. Ye boil the innards."

Mama called Katie from the kitchen. "Would you like to help?"

"Yes, ma'am."

Mama laid strips of white fat on the table. "Take this sharp knife, slice through the fat to the rind, then cut it away like this." Mama slit the fat easily. "Save the skins for cracklings."

Mama's face was flushed from the fire. "Maas, can you pickle the feet?"

Maas's mouth dropped open. "Can a cat have kittens?"

"What did you do with the liver?"

"I'm gittin' ready to skin and boil it, anytime you're ready fer hit."

"Good. Malcolm, I'll stop now and fix something to eat. Why don't you walk out and look at the cows?" She turned to Jane. "Jane, will you put on the grits?"

Daddy sauntered toward the live oaks where the steers stood. Mama had the brains in a bowl and was washing them. "Are we going to eat brains?" Alice asked, horrified.

"Children, your father enjoys brains, and it might cheer him up if we have them for supper."

They looked at each other and rolled their eyes. Even Archer looked squeamish.

When the grits began bubbling, Mama placed an iron skillet on the stove to warm. "Alice, will you please crack these eggs?" Drying her hands, Mama spotted Maas's gun propped by the kitchen door. "Archer, take Maas his gun. I wish he wouldn't leave it in the house. It could accidentally go off."

When Archer came back, Mama began stirring eggs with the brains. "You children have a psychological phobia," she told them, and Katie knew that had something to do with their sanity. "Brains are like horse meat. You would not eat horse meat, would you? But why? Only because we have never eaten horse meat. Horses eat grass even as cows do. They are clean animals. They may not be as fat as pigs, their meat may not be as juicy as a steer's, but it is meat that can be eaten. Indians ate horses, and they are a noble race."

"They also ate dogs," Archer added. "Do you want us to eat dogs?"

Mama threw back her head and laughed. "Seriously, children, you must be guided by fact, not prejudice. The brain of the pig is as clean as the pork chop. You are prejudiced against brains because you don't like the looks of them." Mama poured the mixture in the skillet and began stirring it. "Stir the grits," she told Jane because it was plopping all over the stove and nobody liked lumpy grits.

After Mama's speech, Archer dared Katie to eat brains, so she had to. But the twins ate eggs and cheese and, when the brains were served, would not eat at the table.

Daddy did not seem cheered by his special treat. He helped prepare the shoulders and hams for the smoke-house and showed Brother how to chop and grind the back meat for sausage. They all worked far into the night, and the next morning Daddy did not get up until very late.

Mama was mixing the sausage with a wooden paddle. Adding sage, she tasted the meat and added more sage. Daddy stood in the doorway watching her. "Malcolm, will you change the fittings on the mill and show the boys how to fill the casings?"

He obeyed and soon the little tubes were being filled to a uniform size, like a balloon. Katie's chore was to twist the sausage at intervals to make links.

Daddy dressed in his pin-striped suit and waited for the boys to fill a bushel basket with sausage for him to sell in town. Mama brushed his suit with the whisk broom and straightened his tie. His quietness had a strange effect. No one talked and everyone looked sad.

When the car was loaded, Mama and Katie stood in the doorway watching him leave. The Cadillac backfired all the way across the flat and usually that made them laugh. Instead, Mama just shook her head and went back to work.

The liver was ground and mixed with cornmeal for liver pudding. "Can't you call it by some other name?" Alice asked as Mama spooned it into pans. "Liver *pudding*—that sounds awful!"

"It has many different names—they all mean the same thing." She called Archer. "Be sure you have hickory sticks for the smokehouse." The fire was made in an iron pot and burned constantly. "Katie, I'm going to be making soap. I want you to take care of Timothy and keep him away from the lye water because one drop can be very dangerous."

Mama's face was very white. Katie followed her into the yard. Maas was putting coke under the pot. "Time was when a woman didn't have sto-bought lye. All she needed was some good white hickory ashes and a barrel. She'd jes' drip water through them ashes, git all kinds o'lye."

"Pour in the grease, Maas," Mama said, in no mood for nonsense. Mama stirred as Maas poured and the mixture turned to a thick gravy.

"That's gonna' be purty soap," Maas said admiringly.

"Why don't you render the lard, Maas."

"Trouble with you is you don't take time to enjoy what ye're doin', Miz MacLeod. Set a spell an' watch that thar soap ye're making. Tarnation, ain't no sense in goin' like a house a'fire."

Mama was leaning over the pot and Katie saw her catch Maas's arm to keep from falling. "Keerful," he said. "Steady now."

"It'll pass . . ." She continued to hold on to him.

"Let's git away from this lye pot," he said.

Alice and Jane came outside. "Mama, what's the matter?" Jane asked.

"Nothing."

"You're so white!" Alice said.

"It's nothing," she said crossly. Maas eased her down to sit on a rock. "Go back in the house. Take Timothy, Katie. Leave me alone."

They obeyed. Only the twins went in the bedroom, leaving Katie and Timothy in the kitchen. They thought no one could hear them whispering.

"Do you reckon Mama's pregnant?" Alice asked.

"I'll tell you something if you won't breathe a word of it," Jane said. Alice promised and Jane leaned closer and whispered something in her ear.

When Mama felt better, she came inside. "Now, not

a word of this to your father, do you hear?"

They promised.

When Daddy came home he had to walk up from the creek. "That darned car's broken down again," he said.

"Did you sell the sausage?" Mama asked.

"Every bit of it."

Mama was ironing, heating the irons on back of the stove and rotating them. Jane was the one who told Daddy. She told him right in front of Mama which made Mama awfully mad.

"Overwork," Mama said. "That's all there is to it. Trying to do too much. Nothing to worry about."

Daddy looked at her, worried. "Look what you're doing now. Why don't you let the girls help you? You don't have to do all that ironing."

"The chidren go back to school tomorrow. They have to have something to wear." She spread a shirt on the board, smoothed it with her hand, then rubbed the iron over it, pressing hard, steam rising.

"Stubborn woman," he said. "Let's go for a walk, Becky." But Mama wouldn't. Daddy went to bed.

School no sooner began after the holidays than the Cadillac began breaking down first in one place and then another. "We need tires awfully bad," Brother told Daddy.

"I know," he said, and there was an edge in his voice. "I'm going to take some more sausage in town and if it sells I can buy a tire for the front end."

"That sausage is green, Malcolm. Leave it in the smokehouse. If the weather is as warm tomorrow as it is today, it might spoil."

"It's a chance I have to take, don't I?"

They took the basket of sausage with them on the way to school, on the back seat between their feet. That afternoon, only the basket was on the back seat but no one asked Daddy if he sold the meat. Mama asked him when he walked in the house.

He shook his head grimly. "Tainted." He slumped at the table and rubbed his hand over his face.

After supper, Daddy sat alone at the kitchen table. Brother joined him, spread his books and moved the lamp so it would shine where he wanted it. "Dad," Brother began, "the government is giving surplus commodities to families in need. Right now, to fatherless families."

Daddy seemed not to hear. "I'm going to bed." But he continued to sit at the table. He drew out his pocket watch, fingering it lovingly, rubbing his thumb over the gleaming gold. "This watch belonged to your great, great grandfather." He stared at it. "Your great, great grandfather was one of the biggest mercantile men on the eastern seaboard. Knew how to make money; Brother, there isn't a MacLeod that doesn't know how to make money. Use your head, son, not your hands. Remember that—your head, not your hands." He snapped open the lid, closed it, ran the chain over his forefinger and slid it back in his pocket.

The chill January air stirred the curtains. Katie was huddled by the kitchen stove to keep warm. "Come to bed," Mama called and Katie obeyed.

When the sausage was cured, Daddy tried again and again to sell it, but everyone else had killed hogs about the same time and there was no market for cured meat. On the way home, Daddy would stop by a gas station where Katie knew he could charge groceries. In a week or two he no longer traded at that place.

Daddy never sang anymore. There was a bleakness in his eyes, a vacant stare. At night he went to bed early, sometimes before family prayers, yet in the morning, after a long sleep, he was never ready to get up.

Mama was plainly worried about him. At night she would rock Timothy long after he was asleep, and all the time she was rocking she would be singing, "I come to the garden alone. . . ."

Timothy's birthday was in February, but he did not feel well that day. Katie also had a fever and stayed home from school. Timothy looked at the candles on his cake, his eyes shining but he did not feel like blowing them out. "He's a sick child," Mama said. "Fretful all day."

In the morning there were red spots on Katie's stomach. "Measles," Mama said, "and Timothy will be next."

None of the others could go to school the next day because Maas and Brother could not get the car to budge. Daddy asked Mama to come look at the motor and that's when she had another weak spell. Daddy brought her home and made her lie down on her bed.

"Becky, are you—"

"No. I'm not sick," she said firmly.

"When have you . . ."

"Malcolm, it's not what you think. I've missed three times but it's not what you think. You know it isn t."

"Are you sure?" he pressed.

"Of course, I'm sure. Women have this occasionally."

He rubbed his face in his hands. Maas and Brother were coming into the kitchen. Daddy met them.

"Mr. MacLeod, I hate to tell you, but I think hit's the end of the road for yer Cadillac." He stood his gun by the door.

Daddy waited a long time to answer. Brother was looking at Daddy carefully. "I think he's right, Dad."

Mama got up and poured them coffee. "I don't want any," Daddy said, and he went into the boys' room to lie on the bed.

It was the next morning that it happened. Katie woke up at the sound of voices in the kitchen. Brother was down the hill working on the car, but the others were at the breakfast table. Alice and Archer were having words. Daddy yelled at them, and that scared Katie. Daddy never yelled! She leaned over the foot of the bed she was sharing with Timothy to see into the kitchen. The screen door banged—someone had gone outside. Mama was talking softly to Daddy, and Katie could not hear what she was saying. Again his voice was loud. "You hear me!" he roared. He jumped up from the table and ran outside. Katie put her head under the covers. The door banged, he was back inside. There was a scuffling sound. Katie peeked around the corner. "Sit down, Malcolm," Mama was saying quietly. He sat down, took his plate in his two hands and smashed it on the floor. Daddy turned toward the door and when he did, Mama dashed across the room and went outside. He went to the door, following her.

Katie jumped out of bed and fell across the cot to see out the screen. Mama was standing in the yard with Maas's gun in her hands. "Malcolm, wait." Her voice was steady. "If you come any closer I'll have to shoot." There was a tremor of fear in her voice but no anger.

Daddy turned and came through the bedroom.

"Jane, get Brother," Mama said and Jane raced down the road.

Daddy snatched his trench coat off the hook, kissed Timothy, walked through the boys' room, and went out the door at the other end of the house. Katie watched him heading across the flat in the wrong direction. Brother was running up in the yard followed by Maas. Mama handed Brother the gun.

"Dad!" Brother called.

Daddy turned and waited for him. Brother approached him cautiously. Daddy pulled his watch out of his pocket, and when Brother reached him, he put the watch and chain in Brother's hand without a word. Then he turned and trudged across the flat without ever looking back.

BULL CREEK, PART II

ELEVEN
The
Norther

Timothy and Katie were well of the measles, and still Daddy did not come home. The boys had looked for him, scouring the bluffs and underbrush, although they thought it was unlikely that he had met with an accident or foul play.

Katie sat on the doorstep listening to the older children and Mama talking in the kitchen.

"He's probably gone to Tyler," Jane said. "Oh, Mama, what do you suppose came over him?"

"Malcolm was not himself," Mama kept saying.

Katie held Ethel on her lap, smoothing her feathers. The wind was brisk, and Katie tucked her dress under her legs, trying to keep warm. The hateful red rooster was scratching in the weeds, pecking at the dirt. Catching sight of Ethel, he stood on one leg, the other foot curled beneath his breast, posing, cocking his head this way and that, but Ethel paid no attention. Katie wished they would eat the rooster; he didn't lay eggs, only strutted about and attacked people.

"Katie," Mama called, "don't stay outside too long, you'll catch cold."

But with the screen wire all around the house, it wasn't much warmer inside. Katie put Ethel down and watched her fly up in the tree to roost beside Archer's bantam.

"I'll try to get into town again tomorrow," Brother said. "There'll be a letter from him. I know there will be."

Going to town was difficult. With the Cadillac out of commission, there was no way to get there except to hitch a ride, and some days nothing passed on the road, not even a wagon or a rider on horseback.

Katie took one long last took at Lookout Point before going inside for supper. In the fading light of the winter sun, the road was scarcely visible. There were no lights—nothing was coming or going on the road.

When Katie stood, her dress was turned up. She kissed the turned-up place and made a wish. *I wish Daddy would come home.*

The next day, although he tried for hours, Brother could not thumb a ride to town. "I could walk to town," he said, "and I will if I have to, but it's too far to go and come in the same day." He was eating as he talked, wolfing down his food the way he did when he was nervous. "What are we going to do, Mama? This is the second week the children have been out of school."

Mama served Brother more lima beans. "I worry more about your being out of school."

"Forget about me," Brother said bitterly. "I'm all washed up. There's no way I could pass now."

"The only way a person is washed up is by giving up. Never give up, Brother. Never, never, never give up."

Brother stood up, kissed Mama on the cheek, and went to bed.

Katie felt very sorry for Brother, but because she was not supposed to know the "family business," she could not tell him she was sorry. Mama never talked "family business" in front of the children. Brother, of course, was grown. He knew everything that was going on, and now that the twins were fourteen, they were included. Most of all, Mama did not want outsiders to know their "personal affairs," as she called them. Mama told Maas Daddy was away on business.

The next time Brother tried to go to town, he succeeded. An hour after he left the house, Alice saw a wagon on the lower cut headed toward town and called Mama. They stood in the yard watching the slow ascent of the mule and wagon. "Hauling coke," Archer said.

"I hope Brother is on that wagon," Mama said.

After a while, when he did not return to the flat, they knew he had caught a ride. All day long, Katie kept an eye on Lookout Point, waiting for Brother to come home. Only one car came down the road, a yellow roadster; then later, it went back toward town.

When darkness fell, Mama said they wouldn't hold supper any longer, and after supper they had family prayers. They were lying across Mama's bed, waiting, when True Luck started barking. In a few minutes Brother yodeled back; they opened the door and True Luck bounded outside to meet him. They stood in the yard, peering in the darkness to catch a glimpse of Brother. They heard him running and shouting, "We got a letter! We got a letter from Daddy!"

By the time he reached them, he was out of breath. They hurried inside; Mama held the letter up to the lamp briefly, then opened it carefully.

"There's a money order for twenty dollars," she said, her eyes on the letter, reading it to herself.

"What does he say?" Jane asked, unable to bear the suspense.

"He says to get the license tags for the car and keep the children in school."

"Is that all?" Brother asked.

"That's all." She handed the letter to him. Her disappointment was plain to see.

"It's mailed from Tyler, Mama. He's with Granddaddy. He'll be home soon," Brother assured her.

But he wasn't. When another week had passed, Brother borrowed Maas's horse and rode to town. When there was no mail, Mama decided to write to Granddaddy. Brother took the letter to town the day he enrolled Katie and Archer in Pleasant Valley school.

The school had grades one through eight, each row in the classroom a different grade, and a pretty French girl taught all eight grades. Because the twins were in ninth grade, they couldn't enroll.

Katie sat on the fourth row and Archer on the sixth—instant curiosities for the other children. Because they were in the proper grades for their ages, and Katie was a year ahead, the other children considered them to be superior oddities.

Rosabelle Zeigler, who rode a jackass to school, was three times bigger than Archer, and she was only in the sixth grade. Rambler Taylor, who seldom came to school, was thirteen and sat on Katie's row, but he could not do fourth grade work.

Ruby, who looked like a grown woman, came to bring her little sister. They rode bareback on an old white mare. Ruby's sister was called "Shadow" because everywhere Ruby went, Shadow went. Nobody liked the little sister because she told tales on Ruby, and their papa would tie Ruby to a tree and beat her with a rope.

The two Bracey boys from up the creek, Oren and Willie, also had a mean father. Their pa had a silver plate in his head from the war and that made him loco at times. When he got really bad, the boys would leave home and stay with people in the hills, first one place, then another. Willie, the youngest, liked Katie from the start. He wore a wide-brimmed hat indoors and out, but he still had freckles all over his face—more than Katie had.

The Roper children lived on Cat Mountain, all twelve of them. They were the MacLeod's closest neighbors and sometimes they came to the spring on Saturdays when the MacLeods were washing clothes. Sophie was the only ambitious one in the family and she had finished Pleasant Valley school. The other Ropers did not come to school often because nine of them were girls and each in her turn would marry as soon as someone came along.

Miss Lucretia, the teacher, was the most interesting of all. She came from Louisiana, which explained why she talked the way she did. Because she boarded at Miss Daisy's ranch, everybody knew all her business. Miss Daisy said Miss Lucretia pined over Jack Taylor all the time he was in prison, but when he was let out, Miss Daisy wouldn't allow him to set foot on her place. So Miss Lucretia met him in the woods.

The Taylor children told Katie and Archer all about their famous Uncle Jack—how he had to learn to walk all over again after he got out of prison. Because his cell was small, he had stayed on his bunk morning, noon, and night, and when he got out he couldn't walk, or so they said. The Taylors said Jack went to prison for a crime he did not commit—shooting a man in a fight— but Maas said he did shoot the man. They said Jack was a good-looking hombre with long sideburns and little black mustache. His britches were made out of snake-skin cloth and he rode a seventeen-span sorrel. According to them, there wasn't a rope trick he couldn't do, and he could flip a jackknife thirty feet and hit the bull's-eye every time.

Mama was not at all pleased with the news Katie and Archer brought home from school, but Alice and Jane were eager to hear. Brother kept saying, "Dad wouldn't like this."

There were other things Daddy wouldn't like either. For one thing, the weather.

Early in March a norther struck without warning. Katie woke up freezing cold, the wind roaring through the house, curtains standing straight out from the screens on the north side. A kettle, blown off the stove, clattered onto the floor. Mama and the twins were up, frantically trying to put a blanket over the screens. It was flapping furiously. "Brother! Help!" Mama shouted, but the wind carried away the words.

Brother came running into the room, buttoning his pants. Alice was trying to light the lamp, but the wind kept snuffing it out. "Get the lantern! Get the lantern!" he shouted. "Somebody wake up Archer!"

True Luck was barking and racing about the house excitedly. Sleet was striking the screens with force. "If we don't get these windows covered, we'll all have pneumonia!" Mama shouted above the wind. "Alice, get back in bed! Katie, pull your cot away from the screen. Better wrap up in that quilt and stay by the fire. You could take croup."

Alice kept right on helping, trying to get the blanket nailed to the window. Katie was shivering as she pulled the quilt around her shoulders and huddled by the stove.

"Brother, don't we have some corrugated boxes in the cook tent?" Jane asked, and before he could answer, Mama said, "You and Archer bring me those boxes!"

The wind was battering the branches of the oaks, scraping their branches against the roof. As the boys flung open the screen door, a hail of ice pellets blew inside and bounced in a crazy dance across the floor. The boys were running across the yard, ice crunching beneath their shoes. Katie's teeth were chattering. She put more wood on the fire.

Archer came back with some boxes, threw them on the kitchen floor, and went back for more. Mama tore a box apart, took one side of it, and held it up to the screen. While Jane hammered, Mama braced the cardboard to hold it against the wind. Alice cut and tore the boxes as fast as she could, handing the flat pieces to Mama. Her poor face was white from the cold.

Brother dragged a piece of frozen canvas into the kitchen. "I found this," he said, dropping the heavy bundle on the floor. Rubbing his hands over the stove, he shivered. "That sleet hits you like needles—hurts like the devil!" Archer touched Katie's face with his ice cold hands.

"Put the smoothing irons on the stove to heat," Mama called to Katie. "And keep the fire going."

They worked most of the night, bit by bit shutting out the wind and ice. Finally, all the screens in the three rooms were covered. They were exhausted, numb with cold.

Mama put her finger to her tongue and tested the hot iron. "Here, Jane, wrap this in a towel to put at our feet."

"Mama, there's not much dry wood," Archer reported.

"Well, we'll feed the wood sparingly. It's almost daylight. There might be some stumps we can find to burn. Katie, get in bed. Get in bed with Timothy, he'll keep you warm. Alice, Jane, find all the cover you can—look in the cedar chest and get that old lap robe. We can use all the coats."

Timothy was warm as toast; Katie snuggled close to him. The weight of all the cover they piled on the bed was heavy, but the warm iron at the foot of the bed felt good. Mama settled the others, then crawled in on the other side of Timothy, put her arms around both of them, and drew them close. Katie felt warm and safe again. Even the moaning of the wind outside did not bother her. True Luck, bedded down behind the stove, thumping his tail on the floor, slept fitfully.

When Katie woke up later, she could not get her bearings because the screens were boarded up; only pinpoints of light showed through the cardboard. She lifted a corner of the canvas to look outside. The morning was bright and clear, but everything was encased in ice—the woodpile, the chicken house, the pigpen, an old tire, the smokehouse. Trees were bent down to the ground like horseshoes. Katie thought about Ethel and bounded out of bed to get to her.

"Where do you think you're going?" Archer called as she darted through the kitchen.

"Ethel's out there!" she yelled over her shoulder,

and she dashed out the door. She hit the step and her feet slipped out from under her—she went sliding across the yard.

Archer stood in the door laughing.

"Are you hurt?" Mama called from the cook tent. She and Brother were trying to dig stumps out of the frozen ground.

"No, ma'am."

"Don't laugh, Archer. If your sister broke her arm or something up here, whatever would we do?"

"Set it ourselves. You sure couldn't get a doctor."

Katie found Ethel and Archer's bantam under the house as dry as toast, but the red rooster was having a hard time strutting on the slick ice. His feet spraddled in different directions as his wings flapped to keep balance.

"Two of the Plymouth Rock hens are frozen," Brother reported. "They must have fallen off the roost."

"How much sausage do we have left?" Mama asked.

"Not much. There's some fatback."

Archer came outside to throw sticks in the trees to shatter the ice. Katie stood looking out over the flat, moisture rising like steam from the glaze sheeting the ground, the frozen cedars frosted, glistening in the dazzling sun. "A veritable fairyland," Mama said, her breath white in the cold air. "Be careful, children, we don't want any broken bones."

The pecan trees had not survived—their tortured limbs lay in all directions, ripped and split from their trunks, but the live oaks were undaunted.

Ice was melting, snapping and tinkling as it fell to the ground. From the trees, drops of water splattered on their heads.

Most of the day, the MacLeods stayed in the kitchen eating pecans and trying to stay warm. They tried to play dominoes but argued. Being shut in, unable to pull aside the coverings and look out, made them cross.

"Come, children, let's feed the birds," Mama said as she began crumbling stale pancakes. They stepped outside to scatter the crumbs, but none of them glanced toward Lookout Point. There was a special heaviness inside knowing Daddy could not possibly come home that day with the road iced over.

When conditions improved and Katie and Archer went back to school, the heaviness was still there. As they passed the old Cadillac at the foot of the hill, there was still ice on her shady side. Sometimes Archer would stop with Katie at the car. He would climb behind the wheel and pretend he was driving, and Katie would rub her hand over the worn upholstery and remember Daddy. The poor old car was really dead, leaning helplessly on one side, but the familiar smell of tobacco and dust inside gave Katie a feeling she never wanted to lose.

At school the children were talking about a crazy man hiding in a thicket across the highway. "He's an escapee from the insane asylum in town," Archer told Katie. "There's somebody comes in a yellow roadster, puts food in that tree for him." Archer was pointing to an oak across the road. "But you better not tell Mama or she'll keep us home from school." Then Archer told her what crazy people did to little girls and how she'd better be careful.

Katie was too scared to go to the spring at lunchtime even though all the children went. At the spring they competed to see how many dippers of water each of them could drink. Rambler Taylor had the record with seventeen dippersful at one time.

"'Fraidy cat," Archer teased, and after school he wouldn't wait for Katie but ran up the hill ahead of her, laughing, yelling back that she better hurry, the crazy man would get her. Katie ran, terrified, but Archer never let her catch up with him.

The night Mr. Roper woke them up, knocking on the door, Katie sat straight up in bed, her heart pounding in her chest, sure it was the crazy man. Mr. Roper came inside, grizzled and dirty. "Miz MacLeod, my woman's 'bout to have the baby. Told me to come fetch you."

"All right, Mr. Roper," Mama said. "Have a seat. I'll be with you in a few minutes." She left him in the kitchen and came to the middle room to dress. Katie watched Mr. Roper, standing in the kitchen, trying to peek around the door to see Mama.

Mama was gone all night. The next morning, Katie had already eaten breakfast and put on her clothes when Mama came home. Jane poured her a cup of coffee, and the older children sat around the table listening to Mama tell them about the night. "It was all over when I got there," Mama told them. "That poor Sophie Roper had delivered her mother's baby all by herself. Think of it; why, she's only a year older than you girls, fifteen, and she delivered her own baby sister into the world."

Alice spooned oatmeal from the three-cornered pot for Mama. "That poor girl looked like she had been through a keyhole. This morning when I was cooking breakfast for them, Sophie came in the kitchen with Lester slung on her hip the way she carries him, and I made her go back to bed. That sorry father, he's not fit to kill."

The news of Sophie Roper delivering the baby was the talk of school. The children forgot the "loonie," as they called the crazy man, and no longer looked for the roadster. Archer said he bet there wasn't any crazy man to begin with, that it was just a lie. But Katie wasn't so sure; she had seen the yellow roadster once on the road.

Katie's birthday was due in April, and she told the Lord that if he would please send Daddy home for her birthday, she would never ask him for anything else. She was thinking about her request as she walked home from school.

She remembered other requests she had made, like the time she had asked the Lord to turn the honeycomb rocks into gold. She had really believed with all her heart that when she opened her eyes the rocks would be gold, but they weren't. That's why she wasn't real sure Daddy would come for her birthday, but she wanted the

Lord to know how important it was to her.

Archer had run up the hill ahead of her, and when Katie reached the Cadillac she decided to stop and sit in it a while. Crawling behind the steering wheel, she placed her hands the way Daddy did. But her hands were so small—they didn't look anything at all like his with the hair on his knuckles. She tried to blow the horn but it wouldn't work and the gear shift wouldn't move. She squeezed the brake handle and was trying to pull it back when she heard something. Someone breathing! Somebody was in the car! Katie wheeled around and there was a man lying on the back seat.

"Don't be afraid, little girl—"

Katie flung open the door, jumped out of the car, and hit the ground running. She flew up the hill screaming. Racing toward the house, she ran with all her might.

"What in the world?" Mama cried, running toward her. Katie jumped in her arms and Mama fell backward. Katie clung to her for dear life. "What is it, Katie? What happened? Tell me!"

She was breathless, terrified.

"Crazy man! I saw the crazy man!"

"Crazy man? What crazy man?"

Archer spoke up. "A crazy man escaped from the asylum. He's been camping in the woods down by the schoolhouse."

"What?" Mama rushed Katie into the house. Wrapping her in a blanket, she held her in her arms trying to stop the chill. "Katie, tell me what happened."

Katie was shaking uncontrollably. "I was in the Cadillac. I looked around and there he was!" She clutched Mama's arm tighter.

"Archer," Mama called. "Load the gun and bring it here." Then to Katie, she said, "Now listen to me, Katie. Did that man touch you?"

Katie shook her head, her teeth chattering.

"Are you sure?" Mama was very serious.

"No, ma'am, he didn't touch me."

"What did he look like?"

"Old. He was an old man and he had on white clothes."

"Jane, pour some coffee for Katie." Mama rocked her, holding her close, trying to stop the shaking. Jane brought the coffee. "Try to drink this, Katie, it will warm you."

But Katie couldn't swallow.

"I think I better put you to bed." She carried Katie into the bedroom. "Jane, put the smoothing irons on to warm."

When Katie was tucked in, Mama kept going to the door and peeking out.

It was not long before Brother came home. Maas was with him. Mama told them what had happened.

"I'll blow his brains out," Maas said.

"Maas, we won't shoot anybody unless we have to."

"It's the onliest way to get rid of a loonie. I'm goin' to git my dogs."

TWELVE
The Escapee

No one ate supper, and when darkness fell they continued to sit in the kitchen without lighting the lamp. "No use attracting attention with a light," Brother said.

Alice and Jane had crawled into bed with Katie. She was warmer, but her eyes were wide open as she listened for suspicious noises outside. Every little sound scared her. It seemed as if they had been waiting hours for Maas's return, but it wasn't yet night when they heard his dogs barking in the distance.

"Sounds like Maas is on the man's trail," Brother said.

"You don't think Maas would shoot the man without cause, do you?" Mama asked.

"Maas will shoot first and ask questions later," Brother answered.

They could hear the chickens, unsettled and flopping about in the henhouse. True Luck growled.

"You want me to check the chicken house for polecats?" Brother asked.

Mama shook her head. "I don't want you outside tonight."

True Luck stood up and began barking.

"It's probably a fox," Archer said.

"Well, if it is, it can have the chickens, you aren't going outside," Mama said determined.

"I'd like to have the hide," he argued.

"Well, you'll have to wait for another opportunity."

There were more noises; the chickens were cackling as they jostled on the roosts. "We sure can't afford to lose any more chickens," Brother said as he pulled back the canvas to look outside. "Can't see a thing, it's pitch black."

True Luck would not be quiet. "Lie down, True Luck," Archer ordered, but the dog continued whining, sniffing at the door. A bucket rolled in the yard.

The three girls sat straight up in bed. "What's that?" they said, alarmed.

"Shhh," someone said. Brother and Mama exchanged puzzled looks. Mama peeked out the canvas. "Brother," she whispered, "isn't that a man?"

Brother took a look. "Where? I don't see anything."

"In white, standing by the hitching tree."

"Oh. . . yeah." Brother was quiet. "He's moving. What do you want me to do?"

"Fire in the air."

"I can't see him." Brother moved from the window. "Hold True Luck." He flung open the door and shot once straight up in the air. Someone was running away.

Brother took a step or two in the yard, looked all around and came back inside, white as a sheet. "That was him all right. Do you think he'll come back?"

"Maybe. We'll have to wait and see."

They had not waited fifteen minutes before they heard hoofbeats, Maas galloping across the flat. He reined up in the yard and ran to the house. "Open up," he hollered. Brother swung open the door.

"You all right?" Maas asked worriedly.

"Yeah. We're okay," Brother answered.

"I heard a shot."

"He was here, Maas," Brother said.

"The loonie?"

Brother nodded. "We heard something in the chickenhouse—thought it was a fox or something—but Mama looked out, and, lo and behold, he was standing right by the tree where you hitch Sam."

"I'll be hornswoggled! You shoot him?"

"No. I just shot in the air to scare him off."

"You shoulda' shot him." Maas struck a match and lit the lamp. "You git a good look at him?"

"Not really. It was pitch dark. We wouldn't have seen him at all but he had on white, you know, like they wear in the asylum."

Mama poured Maas a cup of coffee.

"We heard your dogs barking earlier and thought you were on the trail," Mama said.

"Them goldurned dogs! I brung 'em to the Cadillac to git the scent o' the loonie, only a polecat had went thar before. Them loco dogs smelt one whiff of that polecat and they took off! I been chasin' them all night long. They's stragglin' acrost the flat now, their tongues lolly-waggin'."

It was a long night, but Katie wasn't afraid so long as Maas was in the house. As soon as it was daylight, he and Brother checked the chicken house. Sure enough, one of the pullets was missing. "We'll git 'im," Maas said confidently.

Until the crazy man was caught, Mama said Katie and Archer could not go to school. What's more, they couldn't go to the spring and they couldn't go to the woods. "You'll use the chamber pots," she said. Katie and Archer played "Annie Over," but when they asked to pitch horseshoes, Mama said that was too far from the house. Alice and Jane did not mind staying in the house because they were embroidering and reading, doing what they liked to do most. Mama kept the gun handy at all times. Brother went with Maas to look for the man, but when they came home for supper they hadn't found him.

"We see whar he's camped out, but they is old sites,"

Maas said. "No tellin' whar he's holed up. Old fool pr'bly got no more sense than to haid for Johnson Hollow." Maas turned to Brother and grinned. "Can't say 's I blame him with the likes of you blastin' away at him."

After several days, Maas gave up the hunt and stayed on his ranch to catch up on chores. Brother went to town again and brought home two letters, one from Granddaddy and the other, another money order from Daddy. It was for ten dollars. There was nothing else in the envelope.

"It's from Brownsville," Mama said, frowning. "That's near the Mexican border."

"So?" Jane questioned.

Mama didn't answer.

"See what's in Granddaddy's letter," Brother said.

Mama read the letter through to herself, then she read parts of it over again. She handed the letter to Brother with a downcast look. "He says he has not seen Malcolm—that your father has problems that would only be aggravated by our trying to find him."

"What's he talking about?" Jane asked.

"Well, there may be business difficulties concerning the hotel in Tyler," Mama explained.

"What's Daddy got to do with that?"

"I don't know," she said impatiently. "Some legalities that you would not understand."

"Is he in trouble?" Jane pressed. "Is that what Granddaddy said—that he's in trouble, legal trouble?"

"*No*, he did not!" Mama said indignantly. "And I would thank you not to pitcher-pump me any more, young lady."

Brother had read through the letter twice. "He says he has not seen Dad. That's a story. You know good and well if Dad sent us a money order from Tyler, he saw Granddaddy."

"Shhh," Mama said. "Eat your supper."

Mama hardly ate anything and after supper she sat rocking Timothy, looking off into space, not singing as

154

she usually did. Katie and Archer were playing "Forty-two" and the girls were sewing. Brother was lying on his bed.

True Luck started growling. "What's the matter with you, True Luck?" Archer asked.

They all heard it at once, someone stumbling in the yard. Brother was in the kitchen in an instant, gun in hand.

"Be careful, son, it could be your father," Mama cautioned.

Katie's heart was pounding wildly. True Luck was in a frenzy. "Who's there?" Brother demanded through the closed door. No answer. "I say, who's there?" He cocked the gun. "I've got a gun!"

Brother whispered to Mama. "What do you want me to do, throw open the door?" His face was white as a sheet, and he was trembling.

Mama took the gun. She pulled a corner of the cardboard away from the screen and peeked out. "It's him," she said.

"Who?"

"See, he's all in white."

Katie grabbed Brother's arm. Archer begged, "Lemme shoot him, Mama."

"Who are you?" Mama called out into the dark. They could hear the man coughing hoarsely. Mama took another look. "He's fallen down. He's lying on the ground." Carefully, she opened the door a few inches. They all crowded to peer outside. Katie could hear the man breathing—a raspy, awful sound.

"He's sick," Mama said.

The man was struggling to get to his feet.

"Help him," Mama said. Brother looked at her, quizzically, then obeyed. Mama kept the gun trained on the white-clad figure. Archer held the lamp high and they could all see him, an old man so thin his bones showed through his skin. Brother held him by the arm, steadying him on his feet.

"I'm not crazy, ma'am," the man said with difficulty.

Brother eased away from him and he stood alone, kind of weaving in the wind, his white hair wild. "I've got asthma."

"Don't come any closer," Mama warned, the gun still pointing toward him. "What is your name?"

"I'm Elmer Frady, ma'am. I'm not crazy." His voice was thin and weak. "They sent me to the asylum because I'm sick and too old to work." He felt for a tree and leaned against it.

"Who sent you there?" Mama asked.

"My son's wife. Couldn't be bothered with me." He was breathing funny.

"How did you get out?"

"My grandson helped me. Knew I'd die if I stayed there." He was wheezing.

"What are you doing in our yard?"

"I'm hungry, ma'am. I was after a chicken." He began coughing and slid to a sitting position beside the tree. Mama lowered the gun. After the spasm was over, he spoke again. "I'm sorry I frightened your little girl. I was only resting in the car." He struggled to get up.

"Just sit right there, Mr. Frady, I'll fix you something to eat."

Brother stepped to the door and took the gun.

"Oh, ma'am, I would be most obliged." The old man gasped and slumped to the ground again.

Brother guarded him while Mama scrambled eggs and warmed biscuits. As she worked, she talked to Alice and Jane, trying to calm them down. "He doesn't look insane to me."

"They don't have to *look* crazy, Mama," Jane argued.

"I think I know a crazy person when I talk to one," Mama said.

"When did you ever see anybody who was crazy?" Alice asked.

"Lots of times."

"Daddy looked crazy the morning he left," Jane said.

Mama wheeled around from the stove and looked at

her sharply. "Whatever in the world would make you say that?"

"He did, Mama. His eyes were glassy."

"Be quiet."

Mama served the eggs, grits, and biscuits, and the poor man ate as if he were starving. "Cedar helps my condition," he explained. "If I could just have me a little place in the cedar brake, I could get well."

"Where's your camp?" Brother asked.

"No one place. I've been moving all over to outwit the dogs. Nearly went down in the mud bog crossing to the other side of the creek. If I were ten pounds heavier, I would have sunk."

Finished eating, he handed the plate to Brother. "I'll be moving on if you don't mind—"

"You mustn't leave just yet," Mama said. "Let me get you some coffee."

Katie figured Mama was stalling, trying to make up her mind what to do.

The man continued talking with Brother. "My grandson has been bringing me food but I've missed him several times because I was on the move. That's why I had to steal your chicken. I'll pay you back as soon as I see my grandson."

Mama served him the coffee. "Have the authorities been looking for you?"

He shook his head. "They know my case. They won't come after me."

"Don't you know the mountain people will shoot you, Mr. Frady?" Mama asked.

"Indeed, I do, but it would be easier to be shot than to have to live in that asylum." He rose unsteadily to his feet. "Ma'am, you won't turn me in, will you? If you turn me in, I'll have to go back, and you know I'll die."

"No, Mr. Frady, I won't turn you in," Mama said, and Katie knew by the tone of her voice that she was planning to help him.

"God bless you, ma'am. I'll go now."

"Wait." She paused. "What would you think of sleeping in our cook tent tonight? The dogs won't bother you in there and no one will hurt you."

Brother frowned and almost said something.

"Oh, ma'am—" His voice trembled and his rheumy old eyes were pitiful.

"Brother, find some old blankets and a pillow. That lap rob would be good. Make Mr. Frady a bed and give him the lantern."

After Mr. Frady was settled in the cook tent, Brother returned to the house, fuming. "Mama, what's the big idea asking a lunatic to spend the night?"

"Would you let him go back into the woods? Some-one would shoot him at the drop of a hat. Besides, if he is insane, I would rather know where he is and keep my eye on him."

"What do you mean, keep your eye on him?"

"I'm going to sit up tonight. You just make sure the gun is loaded properly and I'll have it right here beside me. If there is trouble, I'll call you."

"Well, I'm not going to let you sit up alone." And he didn't.

There was no trouble, and in the days that followed, Mama invited Mr. Frady to meals, and he helped with the chickens. Maas, who thought at first she was foolish to have a "loonie" about the place, came to trust the old man.

"Say ye got a little pension, Mr. Frady?" Maas asked. "Next time thet yallar automobile comes down the road I'll make it my business to see thet grandson o' your'n and see that you git yer money." Maas carved his thumbnail with a pocketknife. "In the meantime, I'm gonna set ye up a camp in the cedar brake over yonder." He waved his hand toward the back of the house where the cedar was dense. "I kin buy yer vittles when I buy mine."

Back at school, Katie and Archer never told the other children what had happened. In time, they talked of

Mr. Frady who lived on the flat for his health, but no one realized he was one and the same as the escapee.

Maas became fond of Mr. Frady and visited him from time to time to swap yarns. Maas saw to it that he had beans and coffee and asthma cigarettes. Mama sent him water every day, and when they had something good to eat, she sent him hot food. Seeing the smoke of Mr. Frady's campfire trailing up from the cedar brake meant they had a neighbor on the flat, and Mama said that was comforting.

The weather was warming, and the whippoorwills were calling their mates. Archer sat on a honeycomb rock and taught the girls how to imitate the birds with "Jack-married-the-widow," and the whippoorwills answered them. In a few days, Katie's birthday was due. As she listened to the birds' calls, she cherished the hope that in only a few days, Daddy would be home.

April came and with it, bluebonnets, covering the ground like a carpet. Mama ripped the cardboard from the screens so everyone could see them. The view was breathtaking—bluebonnets spread the length and breadth of the flat.

When Daddy did not come home for her birthday, Katie concluded that God had sent the bluebonnets instead. As lovely as they were, it was not a fair exchange.

Mama called to Katie. "Come, let's get a closer look." They walked among the flowers, stooping down to examine their stems, feeling the texture, trying to smell them. "See, Katie, they're a kind of lupine. See?" She spread the petals to show the flower's structure.

"Uh-huh."

"I wonder if Helmut and Ethel could grow these?" she mused. "They need lime."

Katie sat down, hugging her knees. *If only Daddy could see the bluebonnets in April*, she was thinking, *he would never in a million years leave the flat again.*

Mama stood up and her shadow fell across Katie.

"What are you thinking about, Katie?"

Katie groped for words. "Oh, Mama, it's so hard to wait."

Mama's eyes were as blue as the flowers and ever so soft as she looked down at Katie. Slowly she turned, lifting her face toward the wind that pressed the faded dress against her body and fixing her gaze on Lookout Point. She spoke softly, "I know." Then she sighed and the sigh was full of sadness.

THIRTEEN
The Way to Be Brave

For Katie's birthday, Alice and Jane gave her a beautiful handkerchief they had embroidered with pink rosebuds. "Little French knots," Alice explained proudly. Alice and Jane truly loved her, Katie knew; it was just that she was their little sister, and that's all she could ever be to them.

Archer gave Katie a slingshot he had made and used for a while; Brother caught her an armadillo for a pet; and Mama and Timothy gave her a photograph. It was a picture of Katie and Daddy made at Twenty-nine, he in his homburg, as Mama called it, and she in her baseball cap. Mama had framed the picture, using some of Grandmama McIntosh's lace, and set it on the washstand where Daddy used to shave. At first the picture disturbed Katie; it reminded her of something dark and painful, something she wanted to forget.

The armadillo was the best present of all. It was a curious creature, covered with a hard shell, plated together in sections so the armadillo could roll up in a ball if it wanted to and be completely protected from its enemies. Brother said the armadillo could not see very well, but he could smell and would stand on his hind feet, wobbling from side to side, smelling and listening. If there was danger, he hit the dirt digging. He could dig to China, Archer said.

Katie tied a stout cord around the armadillo's foot, and, perching on a low limb of a cedar, watched him for hours as he rooted in the cedar needles for bugs and other edibles.

The more she watched him, the more she envied him. *It must be nice to roll up in a ball*, Katie thought. *It must be nice to be covered with a shell so thick nothing can get through. Nothing can hurt him. He doesn't have to even see what is going on. He can stay underground in the cool dirt, for hours and hours, all alone; all by himself. He can live and be buried at the same time. When he wants to come out he can, and it is like coming out of a grave. If he doesn't like what he sees outside, he can roll up and hide again, perfectly safe. Living in a skin the way a person does, means getting hurt all the time. Even when your eyes are open and you see everything going on around you, there's no place to hide. You can't crawl up inside yourself and say, "Stay out." You keep on feeling the pain, over and over again. You keep on looking because you have to; you keep on seeing and feeling and hurting. That's what it's like being a person. I'll have to wait and wait and wait, and maybe he'll never come. Maybe he won't even write to us again!*

Katie wiped her hands across her eyes. *There I go*, she said to herself. *I bet my face is all smeared and they'll know I've been crying and they'll go around behind my back saying, "Poor Katie," and I'll wish I was dead!*

Katie climbed down from the tree, staked the armadillo, and lifted her dress to wipe her face. By being careful, maybe she could get to the rain barrel and wash her face before anyone noticed her.

There were no more letters from Daddy, no more money orders. Brother went time and again to General Delivery but there was nothing. "Maybe Daddy's letters were returned to him," Brother suggested. "Remember he used to have 'After Five Days Return To' above his return address? If he had that above his return address, it could have been returned to him because we have gone more than five days without getting to the Post Office."

"It's possible. However, these last two letters from Malcolm had no return address," Mama said.

Brother asked Mr. Taylor for a job and got work cutting wood at one dollar a cord. He worked very hard from sunup until dark. "I cut more than a cord a day," he told Archer. But, after several weeks, Brother learned that no matter how much wood he cut, Mr. Taylor always reckoned it to be a cord. The five dollars each week bought groceries, kerosene, and some shotgun shells from week to week.

Brother would come home so tired he had to lie down before he could eat. Katie was lying on her cot gazing at Lookout Point and waiting for him to wake up when she decided to pray one more time. She thought a long time before she decided what to ask. *How would it be*, she thought, *if Aunt Ethel and Uncle Helmut would pay us a visit—not a long visit—just if they would come and bring us some money.*

"Please, God," Katie prayed, "when I open my eyes, let me see Uncle Helmut's little Studebaker coming across Lookout Point." She waited a few minutes before opening her eyes because she wasn't real sure, not as sure as she had been when she asked that the honeycomb rocks turn to gold. Opening her eyes, she saw there was nothing on the road.

With Brother working, Katie and Archer were responsible for getting water from the spring. Because Katie was not allowed to carry a two-gallon bucket as Archer did (her tin milk pail held scarcely a gallon), they had to make two trips a day.

They crossed the flat to the north and followed a cow trail that clung to the steep, rocky bluff down to the field below. They knew by heart every foothold on the cliff, every hazard. After the bluff, from there on, it was easy. The trail edged the field to the creek and followed the cottonwoods along the bank until it reached the spring near the highway bridge.

On warm days, animals would cool off in the spring, so if the water was stirred up, Katie and Archer would play until it cleared.

At the spring the creek ran in riffles, the shallow water pouring from ledge to ledge over limestone shelves, seeking deep holes to fill. Where the streams spread out flat and still, they looked for snakes gliding across and skipped flat stones on the surface. "Lookit, Katie! It skipped eight times!"

Minnows darted about, hiding in the shadows of great rocks. Sometimes Katie and Archer seined for minnows to use as fish bait.

In the cottonwoods squirrels chattered, and from the field came the liquid calls of bobwhites.

While Archer swung out over the creek, hanging onto a grapevine, Katie explored a washed-out place where the roots of a tree showed. Wild flowers struggled to live in the little hollowed-out spaces between the water and the bank. Considering the flash flooding of the creek, the little flowers were courageous, to say the least.

Katie lay back on the bank, listening to the grasshoppers singing across the grass, hearing the lazy clunking of the cowbell. Buttermilk clouds drifted through the sky. "Come on," Archer hollered. "We gotta go."

Katie took her small bucket and sank it carefully in the spring so as not to disturb the bottom and to avoid sucking water spiders into the pail. The sparkling cold water, pouring from the heart of the earth, was pure and clear. Face down, they drank their fill.

As they started the long hike home, Archer began swinging the full bucket in an arc by his side, up—over his head—and down again without spilling a drop. "Centrifugal force," he told Katie. Katie tried the same trick, panicked and soused herself.

Archer, who was not given to lectures, explained the grave consequences of fear. "The way to be brave," he told her, "is to face things head on. Know what you have to do and do it. Don't hesitate. The trouble with you, Katie, is you stop to doubt and you lose your advantage. I know in my head that the water won't spill so long as I keep up the speed. You are never quite sure."

"I'm as brave as you are!" she said and ran ahead of him. She could do that because her bucket was not as heavy as his—she could run all the way up the cliff. "Fleet as a deer," Brother had called her, but Archer called her a mountain goat.

Katie waited for Archer on the top of the cliff. Standing high on a rock, looking down, Katie felt giddy from the sheer thrill of the view. The same wind blowing against her thin body swept over the field below, bending the dry grass, wave after wave as on an ocean. The moving shadows of clouds following, mottled the sere parched landscape. *If only I could paint pictures like Alice and Jane can,* Katie thought, *I would paint this one—the sky, the field, the cottonwoods—with the wind blowing and the clouds just as they are now.*

Mama had started the twins painting again, setting up their easels outside and helping them get their brushes in good condition. Even though they liked to paint and embroider, Katie knew Alice and Jane would like to have friends or at least visitors. No one but Maas ever made it up the hill. Even Mr. Frady stayed to himself like a hermit. The university students had stopped having Sunday school because no one but Sophie came. The only outsiders the girls saw were at the spring on wash days and then not every Saturday.

When Maas suggested a fish fry, Mama consented. A fish fry brought all the mountain people together. It lasted all night with men running trotlines, women cooking fish and everybody fiddling and frolicking.

The MacLeods were the first to arrive at the creek,

going down by the side of Goats' Cave to the one place by the water where there was level ground and space for wagons. Maas could not come; he had a sick cow, which, Mama said, was providential because Jack Taylor came to the fish fry.

Before sundown, people began to arrive—walking, on horseback, in wagons, or on rickety trucks. Some of the men began running the trotlines; others started cleaning fish or building fires.

Rosabelle Ziegler left the jackass at home and rode her brother's white stallion to the fish fry. She was plainly sweet on Brother and wanted to show off in front of him. She spurred the horse to make him show his speed, and the animal thundered past the campers, his great mane flowing, his nostrils flaring. But there was an end to the narrow strip of land beside the creek and when the stallion cut sharply to dodge disaster, big Rosabelle was flung over his head, landing in the creek. The crowd whooped and hollered! Brother fished her out, she as mad as a wet hen and looking worse.

Katie lay on a blanket beside a blazing fire listening to the sounds of paddles bumping the sides of the boats and men's coarse voices carrying over the water. Bull Creek had never been more beautiful. Crickets sang, and overhead stars by the millions glimmered. A lantern in one of the boats cast a shimmering reflection in the water; fish jumped with a splash. Mama was frying cornbread in one pan and fish in the other and the smell of it and the boiling coffee was mouth-watering.

A screeching sound came from Cat Mountain. Jane jumped. "What was that?"

"A screech owl," Katie answered.

"Screech owl, my foot!" Archer said. "That's a mountain lion. If you listen you'll hear him again."

And they did. Katie jumped.

"Jane, Alice, take over the frying pans," Mama said.

Mama walked Katie to the edge of the creek. Stars reflected in the water. "Look up, Katie. Trillions and trillions of them." Then Mama quoted the Bible:

When I consider thy heavens,
   the work of thy fingers,
The moon and the stars
   which thou hast ordained;
What is man,
   that thou art mindful of him?
And the son of man
   that thou visitest him?

In a little while the music began, and they couldn't hear the lion. Mr. Bracey was sawing on the fiddle, stomping his foot; Harvey Pittman, a friend of Jack Taylor, was playing guitar; and Sam Roper picked his banjo. Harvey also had his harmonica and washboard to play.

In the middle of "Redwing," Jack Taylor came swaggering through the crowd, dropped the reins of his horse, and swept the crowd with his dark brown eyes. The music stopped and all heads turned his way. Jack Taylor was every bit as handsome as the school children claimed.

"Howdy," he rumbled. Broad-shouldered and dressed in black shirt with white braid, snakeskin pants, high-crowned Stetson, silver spurs on his boots, he made a "dashing figure," as Alice was fond of saying.

He was twirling a rope over his head, the big loop passing downward over his body and up again, his eyes never changing, his teeth white against his dark skin.

"Lookit that saddle!" Archer exclaimed. The saddle was brand new with silver studs on the side panels.

Jack lassoed a brake handle, a bush on a sandbar in the middle of the creek, and then a little girl who squealed. He gave her a silver dollar, flipping it to her across the fire.

Miss Lucretia kept her eyes on Jack Taylor, but he never once looked her way. He spoke to Alice and Jane and smiled at Mama, tipping his hat.

"Lord help us if Maas comes," Oren Bracey whispered to Brother

"Well, this isn't Maas's land, nor Taylor's."

"Don't matter. A Maas an' a Taylor can't be 'round each other long without a knifin' or a shootin'."

Miss Lucretia came over to where Brother was sitting and started talking to him but Brother was so tired, he excused himself and stretched out on a blanket. Soon he was fast alseep.

The music was starting again and people were forming a circle—men, women, children—all were stepping to the music, "Skip to My Lou, My Darlin'." There was a game to it, a weaving in and out, putting first one person, then another out of the circle.

Mr. Bracey drew the bow across the fiddle on the last note, the crowd clapped, and Mr. Bracey started another tune. That set them all in motion again, skirts flouncing— singing the words to "Green Gravel":

Oh, Alice, oh, Alice, your true love is dead,
He wrote you a letter to turn back your head. . .

As people tired, they dropped out of the frolic, found a place by the fire, and ate or drank coffee. When all the crowd was exhausted and ringed the fires, the musicians settled back, singing the old sad ballads—"Cowboy Jack," about a cowhand who waited too long to go see his sweetheart, for the girl died. Oren Bracey followed that sad one with another, "When the Work's All Done This Fall." It told the story of a son who waited too long to go home to see his mother.

Alice and Jane looked beautiful in the firelight, their red pajamas reflecting color in their cheeks. Like Mama, they knew how to talk and laugh with people, keeping their distance, but friendly.

Nearly everyone had had his fill of fish when Ruby and Shadow rode up on their big mare. They were too shy to talk, too shy to eat, too shy to play, and before it was very late, Mama gave them a mess of fish and sent them home so their Pa would not come looking for them. Katie stood watching them as they rode away bareback, Ruby in front, Shadow behind. The old mare was swaying from side to side; Shadow's hand rested on the horse's rump as she propped herself up, and her face was turned backward, catching a last look at the fun. When she saw Katie watching her, Shadow slowly and deliberately stuck out her tongue. Katie felt a surge of pity for the mean little girl.

The boys were calling from the campfire, "Katie!" She went back to the fire. Willie Bracey, his freckled face hidden by the monstrous hat, spoke sheepishly. "This un's for you, Katie." He strummed the guitar a few times and, in his strained young voice, began singing, "Little Joe the Wrangler. . . will wrangle nevermore. . ."

Why Willie Bracey would think she liked that song was more than Katie could understand. It was about a boy whose stepmama whipped him every day until he ran away and joined some cowboys. Called out in a stampede, he was trampled to death. The song always made her cry, so Katie only pretended to listen and kept her mind on her armadillo, imagining what he was doing or how he was sleeping.

Willie's song was not the last. The music, fishing, cooking, laughing, eating, and playing went on all night long. Timothy lay in Mama's lap, his blond hair in ringlets about his forehead. Katie nuzzled his neck and wondered that he could sleep through the fun.

Mist hovered over Bull Creek, drifting silently with the breeze. As the night wore on, the screeching of mountain lions became blood-curdling and sent chills up the spine.

Suddenly Jack Taylor was the center of attraction again. Dramatically, he flipped a jackknife in the air, its steel blade glinting, spinning fast. He caught the handle and flipped it again, striking a silver dollar in midair.

Harvey set up a Nehi bottle thirty paces away and Jack, standing with his back to the target, snapped the knife between his legs and hit the bottle squarely. As if that were not enough, Harvey stood with a cigarette between his teeth and let Jack cut it in half with a spin of the knife.

As a finale, Jack turned sideways to the crowd, opened his mouth and pretended to swallow the knife whole. The people clapped; the show was over.

The music started up again and did not stop until the first sign of light began to show over Cat Mountain. Jack Taylor folded his jackknife, and, as if it had been a sign to them all, people began rolling up blankets and packing their belongings to leave. Rowboats were secured, fires doused with water; children, dogs, and husbands were counted, and the people began moving homeward.

When everyone had said good-bye, the MacLeods began their weary ascent up the cliff. Archer went ahead, carrying the blanket and skillet. Brother held Timothy in his arms and the rest of them followed, more asleep than awake.

As they came onto the flat they could hear Archer at the house yelling. *Maybe Daddy's come home*, Katie thought, and sprinted ahead as fast as she could run. Before she reached the yard, Archer was hollering, "They're dead! They're dead! The bantams are dead."

"Dead?"

Feathers were everywhere, clumps of them and single ones scattered all over! Blue-green ones and the beautiful copper-colored feathers of Ethel's wings and tail.

"Coulda' been a bobcat," Archer said. "Most likely an owl."

It didn't matter. Katie crawled into her cot and wept softly. When Mama tried to comfort her, Katie broke into sobs. "Daddy gave her to me, Mama—*Daddy!*"

Alice and Jane started crying.

Brother stroked Katie's hair, his hand by now as rough as Maas's. "You have your armadillo, Katie. Don't you want to play with your armadillo?"

It wasn't the same.

"Wanna go to the spring?" Archer asked. Katie did

not answer but rolled over on her stomach, sobbing her heart out.

That night Katie was sick. She woke up coughing a strange, hoarse cough. Mama jumped out of bed. "She's got the croup!" She went in the kitchen and in a few minutes came back holding a spoonful of damp sugar. "Here, Katie, take this."

Katie forced down the strong-tasting remedy, then started coughing again.

Nothing helped, every breath was a cough. It finally woke everybody in the house, even Archer. Brother stood at the foot of Katie's cot looking scared. One coughing spasm followed another until she lost her breath. "Mama, I can't breathe!" Katie croaked, frantic.

"Help me prop her up higher," Mama said. Katie clutched Mama's arm, coughing, gasping, struggling to breathe.

"So much phlegm! Jane—Alice, fix some warm salt water. Brother, let's take her outside in the fresh air."

Brother lifted her out of bed. In the yard, he put her, still gasping for breath, in Mama's arms. They walked up and down but it didn't help.

"Jane, hurry up with that salt water. . . Archer! Where's Archer? Archer, run up to Mr. Frady's. Ask him for one of those asthma cigarettes."

Katie was lashing out, fighting a terrible blackness— she couldn't breathe, couldn't breathe!

"Brother, try to get a doctor!"

"Oh, Lord!"

Katie could hear them coming and going, but she couldn't *see* them! She couldn't speak!

"Here, Katie, drink this." Katie tried, but she couldn't—she couldn't swallow.

Archer came back with Mr. Frady. "This child won't live!" she heard him say.

Katie felt like she was sinking! She dug her fingers in Mama's arm; then she couldn't hold on any longer.

"Drink this," Mama was pleading. "Drink this, it'll make the phlegm come up. Katie, open your mouth— let me put my finger down your throat. Please! Katie! Please!"

"Mama!" someone cried, "she's turning black!"

Katie was sinking down, down, down. *Lord*, she prayed, *let me speak to Mama.*

Two words came. "Mama, pray."

That was all.

FOURTEEN
Mama's Dream

The next time Katie roused, daylight was coming on. She closed her eyes. Brother came into the house and tiptoed across the floor to the foot of the bed. "How is she?" he whispered.

"She's better, thank God. I thought we had lost her."

There were others around the bed. Katie opened her eyes. There were Alice and Jane, hollow-eyed and pale; dear Brother, his eyes wet with tears; and Mama, smiling, patting her. "Mama, can I go to school?"

Mama raised her eyebrows. "School? Oh, no, honey, you won't go to school for a couple of weeks. Go back to sleep. You need to rest." She turned to the twins. "Go to bed, girls."

They obeyed, and in a little while Brother went to his room. Katie closed her eyes. She felt perfectly well.

Katie spent one day lying on her cot, looking out at Cat Mountain, watching for a car to pass. The family acted strange, moving and speaking quietly the way they did after the sale when Daddy was in bed. They kept asking if there was anything she wanted. They thought she was sick. Katie knew God had made her well.

The next day Mama let Katie get up, and on the third day she went back to school. From time to time they spoke of her illness: how two glasses of salt water brought up the phlegm; how Mr. Frady blew smoke in Katie's face and saved her life. Katie let them talk.

When Saturday came, Katie took the armadillo out to the cedar tree, climbed up in it, and let the armadillo root around in the leachings. Mama and Archer were a distance away trying to uproot a cedar stump to burn in the stove. As she watched them, Katie was thinking about God. She thought about her dream, the one she had when she was five years old and in kindergarten. That was a long time before, but the dream was as real as could be. What really did the dream mean? Did Jesus want her to die and leave Mama? Was that why she was so sick? Did Jesus let her come back because he knew she couldn't leave Mama?

Katie thought about all the silly prayers she had prayed—asking the Lord to turn rocks into gold—"the very idea!" Then she thought, *Well, he might have brought Aunt Ethel and Uncle Helmut, but, so what, he's got a mind of his own.*

Katie drew in her breath and felt the air going all the way down in her chest. What was to come next was hard for her to say. Katie prayed silently: *And when I asked you to bring Daddy home for my birthday, I know you had your reasons. Will you take care of him wherever he is and, please, Lord, won't you bring him home?*

Brother was coming toward her, dragging his axe behind him. He never brought his axe home from work. He stopped under the tree, reached up with his hand, and rested it on the limb beneath Katie. He was so thin he looked sick. When he looked up at her there were tears in his eyes. He looked like Daddy when he was sad.

"I lost my job, Katie." He took a deep breath. "How am I going to tell Mama?" He put his forehead against his arm and leaned hard against the limb.

Mama and Archer were coming toward them, dragging

the stump. Mama stopped, staring their way. She told Archer to go on to the house, and she moved toward them.

Mama took a closer look at Brother and asked, "What's the matter, Son, did Mr. Taylor lay you off?"

He took his head down from his arm, his face filled with grief. "Yes, Mama. He's going to work for the highway. Doesn't need me any more."

"WPA?"

He nodded. "As a foreman."

"He didn't have a place for you on the crew?"

"There's only one man on the crew who isn't a Taylor. He's put his whole family to work."

"Well, don't worry about it. The Lord will provide."

"I wonder," Brother said bitterly.

Maas took the news characteristically. "Wal, what more could you expect from a Taylor?" He lit a cigarette.

"Brother, thar's always coal kiln work. Young man like you ort to go into business for hisself and there ain't no better business in these parts, unless, o' course, it's makin' likker and I don't reckon ye'd be interested in that." He waited, thinking Brother might be interested.

"Maas, I don't know anything about coal kiln work—" He was trying to be polite.

Maas tucked the cigarette in the corner of his mouth, squinting against the curl of smoke, and began breaking twigs about six inches long. "I'll show ye all ye need to know," he said. "Ye take poles like these here sticks and ye stack 'em against one another. Sorta' like a injun's tepee, ye lean 'em together. Then ye pack dirt all over this here cone-shaped kiln. When ye git done with that, ye make shore ye got a good draft hole and ye build a fire inside." He paused to take short puffs on the cigarette.

"What happens when it rains?" Archer asked.

Maas shook his head. "'Tain't nary rain can put out a kiln fire if'n hit's made right. Now o' course, if'n ye don't know what ye're doin'—"

There was no doubt that Maas knew what he was doing.

"If'n ye don't make hit right, ye're liable to have the whole shootin' caboodle blow up in yer face, but if'n ye gits that thar draft hole suckin' out smoke jes' right and yer fire a goin' good, them poles keeps a smolderin' and a smolderin' 'till they is charred plumb through. I kin make the purtiest charcoal ye ever done seen."

"What do they use it for?" Archer asked.

"Women use it under wash pots—any place ye want good clean smoke, slow burnin' fuel. That is, on the outside. Ye dasn't burn hit on the inside." He winked at Brother. "Now if ye'd consider moonshine'n, Brother, I know a feller might help ye with that."

Even Katie knew who that "feller"might be. She and Archer had crossed the creek to Maas's place and were making their way through wild grapevines when they saw a little pipe sticking out of the ground. They were trying to figure out why a pipe was there when they looked up and saw the muzzle of Maas's gun pointing at them and an angry Maas ordering them off his property. They got off his land as fast as they could, and Archer said they had come close to Maas's still.

With time on his hands, Brother was miserable. He walked Katie to school, carrying the buckets to bring water back from the spring. He would stand around and talk to Miss Lucretia until the children arrived, and he would ring the bell for her. In a few days he began coming in the afternoons only it wasn't to walk Katie home, it was to walk Miss Lucretia home.

Mama didn't approve of Miss Lucretia, and she told Brother so. "A young man can't be too careful," she told him. "Bad women were always after your father."

"Why bring him into this? I'm not Dad."

"What do you mean by that?"

He didn't answer.

"Your father comes from one of the finest families in

South Carolina. You have nothing to be ashamed of in him."

"Then why doesn't he write, why doesn't he come home? It's been over three months."

"Well, if you're insinuating that he has left us for no reason, let me assure you that Malcolm MacLeod is not that kind of man. He would never, never desert his children."

"I know he wouldn't, Mama, but I don't know how much longer we can make out here."

"Just remember one thing, Brother, if your father had anything to send us, he would send it. He has always been a good provider. You know that."

Brother changed the subject. "They're having a box supper at the schoolhouse for the close of school. Miss Lucretia wants us all to come."

"When is it?"

"Friday night."

Katie and the twins searched the house for materials to decorate their boxes. Colored tissue paper was hard to find, but there were plenty of ribbons. Alice did most of the decorating, and the three boxes looked like Easter baskets when she was finished with them. Mama fried chicken and apple pies to fill the boxes, and when that was done, they all walked down to the schoolhouse.

All the girls had boxes which were placed on the teacher's desk and mixed up so the boys would not know for sure which box belonged to their girl. Then the bidding began.

Willie Bracey was in the back of the room where the men sat. He was sure he knew which box was Katie's and the men kept giving him nickels to bid on the pink one. The price went up nickel by nickel to the ridiculously high figure of thirty-five cents, and when Willie opened it, the box wasn't Katie's. Katie knew his disappointment was not that he could not eat with her, but that the box didn't have Mama's fried apple pies.

Jack Taylor bid a silver dollar for Jane's box and no

one could equal that. Mama didn't like Jane going off to eat with Jack Taylor, so she sent Archer along with them.

When the box supper was over, they trudged up the hill past the Cadillac, Archer swinging the lantern, casting grotesque shadows before and behind them. True Luck was barking at everything he imagined to be in the woods. Brother was seeing Miss Lucretia home.

Jack Taylor and Harvey Pittman were walking up the hill with the MacLeods. When they reached the house, Mama said politely, "We won't invite you boys to come in. It's late and you left your horses down the hill. I know you need to get back to them."

After they left, Alice asked Mama why she sent them away. "Now, girls, we don't have a proper place for you to entertain. It would be uncomfortable to have them in the kitchen."

"We could sit outside," Jane argued.

"What would we sit on?"

After they went to bed, Mama was in the kitchen reading. Katie fell asleep, but when Brother came home she heard him shut the door. She turned over and heard them talking.

"Why so late?" Mama asked.

Brother didn't answer; he looked sick. "Mama—" His voice quivered and he couldn't go on. He looked ashamed.

"Son," Mama said, "the world is full of loose women."

"But she seemed nice."

Brother sat with his face in his hands, staring at the floor. Mama's blue eyes brimmed with tears. She got up, went over to him, put her arms around him.

After a while, Mama went back to the rocker. To ease Brother's misery, she changed the subject. "Brother, I had the strangest dream. . . I dreamed that two angels came down in the front yard beneath the live oaks. They were carrying a little case about so big." She held her hands about a foot apart. "About this wide. It looked like, I'd say, a jewelry case. It was green with a handle. The angels set the case on the ground at my feet and then they went away."

Brother frowned.

"What do you think it means?" she asked.

"I don't know. What makes you think it means anything?"

"Did I ever tell you about the dream I had when we were living at Twenty-nine?"

He shook his head.

"When we were living at Twenty-nine I dreamed that we had moved to Texas and were living in a small house, not unlike this one. A flood came and we could not leave the house."

He looked at her oddly. "So?"

"Well, don't you see? It was a kind of flood, the creek rising, that sealed our fate. Isn't that logical?"

"I'm too much of a Presbyterian to believe in dreams," Brother said. "Dreams aren't logical. What's logical about two angels delivering a jewelry box to you?"

"I don't know. I don't believe in precognition, but I believe in a personal God. When we need special help, sometimes he gives it to us in unusual ways."

"That's too mystical for me."

"It shouldn't be. You believe in angels, don't you?"

"Sure, but only in the Bible. I've never seen an angel and I don't expect to. I'm surprised at you—you've always been practical, down to earth."

"I am a realist, Son, and I believe angels are as real as this table." She tapped the table top.

"Now, Mama, you're sounding superstitious."

"Superstition has nothing to do with it. Brother, isn't it logical to believe that if there is a God, he will communicate with us?"

"I don't know."

"Yes, you do. Think about it."

Brother stood up, stretched himself. "The only message I want to hear right now is that Dad is either going to come home or that somehow we're going to get off this godforsaken flat." He lifted the lid of the three-cornered pot and ate a spoonful of cold oatmeal. "Why don't you write to Uncle Tom? He has plenty of money. Maybe he can help."

"We don't ask for money, Brother. Malcolm would be humiliated and so would I."

Brother began walking the floor. "Well, what in the world are we going to do? We have four or five chickens left—there's no meat in the smokehouse. There's a sack of beans, some coffee, and cornmeal left. What else?"

"The Lord will provide, Brother. Somehow. He always has." In the lamplight, streaks of gray showed in her hair. "We have plenty of fish and rabbits."

"Mama, you worry more about him than you do us."

"Your father?"

"That's right. You think he's crossed the border into Mexico, don't you?"

"Possibly. If he's in trouble."

"If he's in trouble? Didn't Granddaddy say that was a distinct possibility?"

Mama shook her head, puzzled. "It's an enigma to me."

They sat in silence a long time; then Mama laid her hand on Brother's shoulder. "I'm going to bed." She kissed him on the forehead. "Blow out the lamp when you come."

With school closed for the summer, time lay heavy on their hands. Jane and Alice played dominoes, and Katie spent hours in the tree with the armadillo rooting around beneath. She sat by the hour gazing at Lookout Point. She and Archer went fishing and hunting, but Mama said an idle mind was the Devil's workshop, and she set her mind to do something about it.

"Brother, why don't we build a porch here in front of the house? About this wide, I'd say." She marked the area with a stick. "Between the two front doors, like a patio. We'll use these beautiful field stones scattered about."

Brother made a rickety sled to haul the rocks, and he and Katie went all over the flat selecting stones. They also went up on the wagon road and dug bucketfuls of adobe to use as mortar.

Laying the stones, turning their edges to fit as in a puzzle, reminded Katie of the tiles and the walk she had made for Daddy. How long ago it seemed. *Now*, she told herself, *I'll remember these stones and some day I'll write about them—their colors, their shapes—and the way they feel, some smooth, some rough. And, I'll explain where they came from and how long they've been here and why.*

When they finished the porch, Mama had other ideas for improving the yard. "Let's cover it with adobe," she said. "Then we can sweep it and keep it clean."

Alice and Jane were painting landscapes while Katie and the boys were working. The twins really did not like to do outdoor work and agreed only to hand tools and run errands. Archer grumbled about working, but to Katie, it was fun. The adobe was like white powder, and when it was packed firmly it became a pavement. Mama worked alongside Katie and made her rest from time to time.

Katie was resting in the shade when it happened. She did not see the hawk until it was too late—it plunged to earth, snatched up one of the frying-size chickens, and was flying upward again before Katie knew what was happening. Poor Mama was chasing after the hawk, waving her hat and shouting, but it was too late.

Brother swore and slammed his hat on the ground.

Mama stood with her hands on her hips watching the hawk disappearing over the cedar brake. "Good Lord, what next?" Her face was red and angry. "That leaves us the sum total of three fryers!" She turned toward Katie. "Katie MacLeod, it's your fault. It does look like, with nothing more to do than to sit there in the shade, you would have seen that hawk! I told you a long time ago to watch for hawks!"

"Now, Mama, it wasn't Katie's fault," Brother said.

"There's no excuse!" Mama sat down, her face in her hands. "I might as well give up. Try as I will, there's no use trying. If a polecat doesn't get us a hawk will. There are too many odds against us, children. We might just as well go on relief!"

The word "relief" fell on their ears like a curse. Alice and Jane froze in their tracks, dumbfounded. Katie gulped back tears and rubbed her toes in the dirt. Only Archer looked undisturbed. When nobody said anything, he spoke up. "You don't mean that, Mama." He didn't ask her; he told her like he knew for sure.

After a little while, Mama rose wearily, walked over to Katie and rested her hand on her shoulder. Her voice was calm. "Honey, tomorrow we'll go look for cactus. We'll get one of every kind we can find and bring it here." She gestured toward the center of the yard. "We'll plant them in a little bed right over there."

Katie looked up and met Mama's blue eyes. The fury was spent. Mama was not smiling, but Katie knew everything was right between them. That was Mama's way; she never said she was sorry, she showed you. It was the next best thing.

The next day, before the sun was too hot, Katie led Mama to the cliffside where small specimens of cacti clung to rocky ledges. They found a spindly cactus, several small dome-shaped ones, a couple of broad-leafed types and a spiney one with long needles. Their prize find was a lovely little cactus nestled in a large honeycomb rock, too big for them to carry. Katie yodeled, then yelled, "Bring the sled!"

While they waited for the boys to come, they heard the hum of a motorboat sounding beyond the bend in the river, and Mama and Katie stood on the boardwalk to watch it come into view.

On the broad Colorado, the boat was a tiny speck

cutting a wide swath in the water, moving steadily past Maas's place and continuing out of sight behind the Hollow. Long after the boat was out of sight, they stood listening to the drone of the motor fading and watching the wide chevron of water parting the river, washing to its banks on either side.

"Katie," Mama said, "your life is like that little boat. You may feel small and unimportant but in the wake of your life history is changed."

"Me, Mama?"

"Yes, you, Katie. You and every one of us."

The boys came with the sled. They loaded their collection of cacti onto the little contraption, and Brother dragged it to the house.

In another week they had completed the work in the yard. The ground was paved with adobe from the patio to a border of honeycomb rocks; they had stacked flat stones around the bases of three of the oak trees to make dry-wall benches; and in the center, like the heart of the whole, was the beautiful little cacti bed.

They were sitting on the new benches, admiring their handiwork while True Luck romped in the yard chasing lizards. Suddenly the silverlace Wyandotte came charging after him, head down, wings spread, neck stretched! True Luck spun around, tail between his legs, yelping and dashing for cover beneath the house.

Everybody was laughing. "Thank the Lord!" Mama said. "She's setting! Come on, Katie, let's see if we can find her nest."

At first they could not find it, then they waited until they could follow her. The clutch of eggs was hidden beneath a brushpile near the boys' woods. Mama carefully put the eggs in her apron and carried them to a nest in the chicken house.

"She may not like this," Mama said, "but a predator is sure to get them on the ground."

The hen did accept the change and every day Katie and Timothy watched the Wyandotte rushing about gobbling up whatever bugs and grasshoppers she could find, then hurrying back to sit on the nest. They spied on her as the hen turned the eggs with her beak, careful not to break them.

In less than three weeks, on one of Mama's routine checks of the nest, she lifted the clucking, protesting hen and there were two little chicks, still moist from their shells, and another struggling to get out. Mama let Katie and Timothy hold the downy yellow-and-brown chicks, peeping their first sounds in this world.

"Until these biddies are frying size," Mama said, "we'll eat rabbits and fish."

It bothered Brother that he could not shoot rabbits, but he was no marksman. Archer had to do the hunting, and every time he went out with the gun he came home with fresh meat. Katie helped him skin the rabbits. He hung the poor dead things up by their hind legs, slit open their bellies, gutted them, and peeled back their pelts. It was with the peeling that Katie helped. Archer would cut the skin from the fine membranes that held it to the flesh, and Katie would keep the skin pulled back, out of the way of the knife.

Brother had no stomach for skinning rabbits either. If the rabbit remains were wrapped in paper, he would bury it in the woods for them. Brother spent most of his time polishing his shoes and trying to look his best when he went to town looking for work. Of course, he always checked General Delivery for the mail, but there was never anything.

Brother had walked nearly all the way from Austin the day he told Mama, "They're giving away free commodities in town."

Mama frowned and said nothing.

Hoofbeats sounded on the road from the school-house. "It's Jack Taylor," Archer said. "And that looks like Willie Bracey's pony."

The horses broke into a gallop, their hooves kicking up dust behind them. Pulling up in the yard, Jack hollered, "Whoa," and the beautiful sorrel jerked to a halt, tossing its head this way and that, his flanks lathered with sweat.

"Howdy," Jack said and tipped his hat.

Willie said nothing, his eyes on the ground. Jack dropped the reins for the horse to nibble grass and sat in the saddle leaning on the horn.

"Hello," Brother said. "Won't you get down?"

"Can't stay," Jack said, "but reckon we kin rest a spell." They dismounted, tossing the reins around a cedar branch. "Willie here needs a place to stay. His old man wore the hide offa' him. I found him down by the creek wishin' he could come up here."

"Why, of course, Willie is welcome here," Mama said, full of concern.

Willie didn't raise his eyes. Jack reached over and lifted the boy's shirt. Willie's back was crisscrossed with stripes from the whipping. "Cut the blood outta' him," Jack said.

"Oh, dear," Mama said.

Willie yanked his shirt out of Jack's hand. "Pa'll be all right in a few days," he said defensively.

"Can't I get you something to drink, a bite to eat?" Mama offered.

"No, ma'am," Jack replied. "Me and my hoss done filled up at the creek. The boy here might be hongry if he ain't too touchy to ask."

"Alice, Archer, take Willie in the house. Get him something to eat. Make a pallet for him in the boy's room." They went inside. "Won't you sit down, Jack?" Mama asked, motioning to one of the stone benches.

He shook his head, hunkering down on his spurs. "You got a purty place up here, Miz MacLeod; come a full moon ye ort to have a play party. This here flat would be the perfect place for a play party. Use t' dream 'bout play parties when I'uz in prison."

"Are you working on the highway?" Brother asked.

Jack grinned. "I don't never aim to work on no highway. That's hard work—I mean *hard*! I done it a while in prison, but I shore ain't goin' to do it a free man. They's diggin' adobe outta a pit in this heat. It was more'n a hunnert degrees yesterday." He rolled a cigarette. "'Course, my brother hired the whole durn family, except me, and one drifter." He chuckled. "Pity the drifter—them lazy relatives of mine will let him do all the work."

"Well, you tell your brother to let me know if he can hire another man."

"Shore will."

Archer and Willie came out of the house, their cheeks stuffed with food. They unsaddled Willie's pony and turned it loose to graze.

"Reckon I'll hit the trail," Jack said, putting his hat on. "Tell the girls I'll be back of an evenin' an' bring my guitar." He mounted up and turned the horse onto the road. They watched him galloping across the flat.

"Hope he doesn't meet Maas," Brother said.

Archer and Willie took to riding off on the pony early in the morning and staying gone all day. They claimed they were hunting, but Katie knew they were looking for the treasure Maas and Daddy had looked for, and that meant they were going into Johnson Hollow. But Katie wouldn't tell on Archer, and Mama didn't seem to worry that he was gone all day. Katie would hear the gun fire only once or twice all day long and when the boys would come home they would have only one or two jackrabbits. Archer didn't need a whole day to kill one rabbit. He made the excuse that he was sparing his shells because he had only a few left.

With Willie there, Katie was relieved of the chore of skinning rabbits. The boys brought the dressed rabbits to Mama to fry. She washed and cut up the meat, laying the parts on a platter. With the point of the knife she slit open a thigh only to see water drain from it. She shook her head. "Rabbit fever. Too bad." She dumped the pieces in a paper bag. "Archer, you and Willie scrub yourselves with lye soap. You've handled sick rabbits.

I'll bury this meat so True Luck won't get it. I'll make some pancakes for supper."

"We'll go catch fish," Brother said. "Come on, girls, you can go swimming."

Alice and Jane wouldn't go in the water even though they went to the creek. Katie undressed in the bushes, down to her bloomers, and waded in the warm green water. In the middle of Bull Creek were large boulders with sprigs of brush sprouting here and there. Alice and Jane paddled Maas's boat to one of the rocks and sat there giggling and talking about boys. They were talking about how handsome Jack Taylor was—something they would never say in front of Mama.

After swimming a while, Katie and Brother fished. Lying on a rock jutting out from the bank, her line playing lazily in the water, Katie watched dragon flies darting here and there and hovering near the line. "Snake doctors," Archer called them.

The twins were getting too hot on the boulders in the stream and paddled ashore. They sat under the cottonwoods reading a romance book Sophie had loaned them.

Something ate the bait off Katie's line. She threaded another grasshopper on the hook, wincing at the brown juice oozing. Holding the cane pole with both hands she flung the line over her head and yanked it forward—Alice screamed! The line was stretched taut from the tip of the pole to Alice's arm. She had hooked Alice!

Right away Alice fainted, went limp as a dishrag in Jane's arms. Brother worked frantically with the hook but couldn't get it out. "It's the barb—we'll have to cut it out."

Katie peered at the blueness of the imbedded hook and a wave of wooziness passed over her.

"Katie, run to the house and bring me the razor, quick!"

Katie ran as hard as she could, her heart racing. A snake, as round as Brother's arm, was crawling over a rock slab at the very second Katie was leaping over it, but she did not hesitate; just as Archer had said, to be brave you must not hesitate. She kept right on running through the brush to the trail that scaled the cliff. Reaching Goat's Cave, Katie ran along the ledge, past the rattlesnake den, through the brush to Bandit Cave, and finally onto the flat. On level ground she could run like the wind.

Mama and Timothy were somewhere out of sight. Katie grabbed Daddy's razor and a handful of matches.

Racing back across the flat, she scrambled down the cliff on her bottom, scraping elbows and shins. Dodging boulders and cacti she plunged toward the creek, intent on getting to Brother as fast as she could.

Katie glimpsed him standing at the bottom, looking up the cliff. "Catch!" she called and threw the razor to him. "I brought matches." By the time she reached him, he had the razor open and was kneeling beside Alice. With the flame of a match, he sterilized the blade. Alice buried her face in Jane's lap. Katie could not watch.

"There!" she heard him say and opened her eyes. Brother threw the hook aside and began pressing blood from the wound.

After a while, there was nothing more to do but wait for Alice to feel like going home. Brother lay back in the weeds. "This is a godforsaken place," he said. "Excuse me, Katie, I shouldn't have said that." He came up on one elbow. "In the five months since Daddy left, just look at all the things that have happened to us—that ice storm, why we could have died from exposure—then we got scared out of our wits by Mr. Frady; what if he had been a mad man?"

"And that night Katie almost died," Jane added.

"That was the worst. You can't imagine how helpless I felt running up and down the road trying to find a way to town, knowing it would be too late even if I could get a doctor."

"And now this," Jane said. "Alice could take blood poisoning if we aren't careful."

The possibility scared Katie. "Mama'll put some fat meat on it. That'll draw out the poison," Jane said.

"Jane, we don't have any fat meat. Not one small piece," Brother told her.

"Then you better get right in that boat and go over to Maas's place and borrow some."

"Good idea." Brother jumped up and shoved the boat into the water. "Wait here 'till I get back."

Alice's wound healed without infection. By the time Willie left, two weeks later, only a little scar on her arm showed for the accident.

FIFTEEN
Johnson Hollow Treasure

Willie saddled up one morning with some biscuits in his saddle bag and there was no use asking him questions, he knew what he was doing. The MacLeods stood in the yard as he mounted the pony. Katie thought of "Little Joe the Wrangler" and felt sad.

"Are you sure it's all right?" Mama asked him.

"Yes'm," he answered in his serious way. He tipped his hat, nudged the pony with his bare heels, and leaned toward the road. It was plain to see that he did not want to leave but felt he must. The little pony clopped down the road, and when they reached the top of the hill, they stopped. Willie turned around and waved, then rode down the hill, out of sight.

Later in the afternoon, Katie went hunting with Archer to keep him company since Willie was gone. They saw a lot of animals to shoot, but Archer only took aim, he never fired. "I only got one shell left," he explained, "and we had meat today."

They were walking dangerously close to Johnson Hollow. "Don't you think we better turn back?" Katie asked.

"Katie, do you know what Willie and I been doin'?"

Katie shook her head.

"We been looking for those two rocks with the deer head and the horse head. The rocks Maas told us about."

"I remember."

"We rode that pony all over Johnson Hollow. I'm gonna' find those rocks, Katie."

Katie knew he would. If they were still there, Archer would find them because there was nothing he set out to do that he didn't do.

"You wanna help me?"

"Sure," she said, but she was wishing she had the courage to tell the truth.

They were moving under some low lying scrub. The ground was white and stony, the brush stiff and dry. "Over that little ridge is Johnson Hollow," Archer told her. He looked at the sun. "The sun's three hours up—"

"What time is that?"

"Five o'clock regular time." He looked all around, getting the lay of the land. "You go that way and I'll go this way."

Katie had hoped they would at least go together.

Archer took a stick and measured Katie's shadow. "When your shadow gets this much longer," he showed her on the stick, "you come back here." He made a cut in the stick with his knife. "When your shadow gets here, come back to this place. Wherever you go, keep hollering so when I need you I can find you. Just remember one thing, if you get lost in Johnson Hollow there won't be nothing anybody can do, especially after dark. When I find the rocks, I'll give a long and a short yodel."

Archer ran off with the gun and True Luck, leaving Katie to shift for herself. She looked around, memorizing the landmarks—a fallen tree, a big honeycomb rock, a clump of cactus. She broke three limbs and left them hanging to make sure she would recognize the spot.

Something was moving in the brush. She could hear the dry branches parting—it would run a few steps, then stop, and the silence was worse than the sounds. She picked up a big rock and threw it in the direction of the sound, her heart palpitating in her throat. The animal started moving again and did not stop until Katie could no longer hear it. She breathed a sigh of relief.

Katie could not look for the stones even half-heartedly, she was so afraid of being alone and of getting lost. She forgot to holler until she heard Archer yodeling. She answered him and he yelled, "I told you to keep hollering!" It was comforting to hear his voice.

A snake, a ground racer, appeared on the trail ahead of her and streaked along the ground as if leading the way. She tightened her grip on the stick and waited for the snake to disappear before she moved ahead.

Katie found a gully where the ground was open, so she slid down the side on her bottom and followed the gully to its end. It led to an overgrowth where Katie had to get down on her hands and knees to get through. She was following a small animal trail—which was scary because the animal might be at the other end.

The trail petered out in a little clearing and Katie was glad to be able to stand up, brush off the sticky twigs and needles that clung to her clothes, and rest a minute. Katie remembered to holler, but no answer came. *I won't worry*, she told herself. *Archer's bound to be around.*

But she did worry. There was an uneasy feeling in her stomach.

The clearing was surrounded on one side by a ledge which dropped sharply and she wondered if it was the same ridge they had crossed before. Katie felt guilty for not seriously looking for the rocks the way Archer was looking. She moved to the edge of the ledge and leaned over. Scanning the little ravine, she traced its route both ways. Taking a second look, she saw two stones propped up side by side. She couldn't believe her eyes!

There were two stone slabs side by side! Yelling as loud as she could, she slid down the ravine lickety-split. She was so excited she couldn't think! The one on the right had a horse head and the one on the left, a deer head— unmistakably! "Archer! Archer!" she yelled, but there was no way she could make herself heard from below the ridge. She scrambled back up, cupped her hands to her mouth and yodeled, one long, one short, just as Archer had said. Listening, she heard True Luck in the distance. She yodeled again. Archer answered!

Katie kept calling so he would not waste time trying to find her. He came thrashing through the brush ahead of True Luck. "Over here!" she yelled. "I found them! I found the rocks!"

"Where? Where?"

"Over here!" she motioned toward the ravine.

They stood on the edge, gazing down. "Holy cow! You did! You found them!" They slid down the embankment. Archer touched the stones with his fingers, tracing the drawings scratched on their surfaces. "I can't believe it! It's as plain as day!" he said. "That's a horse head and this is a deer head." He looked around. "Wish we had something to dig with."

"Let's go home and get the pick."

"Okay." Archer surveyed the surroundings. "No wonder we couldn't find them. You could never get down here on horseback. You could never ever see them on horseback." He looked around some more. "Willie and I came right past here—rode through that clearing."

"Come on, let's go tell Mama."

They were a long way from home, but Archer knew every short cut. They raced through narrow gullies and up ravines to avoid the brush. Once they were on the old wagon road, Katie knew where they were and Archer left her to race ahead.

When Katie finally arrived at the house, Maas's horse was in the yard, and the lamp was lit in the kitchen.

"Goldarn," Maas said, "ye buggers mean to tell me ye found them stones?"

"Maas, come on, I'll show you," Archer begged.

Mama protested. "It'll soon be dark. You better wait until morning."

"Tarnation, Miz MacLeod, I roam all over these hills in the dark. It'd be downright insulting if it got out that this Maas was scairt of the dark." He turned to Brother. "Get the pick, Brother, and the shovel and anything else ye can find. Somebody git the lantern."

"You can't be serious," Mama said.

"Ma'am, it'll be a lot cooler digging tonight than tomorrow. Come on, bring the young'uns. Ye stand to git rich tonight."

"Well, I've waited this long, guess I can wait one more day."

"Aw, come on, Mama," Archer pleaded. "We did the hard part—we found the stones."

"All right," she said, taking off her apron. "Do you girls want to go?"

It was a foolish question. Jane had the lantern and Alice was putting shoes on Timothy.

"We don't need the lantern lit yet," Archer said. "Save the coal oil. Come on, let's get started."

With pick and shovel, axe and lantern, they headed toward the Hollow, Archer and True Luck in the lead, Maas, with Timothy on his shoulders, bringing up the rear. Maas hollered to Archer, "Ye make right sure none o' them outlaws sneaks up behind ye to ha'nt ye!"

Archer did nothing to slacken his pace.

The clearing was no more than two miles away, and by walking rapidly, they did not have to light the lantern before they were nearly at the place. When they left the wagon road, Katie was not sure of the way, but Archer was sure. He led them through the same gullies and ravines that he had led Katie through on the way home.

"I don't know what I was thinking about, letting you

talk me into coming up here in the night," Mama said. "Anything could be in these woods."

"It's too early for panthers," Maas said. "Besides, if what Archer tells me is ke-rect, we're only goin' in the edge o' the Hollow. I got my Winchester; ye're perfectly safe with me," he boasted.

Katie heard things in the bushes at every turn but no one else seemed disturbed. "That's only Brother," Jane would say.

"It's right up here," Archer said confidently. When he reached the clearing, he waited for the rest of them to catch up. "Now, here's the rim of the ledge," he said. "Be careful. Stand right here." They lined the edge of the ridge and Archer held up the lantern. "See 'em down there?"

They couldn't see them.

"Well, come on. Follow me down the ledge. Be careful—it's steep."

They slipped and slid but they made it to the bottom. Archer stood beside the two slabs, the light revealing the front sides of the propped-up stones.

"I'll be hornswoggled!" Maas said.

"Lookit, Mama," Archer said, running his finger around the outline of the horse head. "You see it?"

"I certainly do. And this one is the deer head?" Archer shined the lantern on the second one. "Isn't that remarkable!" Mama said, impressed.

"Brother, let's get some wood and make a fire," Maas said, anxious to get to work. They all helped drag up brush for the fire. Maas struck a match and the dry wood blazed. "Put out the lantern, Archie," Maas said. "We kin see by the firelight."

Katie, the girls, and Mama seated themselves away from the fire to watch the men. Maas took the map out of his hat and studied it again. Without a word he settled his foot beside the slab on the right, making sure it was plumb with the stone. "Got to get this right," he muttered. Satisfied, he began pacing and counting. He took twelve steps and motioned for Brother to mark the place. Brother grabbed a stick and held it to the spot as if he were surveying.

Maas went to the other slab, did the same thing, only he counted off eighteen paces, walking dead center toward a cedar tree. "'At's it," he said, "right here is whar them lines cross. Correct me if I'm wrong, Brother."

"You're right, Maas."

"And the ground has settled there, Maas," Mama said. "See the depression?" She was pointing. There was a sunken-in place about the size of a wash tub or bigger.

"We'll dig right here," Maas said, his voice low and controlled to hide his excitement. Tension was mounting in all of them. Something like fear was tightening its grip on Katie's stomach.

Mama talked to the girls in hushed tones. "That is a low spot. Like a grave, any hole in the ground sinks after a while."

The ground was so hard the pick hardly dented it. In no time at all, sweat was dripping off Brother's nose as he swung the pick over his back with both hands.

"Lemme have a go at it with the shovel," Maas said. "I can scoop it out easier'n ye can dig it." He was right. The dry, gravelly dirt gave way to the edge of the shovel so that a cupful was scooped up with each stroke. It was a slow process.

When Maas was forced to rest, Brother took over. Maas lay back on the slope but he suddenly sat up again, his eyes riveted straight ahead. He reached for Brother's arm and pointed toward the brush.

Katie's eye followed the direction of his finger. A man, standing less than thirty feet away! Alice was about to scream, but Mama clamped her hand over her mouth.

No one moved, petrified with fear. There was a neckerchief over the man's face and in the light and shadow of the dancing flames, he seemed to move.

"What d' ye want?" Maas croaked.

No answer.

Maas started to reach for his gun, thought better about it, and held still.

Archer, whose eyes were keener than most, spoke. "Maas, that ain't no man. That's a stump," and without a moment's hesitation he walked boldly toward the man and placed his hand where the neckerchief was supposed to be. "See, it's a stump—lightning musta' struck the tree."

Maas wiped his forehead. "I'll be goldurned."

Alice's voice quavered. "Archer, are you *sure*?"

"Of course, I'm sure. I've got my hand on it, don't I?"

Brother laughed nervously and leaned on the shovel, relieved. Except for Katie, they all saw it for what it was—a tree that had fallen, "Split about six feet from the ground, Katie," Jane explained. But Katie could never see it as anything but an outlaw with a bandanna over his face. She huddled by the fire, wishing they would hurry so they could leave.

Maas was shoveling hard, panting, "It's getting easier."

"Let me take over," Brother said. He took the shovel. "It is easier—dirt's looser." Larger scoops of earth were thrown out. Brother was laboring to get his breath, but he wouldn't quit. Archer picked up the pick. Brother stood aside for him to swing it. The pick struck metal!

"Archer, you hit it! You hit it!" Brother shouted. "Here, let me use this shovel." They were less than three feet deep in the ground. The shovel was flying. Its blade scraped metal. "There's the top!" Both men and Archer were on their knees, clawing dirt with their bare hands.

"Come on, Brother," Maas said, "git that corner an' le's pry hit outta' the ground with the pick."

They tried again and again. "Try the shovel," Brother said. "Use the pick on that side. I'll use the shovel on this side. When I count three we'll heave together." Brother was panting for breath as he waited for Maas to position the pick. "Ready?"

Maas nodded.

"One, two, three!" The men were straining hard, their strength about to give way, when the cache moved a bit.

"I think we dislodged it," Brother said, breathing hard.

Maas wiped his face against his sleeve. "It's heavy. I felt it. It's heavy."

"Let's give it one more try." They positioned the tools. "On a count of three—one, two, three!" They pried in the same direction, leaning dangerously hard against the handles. "It's coming!"

And it did. The metal box came part way out of the hard ground. Brother grabbed a burning stick to hold as a torch so they could see the prize. "Maas, I think we can pry the lid off right where it is."

Maas gripped the corner of the box protruding out of the ground but it was no use. He gave it a bang with a rock. "Rusty," he said and hit it again. The old tin was dented by the blow. Maas took out his jackknife. "I can job through hit," he said and he did. Using the knife like a can opener, he perforated all around the lid. Hands trembling, he lifted the lid. Archer's head was between Katie and the cache.

"Silver dollars!" Archer yelled as he grabbed a handful and held them up to show. They crowded close to see. "Stand back! Stand back!" he shouted. He began hurling rocks over his shoulder. "Maas! Maas! It's rocks! There're rocks in here." He kept throwing them over his shoulder. "Maas, there's nothing but rocks in here!"

A hush fell over them. Archer stopped throwing rocks. He felt inside the cache. Then he stood up, kicked the box, furious.

Mama looked at Maas. He shook his head, reached for the torch. He passed a torch over the hold. "Looks like a few silver dollars and a can full of rocks."

Brother shook his head despairingly.

"That's not fair!" Archer screamed.

"What do you think happened?" Jane asked Maas.
"Somebody beat us to it."

"How?" Archer asked. "We had the map!"

Maas shook his head thoughtfully. "Somebody else had one, too." He poked the shovel in the dirt, making sure they had not dropped any of the dollars.

Brother lay back on the ground. "What a sorry joke."

Maas, leaning on the shovel, looked all around, disappointment in his tired eyes. The wind began kicking up a swirl of dust where the can was. Without a word, Maas began shoveling dirt on the fire to put it out.

"Light the lantern, Katie," Mama said. "We'll be going home."

When the last spark was smothered and the smoke was only a whisper, Maas whistled for True Luck, and one by one they followed him up the ravine.

SIXTEEN
The Feud
Erupts

It was a long time before they could talk about the disappointment. When the speculation about who got the money began, Katie knew the pain had eased. "Maybe that young feller who give hisself up, the one who went to jail, mebbe he got out and come back fer the money," Maas said.

"It doesn't matter who got the money," Mama said. "We found seven dollars we would not have had otherwise. Mark it up to experience that you do not get something for nothing in this world."

Mass grew philosophical. "Wal, we ain't goin' to tell nobody the money ain't thar. So long as nobody knows thar ain' nuthin' up thar, they'll keep a hopin' an' a lookin' and in these days that's what most folks need— a lotta' hope and somethin' to look forward to."

Mama looked Maas straight in the eye. "Maas, you could use a little hope yourself."

"What do ya mean, Miz MacLeod?"

"You know what I mean. When is the last time you have been to church?"

Maas grinned. "Mebbe I went when I 'uz a boy. Can't rightly recollect." He winked at Brother.

"Well, it's high time you considered spiritual matters."

"I ain't much on readin', ma'am."

"Tell me, when is that brush arbor meeting?"

"Next week but, Miz MacLeod, they's havin' it on Taylor land, and no Maas ever sets foot on Taylor land."

"What are you afraid of?"

"Who says I'm afeered?"

"Sounds like you're afraid," she said stoutly.

He sat up straight. "Goldurn it, I'll go! I'll show you who's afeered o' them polecats! I'll take on the whole pack of 'em if need be."

"Maas, they can't object to your going to *church* on their land. Surely, they won't start trouble at a worship service."

But Mama was wrong. Sitting on benches under the stars, surrounded by a thin hedge of scrub, all the women and children of the hills sat singing the praise of the Almighty. Menfolks stayed outside but within earshot, smoking and chewing their tobacco. Only Maas, hat in hand, sat inside alongside the MacLeods, his tall frame conspicuous on the second row. His discomfort had little to do with the Taylor men gathered outside. Clearly, Maas had never been in church before.

Alice and Jane were called up front to help the preacher lead the singing. Other ladies joined them, hovering around the scarce song books, trying to see by the flickering lantern. They swatted and swallowed bugs swarming around them and the nervous preacher sang louder and louder.

Something was going on outside. The men were talking, shouting a bit, passing a jug, and, out of the corner of her eye, Katie could see them picking up something off the ground.

Without looking around, Maas said to Mama, "I

gotta' go," but Mama shook her head and said, "It's not polite to leave church."

The preacher was glancing about furtively, and when they sang the last stanza he directed the women to keep right on singing, starting again at the top.

And then it happened—a rock came barreling over the heads of the congregation and smashed a lantern. "Rock fight!" someone cried. Automatically, the women, still singing, began turning over benches, and together with their children got down on all fours behind them. Rocks were hurled past their heads, down the aisles, bouncing off benches and pulpit. But the MacLeods sat staunchly where they were, singing lustily while the frantic preacher became a fast-moving target on the platform. When he had to jump high to dodge a missile and in the same split second dodge glass falling from a smashed lantern, he threw down the hymn book and began pronouncing the benediction while running through the brush.

The rocks, like rain, pelted everything in sight and narrowly missed Maas's head, the main target.

In a little while, the bombardment let up.

"You ready to go home?" Maas asked calmly.

They filed out, Mama leading the way, Maas behind her, never flinching. She walked lady-like, the way she did when she wore a plumed hat. When the men saw her, smiling and gracious, they stopped dead in their tracks, rocks still in their hands. "Good evening," she said to each one, extending her hand for a handshake. Their rocks were dropped as unobtrusively as possible, hats were doffed, and mumbled pleasantries exchanged.

Maas took advantage of the moment and sauntered over to his horse without looking back, mounted up, and rode away.

The MacLeods were walking home. Jack Taylor caught up with them as they started down the mountain. "Miz MacLeod, I got a buckboard over here. Can I take you all home?"

"Thank you, Jack. We'd be delighted. We've never ridden in a buckboard."

The ride home was fun. Once safe, they could laugh. Archer started it. "When those rocks began flying, that preacher was lifted plumb off the ground! He was sky-high! Talk about a scairt rabbit—I've never seen a jackrabbit run that fast!"

"And the fat lady—" Brother was laughing so hard tears were rolling down his cheeks. "She had her rear end stuck under that bench—couldn't go forward and couldn't go backwards—just stood up and ran holding onto the bench!"

They laughed all the way home. Katie's sides ached from laughing.

Jack stopped the buckboard under the oak trees, threw the lines around the brake stick, and helped Mama and the twins out of the wagon. Mama went inside to make coffee and when she came out, Jack was telling them about the accident.

"They had a man die on the highway today."

"Who?" Brother asked.

"Feller by the name o' Smith. He was a drifter outta' Arizona some place. You remember I told you my brother hired one man outside o' the family? That's him."

"What happened?"

"Got too hot fer 'im. This July sun got to him an' he keeled over. Nothin' they did fer him could bring 'im around. Young feller."

"Did they bury him?" Archer asked.

"Nope. Waitin' to hear from the authorities. Tryin' to find his people, but it ain't likely they will."

"Does that mean your brother will hire another man?"

"Yup. Don't know fer how long. Gov'ment's been cuttin' back. First man gits there in the mornin' gits the job."

Brother made sure he got there first. He left the

house while the stars were still shining. When he didn't come home all day, they knew he had gotten the job.

Jack Taylor had not exaggerated how hard the work was. As Katie watched for Brother to come home, he walked onto the flat, too tired to yodel or wave or anything. He was dragging his feet. Katie filled a dipper of cool water and had it ready for him when he came in the yard. "Thank you, Katie," he said. "I'm going to lie down."

They all followed him into the bedroom. Katie unlaced his shoes, covered with adobe dust. "Archer," Mama said, "get a basin of water and wash your brother's feet."

"What?" he said, but then he thought better about it and obeyed.

Brother lay back on the bed and rested a while before he spoke. He was hollow-eyed and red from the sun. "Mama, you wouldn't believe what it's like. Most of those men are over fifty—too old for the adobe pits."

He was too tired to talk.

"It's too much for you, Son. I won't have you kill yourself."

Brother lifted his hand. "Wait a minute—I'll work only every other week. That'll give me time to rest. I'm working hard so Taylor won't lay me off if the government makes him cut the crew."

"Son, it will kill you."

"No, it won't. The men appreciate my doing more than my share and try to pay me back in little ways. They think cold water will give you cramps in this heat, but when I told them I had to have spring water, they brought it to me. They warned me, 'Sure as shootin' it'll kill ye.' When I didn't double over with cramps they still were not convinced, said I was a different breed."

"You are, Son," Mama said.

Because Jack Taylor had told Brother about the

204

highway job, he thought he would be more welcome to visit the flat. He and Harvey Pittman would come riding up about sundown and sometimes Rosabelle's brother, Pete, was with them. They brought guitars, sat on the stone benches, and sang all the old sad songs. Alice and Jane, who had nothing to wear but the faded red pajamas, sat primly, their ankles crossed, listening to the yodeling and singing, pleased with all the attention they were getting, but very proper. Mama never left the girls alone with Jack Taylor, and she asked Maas to leave his horse tied in the yard whenever he could spare him. If Jack saw Maas's horse at the MacLeod's, he wouldn't come near the flat.

Jack talked about prison and Mama didn't like that at all.

"I met a lotta' nice fellers in the pen," he told them. "They was mostly in there for making likker or runnin' it. And thar was some outlaws. You heered 'bout them bank robbers that hid out 'round Bull Creek here years ago? Wal, the one was caught and I knowed him in the penitentiary. He was an old man and had plumb growed up behind bars. He was sick a lot—took a likin' to me, said he wished I was his son."

"Jack, would you please talk about something more uplifting than criminals?" Mama asked peevishly.

When Jack Taylor came too often, Mama would be cross. Plainly, she was worried, and Katie suspected it was because Alice and Jane were getting shapely like Mama and getting prettier every day.

"Why doesn't that man work?" Mama asked, as if she didn't know. Even Katie knew that a man like Jack Taylor lived by his wits, gambling, bootlegging, stealing, probably.

"Mama, I'll betcha Jack's the one who got the bandit money," Archer said, "I betcha that outlaw he knew in prison told him where to look."

"Yes. I thought about that," Mama said.

Jane spoke up, "Have you noticed he always has

silver dollars? And there were silver dollars in that can."

Mama nodded.

"Wonder why he left those few dollars buried with the rocks?" Alice asked.

"Who knows? Maybe as a joke. Maybe to let people figure out who got it," Archer said glumly.

"Couldn't he tell anybody he wanted to?" Alice asked.

"If he told he found the money," Brother explained, "sooner or later the government would find out about it and come looking for him."

"Or somebody would kill him for it," Archer added. "What do you think, Brother? Don't you think he left those silver dollars in the can so people would guess that he did it but not be able to prove it?"

"Probably. Since Maas is the only other man who has a map and the two are such arch enemies, nothing would please Jack more than to let Maas know he beat him to the money."

"Wait'll I tell Maas!" Archer exclaimed.

"Oh, no, you won't, young man!" Mama said emphatically. "Let sleeping dogs lie. All we know for certain is that Jack Taylor knew one of the outlaws in prison. If you tell Maas even that much, the fat will be in the fire. Maas will jump to conclusions and there'll be the devil to pay. One or both of them could get killed!"

That ended the matter, although Archer kept thinking about the case when he and Katie were going to the spring. Archer was in such a bad mood about Jack Taylor that he wouldn't skip rocks on the creek or anything. When they had filled their buckets, he announced, "I'm not going to climb that old cliff—I'm going home by the schoolhouse. It's easier."

"It's a lot longer," she said.

"Not much. Except for the hill, it's all level ground. Now are you coming or not?"

Reluctantly, she followed him. They trudged along the highway, and Katie hoped the highway truck might come down the road and let Brother off at the school house so they could walk home together.

As the two of them were passing through the school yard, Archer saw somebody lying under the oak tree in front of the building. They approached the stone wall surrounding the tree and looked closer.

"It's Brother!" Katie exclaimed. They scrambled over the wall and knelt beside Brother, who was sprawled on the ground.

"Is he sick?" Katie asked.

Archer listened to his snoring, spied a Nehi bottle, picked it up, and smelled it. "Naw, he ain't sick. He's just . . . tired."

"Tired? He looks more than tired to me." Katie laid her palm on Brother's cheek. He didn't rouse. "What are we going to do?"

Archer shifted to a squatting position. "Tell you what," he said. "You go home and tell Mama that Brother is tired and that he is sleeping it off. That's all you're to say, just tell her he's sleeping it off—she'll understand."

Katie picked up the bottle to smell it. Archer knocked it out of her hand. "Now, go on. Tell Mama exactly what I said and don't you *dare* tell anybody else."

"Archer MacLeod, just because you're twelve years old you needn't to think you can boss me around!"

He picked up a rock. "Get going!"

She snatched up her bucket and left.

He called after her. "Tell Mama I'll stay with him until he's all right."

By the time Katie reached the house, she had figured out what she would do. She took Mama outside to tell her what Archer said. That's when Katie began to cry.

"It's all right, Katie. Brother will be all right."

Jane came out of the house. "What's the matter?"

"Don't ask questions," Mama said bluntly.

"Where's Archer?"

"He'll be home later."

Katie was asleep when the boys came home, and the next morning Brother had gone to work when she woke up. She dug oatmeal out of the three-cornered pot and as she was pouring cream on it, she asked Alice, "Where's Mama?"

"I think she took Timothy to the woods."

Katie wasn't allowed in the boys' woods, but she needed to know that Brother was all right and she needed the roll of toilet paper Mama had. Skipping along the path, well into the boys' woods, she was about to holler when she saw Mama in a tiny clearing by herself. Mama was kneeling beside a stump, her hands folded, her face lifted to the sky, lips moving. She was praying.

A shaft of sunlight broke through the trees, and Katie felt the stillness as if angels hovered in the air. The stillness was as if the music of a great symphony had paused for a pulse beat—like the delicate spider circles on the clear water of the spring—there was a silent presence there.

Cautiously, Katie bent down and backed away, careful not to make the slightest sound. At a safe distance she broke and ran down the path to the house.

"Ka-tie!" Jane was calling. "Here's Timothy. Will you look after him? I've got to scrub the kitchen." She was standing in the yard, Timothy by her side. "What's the matter with you? You look funny. What were you doing in the boys' woods? You know you aren't allowed in the boys' woods."

Katie didn't answer and Jane bounced back inside.

"Build me a coal kiln, Katie," Timothy asked. They sat down in the shade of the oak, and Katie began breaking sticks to make a miniature kiln.

Katie had almost finished the kiln and was going in the house for a match to light the little fire when she heard hoofbeats sounding on the road. Maas came into view, riding Sam at a fast trot. They came into the yard raising puffs of dust behind; Sam jumped the barbecue pit and pulled up at the hitching tree. "I'm ridin' into town today and thought yer Ma might need somethin'," Maas said and swung down from the saddle.

Mama was coming from the woods. "Can you wait a few minutes until I write a letter, Maas?"

"Shore."

"Have some coffee while you wait."

Maas let Katie ride Sam around the flat. There was a special excitement about riding the big horse alone. The jarring of the fast trot ended when she persuaded Sam to canter. If only she could ride more often, she would learn how to control the big bay the way Maas did.

When Katie circled the flat once and Mama had not finished writing the letter, Katie rode around again. Half way around, just as she was streaking alongside the boardwalk, Archer started yelling and beckoning her back to the house.

As Katie was getting down off the horse, Mama handed the letter to Maas. It was addressed to Mr. Thomas MacLeod in Greenville, South Carolina. Katie knew that was Uncle Tom, Daddy's brother.

In September, school started at Pleasant Valley, but Archer and Katie were not enrolled. Katie felt uneasy not going to school, but she did not ask questions. Something was going on that she did not understand— something she did not want to know.

Brother's job lasted until September. Then Mr. Taylor received orders to cut the highway crew; he kept his relatives and let Brother go.

"What more could ye expect of a Taylor?" Maas asked. "Least aways that sorry Jack won't be showin' his ugly face up here no more."

"Why not?" Jane asked.

"Because he ain't got the face after his brother let Brother go. Jack Taylor knows Brother here is yer breadwinner."

Mama stopped stirring the beans, looked straight at

Maas and spoke calmly. "I expect Mr. MacLeod to come home imminently."

Katie looked up surprised.

Brother smiled. "Yeah, Maas, he's going to come riding up in a new Cadillac and take us all to glory. In the meantime we have nothing to worry about because Mama here says, 'The Lord will provide.'" His bitterness was harsh.

There was hurt in Mama's blue eyes but she spoke emphatically. "Yes, Brother, the Lord will, indeed, provide."

The lima beans bubbling in the pot were the last from the bag. There was no more toilet paper; they were using old dress patterns. But for food, kerosene, and ammunition, there were no substitutes. To save oil, the MacLeods did everything they could during day-light hours. They even read the Bible before dark. To save food, they rationed the chickens. Brother took to eating the neck as his "favorite piece" and Mama ate the back. Archer called it "the parson's nose." Mr. Frady always received a thigh and Archer the other one.

The silverlace Wyandotte laid an egg almost every day and sometimes Mama sent the egg to Mr. Frady. "He's a sick man," she explained. "He needs the nourishment."

Every day that Brother could hitch a ride to town, he went looking for work and asking at General Delivery for the mail. The rest of them would wait for him, sitting on the stone benches watching for car lights on Lookout Point. Once a car sounded its horn on Lookout Point—the girls looked surprised. "Did you hear that, Mama?" Katie's pulse was beating fast—it sounded just like Daddy's horn. They sat quietly, waiting. The car rolled down the mountain to the second cut then blew the horn again. The suspense was almost too much to bear.

But it wasn't Daddy. Soon Brother was trudging up the hill, and they would not have known it except True

Luck started barking and raced to meet him.

Sometimes Katie thought Brother had forgotten how to yodel or holler or even to smile, he was so discouraged.

During the day, Mama, Katie, and Timothy went fishing while Archer hunted. Even in late September when all the chickens except the Wyandotte and the rooster were eaten, there was meat of some kind every day. "Why don't we eat the rooster?" Katie asked, and Mama said that she was saving him for a rainy day.

When Archer was down to his last shotgun shell, Katie reckoned that the rooster would soon be killed. Archer got up early that morning to meet the herd of jackrabbits that fed on the wagon road. "Good luck," Brother said.

All the MacLeods followed Archer into the yard and stood watching him as he walked toward the wagon road. Katie was not going with him for fear she would scare the rabbits before he had a chance to shoot.

After Archer was out of sight, they stood motionless, waiting expectantly. Katie was praying Archer would not miss and from the looks on the others' faces, they were praying too.

The shot sounded. "There it goes!" Brother said. No one else said a word, the strain not yet relieved.

It seemed Archer would never come. Katie couldn't stand the suspense; she untied the armadillo and led him to a cedar where he could root around.

"There he is!" Jane exclaimed. "He's got one!"

Mama smiled. "I knew he would!"

They all ran toward him as Archer held up the big rabbit, grinning proudly.

After the rabbit was eaten, Archer argued that the rooster must next be killed. Katie agreed with Archer but Mama said, "Children, stop pitcher-pumping me. We won't kill the rooster yet; we'll all go fishing."

"I'm tired of fishing," Archer said, but he went because the others were going—all of them except

Brother who had gone to town again.

They fished nearly all day and caught only one perch. Even on Maas's trotline there were no fish, mainly because the hooks were not baited, Archer said. The trotline used bait made of cornmeal dough— buffalo bait— and there was nothing to make buffalo bait out of. On the fishing pole lines they used grasshoppers.

At sundown they trudged back up the cliff and instead of cooking supper, Mama said they would wait for Brother.

Katie lay on her cot watching the road. The sun was setting behind the river and the rose and lavender afterglow lingered over Cat Mountain. Cattle on the far side of the flat were meandering toward the creek, their bells clunking, tails swishing. How much Daddy would enjoy seeing them.

Katie had gazed between the branches of the live oak above her cot so many hours she had memorized the shapes of all the strong limbs. She knew every curve and how the branches lay.

When darkness settled in on the flat, the stars began appearing. A sliver of a moon rose over Cat Mountain. The yard with its white adobe seemed awash with light. She watched a star rising; it climbed steadily, first below the limb, then behind it. She waited patiently all the long time it took the star to rise above the limb.

Mama had taught Katie that most stars do not move, that the earth moves, and she was thinking about that when Brother yodeled. Katie hopped down off the cot. Archer and the twins were off to meet Brother; Katie ran after them.

When they met Brother, he was weighted down with two cloth sacks of groceries. "Take this one," he told Archer. Archer could hardly lift it and Katie helped him.

"We'll take the other one," Jane said, but Brother said it was too heavy for them.

"Where'd you get all the groceries?" Archer asked.

"I didn't steal 'em."

"How'd you pay for 'em?"

"Don't be so curious."

"Aw, come on—"

"Let's just say I waited in line for 'em."

"You don't mean—?"

"Shhh."

When they reached the house, Mama opened the door and they dumped the sacks on the table. "Mama, there's lots of canned milk. The lady said to tell you to put milk in everything, in the gravy, everything."

While they unloaded the sacks, Mama mixed up pancakes. As fast as she cooked them, they were eaten. "Alice, wake up Timothy and serve him supper."

"We never ate this late before," Archer grumbled. "It's nearly ten o'clock."

October had come by the time Brother went to town again. He borrowed Maas's horse and rode into town early. That day, he brought a letter from Uncle Tom. "At last," Mama said, and read it to herself. Then she read it again before she handed it to Brother.

"He says he'll pay the freight on our belongings. What do we have?" Brother asked.

"We have three mattresses, the cedar chest, the radio, some sheets and blankets," Mama replied.

"Don't forget the sewing machine," Alice reminded her.

"And your paintings," Mama added. "I wouldn't want anything to happen to them."

Katie did not like what she was hearing. "Mama, what do you mean—" she began, but Mama cut her off.

"Katie, how would you like to have a play party? The moon will soon be full, don't you think that would be fun?"

"Sure, but—"

"You and Archer run to the boardwalk and call

Maas, if you can make him hear, and we'll tell Maas to spread the word."

Katie and Archer did as they were told, and as they stood on the boardwalk yodeling, trying to make Maas hear, they discussed the matter.

"I think Uncle Tom is going to send us railroad tickets to go back to North Carolina," Archer said.

"Why do you say a silly thing like that?"

"Well, why would he be talking about paying the freight on our belongings? Mama wouldn't send our stuff some place if we weren't going too, nut!"

"But what if Daddy comes back and we're not here?"

"He could find us."

By the time Maas had come to the creek, paddled across, climbed the bluff, and crossed the flat, Alice and Jane had all the plans made for the party. While they were telling Maas, Katie went out to be with the armadillo.

She had left it staked under the cedar where she sat in the low limb watching, but it was not there. The armadillo was gone! The stake was still there and even the cord with the loop that had been around its head.

"Brother! Brother!" she screamed. "He's gone! He's gone!" She was running toward the house as Brother came outside.

"Don't worry, Katie, we'll find him." He went to the tree to examine all the evidence. "He's around here some place. We'll find him."

But they didn't. They searched carefully over a wide area. The armadillo was gone. "Well, Katie, just think, he didn't get away with the cord around him; if he had, it would have tangled in the brush and he would starve to death."

It was small comfort. He tried again. "Don't you see," he held up the stake, "if he were dragging this stake around, it would get hung up for sure and the poor armadillo would die. This way, we know he is free and happy."

Katie couldn't help but cry. Brother stroked her hair. "Now, you be a big girl, Katie. You're nine years old. Big girls don't cry. Tell you what—I'll get you another armadillo."

She shook her head. "It's no use." Then she felt courageous enough to ask. "Brother . . . "

"Yes, honey?"

"Archer says we're leaving Bull Creek. Are we?"

Brother waited to answer, his eyes on the ground. "Yes, Katie, we are."

Katie couldn't say anything.

Alice and Jane were very excited during the next few days getting ready for the party. Mama took all the clothes to the spring to wash. Katie stayed at home with Alice until they had boiled the peas for dinner. As much as she liked going to the spring and as much as she hated being left at home, Katie had no feelings about it that morning.

Alice and Katie carried the pot of peas between them, a stick through the handle. By the time they reached the creek, Mama and Jane had already washed several tubs full of clothes and had them spread on bushes to dry. Mama was rubbing a bar of lye soap over the red pajamas lying wet against the wash board. As she scrubbed, suds spilled over the sides of the tub and flew about in the wind. With Mama's head bending over the board, Katie could see that even the little wisps of hair on her neck were beginning to gray.

"Want to rub some socks?" Mama asked Katie.

Mama was being kind. She knew how Katie liked to scrub on the washboard. But, now, nothing mattered to Katie.

"Aunt Nora is coming for us," Mama began. "Uncle Tom's wife. She'll come to the school yard. I don't think we want her coming to the flat, do we?"

"Mama," Katie said, holding her voice steady, "I don't want to hear."

Brother was tending a tub of boiling clothes, lifting

them with a stick, steam escaping like fog. Wiping perspiration on his sleeve, he announced, "I'm going swimming."

"In October?" Alice asked.

"Sure. It's ninety degrees. Come on, Archie, Katie."

Katie did not follow them. As she half-heartedly rubbed the socks, she could hear the boys shouting and laughing, but there was no frolicsome feeling inside Katie. Her heart was breaking.

"Hand me Brother's shirt," Mama told Alice. "I have enough starch for that one." Mama took the socks to rinse. "You're not strong enough, Katie," she said as she doused them again and again in the running water. Twisting them together, Mama held them in a vise grip to get out all the water. "You must squeeze them hard and hold them tight until the last drop of water is out of them."

Mama tried to keep Katie's mind off things as they were, but there were no smiles left in Katie.

When plates were passed, Katie took one and let Mama fill it with blackeye peas, but she could not swallow food. When True Luck came up out of the water, shaking himself and annoying the others, Katie led him aside and put her plate of peas before him. True Luck gobbled the food and licked the plate.

After dinner they had nothing to do but wait for the clothes to dry. The boys went back to swimming and the girls sat under the cottonwoods to read. "Here's one for you," Mama said, holding up a volume of *Our Wonder World* for Katie to see.

Katie shook her head. She waded the creek idly until she came to a boulder where the water was deeper and wider than at the spring. A breeze stirred the leaves of the cottonwood overhead but the water was still. It lay like a pond unto itself, quiet above the gentle spillway that led into the flowing stream. Dragonflies darted about, skimming the water. The russet-colored grass on the bank cast still reflections.

Katie was watching a kingfisher perched on a branch.

As it waited, only its head moved a bit. Then, in an instant, it swooped down, snatched a fish, and flew off down the creek. Only a flash of spray signaled the catch.

If Archer were here, she thought, he'd be skipping rocks on the flat water. Katie felt no urge to skip stones across the pond—no desire to spoil the peace of it.

A little snake swam into view, breaking the surface with a narrow wedge of wake that widened behind it. The wary snake held its arrow-shaped head high, its eye, like a bead, staring.

In the late afternoon, when the clothes were dry, the girls folded them and placed them in the tubs. With someone on either side of a tub they would carry the clothes up the trail by the cottonwoods. Katie did not wait for them. She picked up the washboard and her pail of water and walked on ahead.

Wind blowing over the pasture brought up the fragrant sage smell of the grass and the pungent odor of cow droppings. The fence along the trail was down in several places and served no purpose. The cedar posts were peeled and weathered to a silvery sheen, the strands of barbed wire, rusty and sagging. The steers roamed at will. They were not the kind of cattle Daddy liked to see; their sides were caved in; their ribs and hip bones protruded. As Katie skirted the field, the cows stared at her in their somber way, as if they cared.

As Katie made her way to the cliff, she knew that she would never climb it again. How many times she had raced up the rock face, matching lightning swift speed and balance against the crumbly footholds. "Agility," Mama called it. Now Katie wanted only to take one step at a time, feel every foothold, look at every familiar rock, every gravel slide, all the straggly scrub clinging to the cliff.

When she reached the top, Katie set down the bucket and looked upon all that lay below. The gray and brown grasses, ever restless, battling the relentless wind moving this way and that, was so like her own torment of soul. The rich strawy smell of it and the dry cedar scent pressed in upon her senses as the wind whipped about.

Back of the flat the sun was sinking fast. A soft lavender haze settled on the land below, resting it from the glare of the day, subduing its shadows. Overhead, a pair of hawks, gliding in single circles, searched for prey.

Katie looked up at the sky to find an early star, but seeing none, she watched the hawks turn with grace and fly over the bluff. She could hear Archer's voice. The others were following him up the trail.

Katie whispered softly, "Dear Lord, I don't want to go. Please . . . please . . . please, tell Daddy to come home quickly."

SEVENTEEN
The Play Party

When the day of the party arrived, Brother and Archer dragged a pile of brush onto the center of the flat for a fire. Alice and Jane primped all day, rolling their hair on rags, arching their eyebrows. Brother and Archer helped Mama sweep the yard, and in the afternoon the boys took True Luck to the creek, gave him a bath, and checked him for ticks.

As the sun was setting, spreading gold and amber colors across the sky, the first wagons began arriving. Maas, sporting a clean shirt, was called aside by Mama. "Now, Maas, this is our home," she told him. "Jack Taylor is welcome here. If he comes, you must not cause trouble. Do you understand?"

Maas held up his hands in protest. "Miz MacLeod, you don't understand—so long as them Taylors stays offa' my lan' and I stay offa' thair'n, thar won't be no trouble. Hit's when a Taylor puts so much as his little toe on my property he gits his haid blowed off!"

"Very well," Mama said, "I have your word?"

Maas agreed. "Now if'n you're satisfied, I'm a goin'

up in the cedar brake and bring Frady down."

They could hear the Ropers coming all the way from the schoolhouse, old man Roper gee-hawing at the mule, the wagon slipping and sliding on the hill.

Miss Daisy, making her first appearance on the flat, rode horseback and was puffing on a cigar. "Left that hussy to walk," she said of Miss Lucretia, but in a while Jack Taylor came galloping up with Miss Lucretia on the back of his sorrel.

Jack was sporting a new buckskin vest and new boots which made him the center of attention. He strode about, lariat looped on his arm, enjoying the admiration.

Rosabelle and Harvey came together, he on the stallion, she on the jackass. Her fat bottom bulged over both sides of the poor beast and the poor jackass bellowed his protest. Even Katie smiled at his braying.

Oren and Willie brought their Pa, who was over being loco, ready to do the fiddling. All the Taylors came, but they stayed clear of Maas, who was standing with Mr. Frady. In a suit and tie, Mr. Frady looked ten years younger than the night he stumbled into the yard in the asylum clothes.

Mama spread a blanket for the MacLeods to sit on, and Mrs. Roper spread one for her baby. More mountain people came, people they had not seen since the day of the sale. Last of all, Ruby and Shadow came, stopped the old mare by the hitching tree, and sat there staring. Ruby's stringy blonde hair had not been combed and her faded dress was raggedy. The sight of them disturbed Katie. Their silent misery was painful to behold.

Sophie Roper walked over to them, reached up her hand, and without a word, the sad-eyed Ruby got down from the mare.

Brother lit the fire and the people milled about, choosing positions in a big round circle. The music commenced—fiddle, guitars, a banjo, and two harmonicas. Onlookers clapped, feet stomped out the time, voices sang the words to "Old Joe Clark," and the party was begun.

When the first song ended, another began, "Old Ben Bolt," and the crowd was responding in a frolicsome mood. "Whoopee!" and "Ti-yi" sounded from the men, encouraging the musicians.

When a song was ended, Jack Taylor leaped to the center of the circle to perform his rope tricks. Twirling the lariat above his head, making a fancy loop, he let it fly—sailing over the heads of others and landing around Jane. He drew in the noose and pulled her, laughing and blushing, to him.

"That provokes me," Mama said under her breath. When Jane was free, Mama motioned her to come sit beside her.

The light of the moon showed over Cat Mountain. "First one to see the moon tip the mountain gits to call the game," Mr. Bracey promised.

They danced to "Skip To My Lou" and "Go In and Out the Window," and then it was time for a ballad. When the Bracey boys began singing, "Two Little Orphans," Katie covered both her ears. The song was about a little boy and girl whose mother was in heaven and how the preacher found the children on the church steps, dead in the snow. Tonight, of all nights, Katie could not bear to hear it.

Archer saw the first tip of the moon showing. "I choose 'Dancing Josie,'" he said, prompted by Jane.

There were a few more reels and then Alice asked for "The Miller Boy." Because Alice wanted it, they played it twice.

At last the crowd was too tired to play. Requests for ballads began, and Katie moved away from the circle toward the yard. Sitting down on a honeycomb rock, she gazed at Lookout Point. Archer came and stood beside her.

Rosabelle asked Brother if he wanted to ride the

stallion and, of course, he did. He spurred the great horse to a fast gallop. Rosabelle whistled. "Look at him ride!" It was a sight to see—the white mane and tail flying in the wind as they streaked around the moon-flooded flat. The stallion thundered twice around the flat, and when Brother reined him back into the yard, the horse was still raring to go. He dismounted and followed Harvey, who led the horse to the hitching post.

Well away from the crowd, Harvey Pittman pulled a Nehi bottle from his pocket, uncorked the stopper and offered it to Brother. Archer nudged Katie. "Lookit," he whispered.

Brother turned up the bottle to drink.

"Don't worry," Archer said. "Brother sticks his tongue in the bottle so it won't go down."

"What?"

"Ever since he got sick offa' Nehi, he told me that's the way he does it."

"How come?"

"I told you, nut, 'cause he got so bloomin' sick offa' it. Aw, you wouldn't understand."

The moon had crossed the flat and was sinking behind Johnson Hollow. They had played every game they knew at least twice and had sung most of the ballads. Soon the people would be leaving. Mama motioned to Brother and he stood up and moved toward the center of the circle. In the firelight he looked older than Katie remembered, thinner and taller.

"Friends," he began, " my mother wanted me to tell you that we will be leaving Bull Creek soon. We're going back to North Carolina where we came from. We want you to know how much we have enjoyed being here and we hope some day we will meet again."

Nobody said anything and nobody moved. Brother looked embarrassed. "If there's anything we have that you want, we'll be selling it cheap. Before you leave, if you want to look at it, you may, and tell us what you can give for it."

Jack Taylor strummed his guitar a few times and all the mountain people followed his lead singing "Red River Valley."

> *From this valley they say you are going;*
> *We will miss your bright eyes and sweet smile,*
> *For they say you are taking the sunshine*
> *That brightens our pathway a-while.*
>
> *Come and sit by my side if you love me;*
> *Do not hasten to bid me adieu.*
> *But remember the Red River Valley*
> *And the girl that has loved you so true.*

Nobody made a speech; the song was their farewell. As Katie looked around the circle, the firelight reflected in the faces. They were sad, every one of them. Mr. Frady's cheeks were wet with tears.

When Mama opened the house for the sale of their things, only the men went inside. It was as if the women and children stayed outside out of respect.

"Mrs. Roper," Mama said, "I have some volumes of *Our Wonder World* to give your children. Sophie, you see that they read them."

"Yes'm."

"And, Shadow, if you and Ruby ride back up here after we're gone, there'll be something for you."

In a short time the men filed out of the house. They would come later for the items they bought. Climbing in their wagons, they clicked their tongues at the horses, took the reins, and moved onto the road. The MacLeods stood in the yard watching them leave. Mountain people did not say good-bye but the children looked back until all were out of sight. The MacLeods did not turn back to the house until the last lantern disappeared over the hill. When they turned to go inside, Brother spoke. "Taylor offered me two dollars for the bed, Maas upped it to three. Taylor went to four, and I guess there would have been no end to it, but Mr.

Frady said he would give five dollars, and they let him have it."

"Who got the tools?" Mama asked.

"Harvey—the axe, shovel, and pick—five dollars. Roper wanted whatever clothes we leave, pots and pans, dishes. Jack Taylor staked him five dollars to buy the lot."

"Who gets the stove?" Jane asked.

"Mama told Maas he could have it for hauling our cedar chest and mattresses to Railway Express."

The cedar chest held the little sewing machine, radio, Archer's gun, the girls' paintings, Daddy's briefcase, and the Bible story book. "The express man will have to crate the mattresses and the rocker," Mama said.

After they were all in bed, Katie pulled back the curtain to watch for a car on Lookout Point. An owl, sounding like a child crying in the night, kept her company until the gray dawn began to rise.

In the morning, Katie was awakened by Timothy who dragged her out of bed to come and play. It was the last day before they would leave.

Katie dug the last of the oatmeal out of the three-cornered pot, poured canned cream on it and tried to eat.

Mama was in the boys' room wrapping blankets in a bedspread. "I wrote Tom's wife directions to Pleasant Valley school and told her to wait for us there. I won't have Nora coming onto the flat. She would never understand our living here, and Malcolm would not want her to see the place.

"Mama," Alice said, "I'm surprised Aunt Nora will drive all the way from South Carolina by herself."

"Oh, she won't. One of Malcolm's brothers will drive her to Austin and go on to Tyler."

"Are we taking all the blankets?"

"Yes. Ethel won't have enough cover for all the beds."

Archer killed the rooster and Mama parboiled it all

day before she made chicken and dumplings. The silverlace Wyandotte looked strangely alone wandering about the yard. "We'll give her to Mr. Frady," Mama said. "Maas has promised to look after Mr. Frady and the Wyandotte will see that he has an egg now and then."

Later, Maas came in his wagon. "Brought you something," he said, reaching in back of the wagon for a sack. In the kitchen, he unloaded six dressed chickens. "Thought mebbe you might fry these to eat on the way."

"Maas!" Mama scolded. "You killed all your fryers!"

Disregarding what she said, he continued, "Thought I'd bunk in the cook tent tonight in case you need me in the morning."

Late in the night, Mama was still frying chicken. Katie lay in her bunk peering through the limbs of the oak. The yard was pearled with moonlight and the honeycomb rocks looked like bleached bones. The moon was orange and lopsided, hanging heavy in the night sky. The air was crisp, rustling the leaves of the trees, making the sound of falling rain. A fire blinked on Cat Mountain, marking a coal kiln or a still. On the flat, Maas's horse was rolling in the dirt stirring up dust.

Katie lingered over every detail. Every line, every curve, every scent, every sound must be remembered; it was the only way she could take Bull Creek with her.

True Luck began yowling at the moon. Katie lay back on the cot, closed her eyes, and carefully reviewed everything to be remembered.

By daylight everyone was out of bed, everyone except Katie. She could not bring herself to leave the little cot for the last time. Her chest hurt with the pain of it.

The boys and Maas had loaded the mattresses, the cedar chest and the little green rocker on the wagon to be taken to town. "Katie," Brother said gently, sitting on the side of her bed. "We need to fold up the cot." He reached for the picture on the washstand. "Here, I'll wrap up your picture of Daddy and you can take it with you in the car."

Plainly, he could not think of another kindness. He kissed her, and, without a word, Katie got up and went into the boys' room to dress.

She could hear Mama and the girls as they searched the house looking for something to leave Shadow. "We've packed everything," Alice said.

Outside on one of the benches was the Annie Over ball, Katie went to it, picked it up, and handed it to Mama.

"Are you sure that is what you want to do?"

Katie nodded. Mama put her arm around Katie and hugged her.

"What about True Luck?" Archer asked.

"I packed your shotgun," Mama answered, evasively.

"We're going to take True Luck, aren't we, Mama?" A trace of panic sounded in his voice.

"Son, Maas has agreed to take care of True Luck."

"I'm not going!" he shouted.

"Archer, if there was any way I could take him, I would, but there's hardly room for all of us." Mama's eyes were pleading.

"Archie, boy, I'll see to hit that True Luck gits to run rabbits and hunt squirrels every day. Tarnation, boy, whar ye're a'goin' the only thing True Luck could chase would be an automobile. Prob'bly git hisself kilt seein' as how he ain' use t' city livin'."

Maas took the dog from Archer's arms and set him in the wagon, but True Luck whined and twitched miserably. Archer buried his face in True Luck's neck, trying to hide his tears.

Mama spoke softly to Brother. "Get the bag, son."

Brother set the suitcase and blankets on the stone benches. "Better look around and make sure we're not leaving anything."

Katie followed as they trooped through the house.

The others had passed through the kitchen ahead of her when she spied the three-cornered pot. "Oh, Mama," she said. "Here's the oatmeal pot."

"It stays here."

Katie looked at the blackened pot with its familiar dents. "How will we make oatmeal?"

No one answered. Brother tousled her hair.

Mama's voice was soft. "Maas says the car is waiting in the school yard. Let me see how you all look." Alice and Jane were wearing the red pajamas; Brother had on the green coat and a pair of Daddy's pants; his white shirt starched and ironed. Mama straightened Katie's sash. Archer stood erect, his chin quivering, fighting back tears. His sweater was patched on both elbows and there was a patch on one knee of his pants but he stood straight as an Indian and no one would notice that his pants were too short. Timothy, clutching his teddy bear, was spotless in his white coveralls, his hair golden in the morning sun.

It was Mama whose dress was the shabbiest—the faded blue one, the only dress she had left.

Satisfied that they looked their best, Mama said quietly, "We must go."

Yet they stood, their eyes ranging over all the familiar things—the rain barrel, the hitching tree, the picnic tables, the chicken coop, the barbecue pit, the stone benches, the little cactus bed—until the eyes of all of them drifted across the flat and rested on Lookout Point. No one said a word.

Mama turned and they followed, leaving Maas holding True Luck to keep him from racing after them. They walked in silence, past the boys' woods, to the crest of the hill, too full to speak. Reaching the hill, they stopped, turned around to look at the house one more time. They waved slowly to Maas and he yodeled back to them.

As soon as they were out of sight, on the way down the hill, Mama said, "Children, I want you to go to the bathroom. We have a long ride ahead of us, and Aunt Nora will not want to stop often."

The girls went in the woods on one side of the road, the boys on the other.

As Katie pulled up her bloomers, her dress was turned up at the hem. She kissed it and made her wish one more time.

At the foot of the hill, the old Cadillac came into view, tilted on its side, lifeless and still. They paused, looking longingly at the old car, then moved on slowly, Katie following last in line. One by one, they touched the old car, the tips of their fingers tracing along its side lovingly. Katie, sure that no one was looking, walked around the car, stepped up on the running board, leaned her head inside and kissed the steering wheel.

As Katie hurried over the cattle guard to catch up, she saw a big shiny automobile parked in the school yard. A beautifully dressed lady was standing beside it. Katie, afraid, reached for Mama's dress. "Hello, Becky," the woman called in a high-pitched voice. They came close enough to smell her perfume.

"It's good to see you, Nora," Mama said. "These are my children, Of course, you remember Brother and the twins. This is Archer, and Katie, and Timothy."

"Well, yes, but there won't be room for seven of you. I thought Tom made that clear."

"Brother is going to hitchhike," Mama told her.

"And the other boy—he can hitchhike too."

"Archer? No, Archer is only twelve years old. I wouldn't think of putting him on the highway to thumb."

"Oh?" Nora raised her eyebrows. "What's this—all this?" She was poking the bundle of blankets.

"Those are our blankets, Nora. Ethel won't have enough cover for the beds. I must take them."

Brother lost no time fitting the blankets on the floorboard of the back seat. "I'll put the suitcase in the trunk."

When he was finished, Nora said indignantly, "Well, if we don't look like a bunch of Okies, it's not your fault."

Mama took Brother aside. "Here, Son," she said, untying a sock that held a few bills. "Here is fifteen dollars." She kissed him.

He protested. "That's too much, Mama. I don't need all that."

She kissed him again. "Do be careful, Son."

"I will, Mama." He smiled. "Bet I beat you there."

"I hope so."

They climbed in the car, Mama and Timothy on the front seat with Aunt Nora, the rest of them on the back seat. Brother leaned his head in and kissed the twins and Katie good-bye; then he kissed Mama again.

The motor started, and the car began to roll across the school yard; they were waving to Brother. As they turned onto the paved road, Katie glimpsed the Cadillac one more time. She would see the spring up ahead, she thought, but when they crossed the highway bridge, they were going so fast she missed it.

Alice whispered, "We'll look back on the flat from Lookout Point."

Jane made room for Katie to see out on the right side. They craned their necks to see. For one brief moment, as the high-powered car roared around Lookout Point, they saw the top of the mountain with the little house sitting solitary beneath the live oaks. Then they were gone.

BACK IN CAROLINA

EIGHTEEN
Nora

Jane was mad at Aunt Nora. Balancing the box of chicken on her lap, she gripped it so hard her knuckles turned white. She was so mad her eyes were red. No one spoke. Even Archer kept quiet, staring out the window at the mountain curves slipping past as the car spirited them away.

No one moved on the back seat. As crowded as they were, pressed in beside one another, they did not shift positions. With the blankets on the floorboard, their feet high, knees bent—they were stiff, cramped, silent. The scent of Aunt Nora's perfume whipped about in the car despite the open windows.

Archer ventured to whisper in Katie's ear, "Smells like somebody stepped in cow manure."

Katie paid no attention. Everything was happening so fast—tearing them away from Bull Creek and thrusting them into the unknown. She clutched the little picture of Daddy and prayed. Maybe this was only a bad dream.

Aunt Nora's diamonds glinted in the sun as she held the steering wheel. From time to time she reached for a bottle in the case beside her and lathered her hands with sweet smelling lotion. The traveling case left little room on the front seat for Mama and Timothy. With Timothy on her lap, crowded against the door, Mama rested her elbow on the open window.

The car skirted town and soon they were zooming across the countryside. Katie leaned her head against Alice's shoulder, her chest hurting. Aunt Nora was asking Mama a lot of questions.

"What are your plans, Becky? What are you going to do when you get to Charlotte? Will you get a teaching job?"

"No, Nora. Charlotte schools would not accept my credentials."

"Too bad your parents aren't living. Perhaps your Uncle Robert . . .?" Aunt Nora examined her nails. "Tom is so different from Malcolm, always has been. Steady, reliable—thinks only of his family's comfort." It was as if she were talking out loud to herself. "Tom's building a splendid insurance business, Becky. Now, you know it takes brains to do that in this day and time." Aunt Nora licked her finger and stroked her eyebrows.

"Does Tom still rent those houses by the railroad?" Mama asked.

"Not only those, he has five tenants on Mill Street and several houses scattered over Greenville. Tom doesn't waste a dime—not a single penny. If the money that has gone through Malcolm's hands had gone to Tom, he would be a millionaire today."

"Malcolm has always been a good provider, Nora," Mama said defensively.

"Becky, if I were you, I would hire an investigator."

"That won't be necessary."

"Tom says Malcolm will never come home again."

Mama, as if to answer for all of them, said, "Don't you think we might be better judges of that than Tom?"

There was a lull in the conversation as the car slowed for cattle crossing the road. Mama was watching a

234

hitchhiker standing alongside the ditch. Katie looked to see if the man might be Daddy, but he wasn't. He was thinner and older than Daddy and shabby looking. He stood limply in a swirl of dust and did not raise his arm to ward off the choking, blinding dirt. Katie knew how he felt.

Katie thought about Brother standing by the road waiting for a ride. Would he catch up with them—pass them, maybe?

Timothy looked over Mama's shoulder, his blue eyes watching them, wondering at their silence. Timothy was wise for his four years.

Archer began fingering the box of chicken. "My stomach feels like my throat's cut," he whispered.

Jane gave him a reproving look and he turned his face to the window. He stared out the window, grieving over True Luck—Katie could see him wiping his eyes again and again. Aunt Nora was talking again.

"Now I don't want to give you a false impression, Becky. Tom is doing well, but most of his money is tied up in one way or another. You know how the MacLeods are—they have principles. Tom said Malcolm would not appreciate anyone assuming responsibility for you and the children. Malcolm is a proud man, and he would not want Tom meddling in his affairs."

"Nor anyone else, for that matter," Mama said, annoyed. Mama moved Timothy's feet away from the traveling case.

"Tom gave me this lovely case before I left," Nora said. "He spoils me, spoils me rotten."

Katie moved her leg ever so slightly and Jane shook her head disapprovingly. "It's gone to sleep!" Katie whispered. Jane tried to make more room for her.

Katie was so thirsty. She groaned inside. *Oh, for a dipper of spring water,* she thought.

Hour after hour went by, and the car did not stop. Archer studied the sun. "It's one o'clock," he complained, holding his stomach. They were driving through a small town and Mama was looking at the faces of men on the streets. She was searching, hoping to see Daddy. Jane and Alice were doing the same thing.

"It must be lunchtime," Aunt Nora was saying. "Help me find a cafe."

"There's one on the corner," Mama told her.

Nora pulled up to the curb and stopped the car.

"Nora," Mama said, "you go in and have a hot lunch. The children and I have some very nice chicken."

"Very well. I won't be long."

When Nora went inside the cafe, Archer grabbed the box. "I'm starved!" He snatched two pieces of chicken. "We will have to go easy on the chicken," Mama said.

The girls passed the box to Mama; she took the back with the parson's nose and a drumstick for Timothy. Katie took the neck, Brother's favorite piece. She was feeling pins and needles in her leg. "How long will it take us to get to Charlotte?" Katie asked.

"We'll get there on the third day," Alice said.

In three days Katie figured her leg would be dead.

Archer finished his chicken and licked his fingers. "I'm going over to that filling station and find a bathroom." They watched him cross the street, Mama fanning Timothy with the box lid.

"Look at your arm, Mama, it's getting red," Alice said.

Mama felt it. "I knew it was getting warm but there's not much room and I have to put it out the window."

"Well, if she would move that traveling case there'd be enough room." Jane was smarting from holding in about Aunt Nora.

"Jane, about that traveling case—do you remember the dream I told you about?"

"What dream?"

"The dream about the two angels."

"I remember," Alice said.

"The angels carried a case and put it down at my feet, remember? Well, it was this very same traveling case— it was the same size and same color—green! The angels set it down and left it there."

"What does it mean, Mama?" Alice asked.

"I don't know unless the Lord put it there and expects me to be patient about it."

Archer was beckoning to them from the station. "Come along. Archer has found a rest room. Maybe the man will give us a jar or something to carry drinking water with us."

Aunt Nora was gone an hour, long enough for the girls to take sponge baths in the lavatory.

"Isn't it wonderful having all the water we want?" Jane said. They watched water streaming from the faucet, swirling down the drain.

Katie didn't think it was so wonderful. Nothing was better than scooping up fresh spring water in both hands, drinking it, and splashing it on your face.

When they came outside, Archer was filling a jug from a spigot. "I'm gonna' sneak it under the blankets before Aunt Nora sees it." he said.

Aunt Nora finally finished her lunch and drove the car over to the gas pump. Katie could smell the odor of gasoline as the man pushed the handle back and forth pumping up the gas. There was a special fascination about gasoline sloshing in the bottle glass tank, the level steadily rising above the measuring marks.

Archer helped the man fill the radiator and watched as he lifted one side of the hood then the other to inspect the motor. While the man pumped more air into one of the tires, Archer washed the windshield.

When they were done, Aunt Nora reached in her purse, handed the man two dollars and said, "Keep the change."

By nightfall they had stopped twice for gas and by the time they reached the tourist home, Katie was too weary to talk. Mama told Aunt Nora, "Nora, you need a good night's rest. You take one room and the children and I will take the other one. We can manage very well in a room to ourselves."

As soon as the door was closed behind them, Jane leaned against it and with tears streaming down her face, she croaked, "I hate her! I hate her! I hate her!"

Mama was rummaging in the suitcase and did not look up. "Have some chicken, Jane."

They ate in silence and then Mama spoke about Aunt Nora. "Jane, you must overlook Nora—turn the other cheek. If you don't forgive from your heart, you'll be the loser."

"I can't forgive her."

"God requires us to forgive before we can be forgiven."

"I can't help that."

"Jane, in this life you will meet with greater grievances than Nora's annoyances. Prepare yourself. 'Be ye kind . . . tenderhearted, forgiving one another even as God for Christ's sake hath forgiven you.'" But the Scripture was wasted on Jane.

They each took turns bathing in the sink, then fell into bed—Mama and the boys in one bed, the girls in the other one. In the darkness, Katie hugged her side of the bed, listened to the crickets for a while, then fell asleep.

The next day, Katie was too tired to pay much attention as they traveled. Archer was miserable. He was disappointed because he had looked forward to crossing the Mississippi on the ferry, and Aunt Nora chose to use the bridge. When they reached the Gulf of Mexico, Aunt Nora asked Archer to fill a bottle with Gulf water as a souvenir for her son. The glitter of the sun on the broad water was dazzling. Katie wished she could get out of the car and run on the beach with Archer.

As they waited in the car, Aunt Nora finally noticed Mama's red arm and offered her some lotion.

In the tourist cabin that night, they ate the last of the chicken. Archer licked his finger and dabbed at the crumbs in the bottom of the box.

The next morning when Aunt Nora came out of the restaurant, she brought them a loaf of bread and an opened can of pineapple.

"We're almost there," Jane promised.

But they weren't. All morning long they were moving through towns and cities, stopping and starting, slowed by traffic.

Katie was asleep when they reached Charlotte and woke up as the car stopped in Aunt Ethel's driveway. There was the little stone house as Katie remembered it, the rock garden in front. Aunt Ethel was hurrying down the steps, excitedly trying to see them and glancing at her feet to keep from tripping. Plump, with reddish hair, she didn't look as Katie remembered her.

Uncle Helmut followed Aunt Ethel down the steps, steadying his portly frame by touching the stone wall.

Mama kissed them while Archer took the suitcase out of the trunk. Aunt Nora was jabbering to Aunt Ethel about what good children they were and how eager she was to get on her way, couldn't come inside. Uncle Helmut began giving Aunt Nora directions out of town as the girls climbed out of the car. Aunt Ethel grabbed Katie, smothering her with hugs and kisses.

Archer piled the blankets on top of the suitcase and stood waiting. He looked pathetic standing there in clothes all too small for him. Aunt Nora backed down the driveway and with only a flutter of her hand, she was gone. Jane muttered, "I hope I never lay eyes on her again."

After supper, Mama was helping Aunt Ethel make places for them to sleep. Katie was bedded down on the couch in the living room where Uncle Helmut sat before the fireplace polishing his shoes. He sat in his office chair, made of oak with curved back and arms and his bulky body filled it. Uncle Helmut wore a smoking jacket to save his suitcoat and in the brocade jacket he looked like the gentleman he was. His fine white hair shone in the lamplight, and his thick mustache was neatly trimmed. Obviously, he took care of himself and he took care of his things.

The high-top shoes sat side by side on the hearth like two old friends in church. Uncle Helmut removed the laces and began applying the paste wax with a brush. When he was done, he pressed the lid shut on the can, closed the box, and waited for the shoes to dry. Then he painstakingly buffed the shoes until they gleamed in the firelight. All his motions were slow, methodical, practiced. Uncle Helmut was a person you could depend on.

Mama came in and sat in a rocker across from him. They did not talk at first but watched the flames licking up the back of the chimney.

"Helmut, I know you are wondering about Malcolm," Mama began. It wasn't like Mama to bring up Daddy to anyone outside the family. She must have thought it was her duty to talk about him with Uncle Helmut.

"Yes, Becky, I've given considerable thought to Malcolm. He left in February, didn't he?"

Mama nodded. "February fourteenth, to be exact — Valentine's Day."

"That makes eight months."

"It seems so much longer."

"You wrote Ethel that you heard from him twice?"

"Yes. He sent money both times."

Uncle Helmut reached for the poker and tended the fire. A shower of sparks flew upward. "Was he in trouble of any kind? Could he be hiding from the law?"

"I don't know. Malcolm's father disappeared one time. Mr. MacLeod was president of a bank and something happened at the bank which Malcolm never explained to me. Mr. MacLeod was gone for nearly a year and whatever the trouble was, it cost Grandmother MacLeod her inheritance to settle the matter."

Uncle Helmut put on his wire-rimmed glasses and, fingering the side pieces, fitted them around his ears. Picking up a shoe, he began threading a lace through the grommets. "Men in business can get involved in dealings that pose legal problems," he said.

"Malcolm's father and two of his brothers now have a hotel in Tyler. There may be some kind of difficulty there."

Mama's voice was tired. "I would have stayed on in Texas, but I could not subject the children to another winter in that house. It can be bitter cold out there, and a summer house is not suitable shelter. Our car was beyond repair; we had no way to get the twins to school in town." She was gazing at the fire, watching rolls of black soot bobbing on the chimney wall. "I suppose I worried most about Alice and Jane. They are getting to the age where young men are interested in them, and some undesirable suitors were beginning to visit."

"Did you write Malcolm's father that you were leaving?"

"I only wrote Tom, but Malcolm will know where to find us. He will get in touch with you." Mama sighed. "Helmut, this is Malcolm's pattern. He has always gone ahead of us to a new place. When he was established, he would send for us. When he was building the store in Bamberg, we stayed with Mama and Papa until he could move us there. After Little Malcolm died, we could not bear to stay on in Bamberg, so Malcolm went to Greenwood. As soon as he had an office and a house, we joined him."

Uncle Helmut stroked his mustache. "Yes, I remember when I first met Malcolm here in Charlotte. He was alone. When he began to prosper, he bought Twenty-nine and moved you here."

"It took him longer to make a go of it in Texas but he was well fixed when we went out there. Then the Depression hit real estate. This is the worst financial setback we have ever had to face. When Malcolm weathers it, when he has a comfortable place for us again, he will come or he will send for us."

"I'm sure he will, Becky. But if—"

"Helmut, Malcolm would never desert his children."

"Of course not."

"He's a blue blood, Helmut. They don't come from finer stock than Malcolm. I know his faults, I know his weaknesses, but I'm not ashamed I married him."

Katie dozed. She roused when Uncle Helmut got up

241

to turn off the lamp. Mama had gone to bed. Aunt Ethel came in the living room and stood at the foot of the couch. Katie pretended to be asleep.

"Oh, Mr. Schneider, what do you think? Do you think Katie will live through the night?"

"Ethel, Ethel—"

She was sniffling. "Look at those black circles—that little pinched face. Her limbs are like toothpicks!"

"She's tired from the trip, Ethel. She'll be all right."

"Mr. Schneider, shouldn't I write Uncle Robert and tell him Becky is destitute?"

"Don't you dare! Becky would never forgive you."

In the days that followed, Katie spent a lot of time on the porch looking for Brother, and Archer sat alongside her on the bench. "Katie," he said, "in a few days— maybe today—you're going to see True Luck coming up Laurel Lane."

"Do you really think so?"

"I know so."

But Archer's voice quivered and that meant he wasn't sure—only hoping. Katie wanted to reach over and touch him, but she didn't dare. They sat listening to Mama sewing on the treadle machine, starting and stopping. She was making over used clothing Aunt Claire had sent from Greenville. Aunt Claire was Daddy's youngest sister and by far the nicest one, Jane said.

Aunt Angela, who lived in New York and wrote books, sent a box of ladies' hats, shoes, crepe dresses, and evening purses. Mama gave Katie one of the beaded bags to play with and told her to write Aunt Angela a thank-you letter.

Katie went to the kitchen, away from everybody, to write the letter. She stared at the tablet for some time, awed that she was writing to someone who was a real author. Then she wrote a few lines and signed her name. Mama read it and approved. "Here's the address. Perhaps Ethel has a stamp."

Katie went back to the kitchen and, after addressing the envelope, had another idea. "P.S.," she wrote, "I want to write a book. It's about my Daddy. If you know where he is, will you please tell me?"

NINETEEN
Sweet
As Pie

The worst thing about living at Aunt Ethel's was that there was no place to run. Mama didn't allow Katie to go across the street to the meadow, and there was no place else to run. The front yard was full of flowers and the backyard was laid off in flower beds with boards shoring up the soil. Of course, Aunt Ethel would let Katie do anything she wanted to—run between the beds, leap over them—but Uncle Helmut did not approve and Katie respected Uncle Helmut.

Sometimes Katie followed him as he did his chores. In the cellar he tended his grape wine, mended his shoes on a cobbler's last, and in his office he went over accounts at his rolltop desk.

But Katie couldn't hang around Uncle Helmut all the time. Most of the time she was inside, looking at seed catalogs, trying to find pictures of bluebonnets, but there were none. Walls bothered Katie. In the bathroom, for instance, she wished she could yodel and hear Brother or Maas or Archer answering, but in the small cubicle the sound would go no place, only reverberate against the walls. Sometimes, sitting in the bathtub, Katie would let the tears slide down her cheeks, but even there she couldn't cry for long. Archer was always banging on the door, telling her to hurry up or he'd tell Mama.

It seemed that Brother would never come. In the days they had been at Aunt Ethel's, Mama had made enough clothes for Katie and Archer to start school and in a few more days she would finish the clothes for Alice and Jane.

Katie dreaded every step of the way to Sycamore School. It was an old brick building on the hill across Main Street—the same school Brother and the twins had attended. All the same teachers would be there, and they would expect Katie to be as smart as Brother and the twins.

Katie followed two steps behind Archer. Children were everywhere. Archer made it plain he didn't want Katie walking beside him.

School was a nightmare. The fifth grade teacher, Miss Byrd, used a long rod to lower the windows from the top four inches, then raised the bottom window four inches—precisely that, no more, no less—and she pulled the shades so that they were even, all the same length. It was part of the walling in.

A dusty globe stood in a corner of the room; a picture of George Washington hung on the back wall and a picture of President Roosevelt was above the blackboard over the teacher's desk. On that desk was a paper cutter, probably the very one that had cut Jane's finger, cut it so deep the nail would never be right again.

In the upper right hand corner of each desk was an ink well, and it could have been any one of them that Miss Byrd had spilled on Alice's dress—a new blue wool dress.

Katie felt very small in the enormous desk, her feet dangling. Sometimes she wished she was not a grade ahead because all the other children were bigger than she and they looked at her as if she didn't belong in fifth grade, as if she were cheating.

Miss Byrd called Katie to her desk. The room was deadly quiet and the girl next to Katie eyed her intently as Katie slid out of the desk and made her way to the front. Miss Byrd held a stick pen in her right hand and dipped it in the ink. "Full name, please."

"Katie Penelope MacLeod."

"Penelope" caused a ripple of laughter. Miss Byrd looked at the class reprovingly.

"Birthplace?"

"Greenwood, South Carolina."

"Age?"

"Nine."

"Address?"

"One-fifteen Laurel Lane."

"Living with your aunt?"

Katie nodded.

"Mother's name?"

"Becky MacLeod."

"Father's?"

"Malcolm MacLeod."

The sound of the pen scratching was magnified in the silence. Miss Byrd studied the completed form, laid down the pen and looked at Katie over her glasses. "Where is your father, Katie?"

Katie's head reeled. She turned away from the woman's merciless eyes. "He's dead," she mumbled.

Miss Byrd dropped the card in its folder and handed Katie a list of books. "Tell your mother she should be able to buy these books in the neighborhood second-hand. If she can't, we have new ones."

Miss Byrd left the room and Katie went back to her seat and put her head on her desk. She wanted to die.

When the dismissal bell rang that afternoon, Katie did not wait for Archer. She raced home alone. Running down the hill, crossing Main Street, passing the bakery, turning down Laurel Lane, Katie did not stop until she came to Twenty-nine. A woman was sweeping the porch steps, so Katie ambled along in front of the house, gazing lovingly at the old stones and shingles. If only she could walk up the driveway, climb the steps and sit there. Then the yellow Packard would come and Daddy would jump out, spring up the steps two at a time, grab her up in his arms, hugging and kissing her.

The woman stopped sweeping and stared at Katie. Katie looked away from her to the side porch. She frowned. Something was missing. The redbud tree—! The redbud tree was gone! Katie tore across the lawn to the place where it had been planted. The wood of the stump was still raw, and fresh chips were on the ground. "You cut down our tree!" she screamed at the woman.

The woman looked annoyed. "Young lady, you get off my property this instant!"

Katie ran up the street as hard as she could. When she reached Aunt Ethel's house, she ran inside. "Mama! Mama!"

"Mama's in the greenhouse," Alice told her.

Katie bounded outside and found Mama watering plants. Aunt Ethel was potting ivy and talking. "Your children are the most unselfish children I have ever seen, Becky. Hello, Katie, how was school?" Not waiting for an answer, she kept on talking. "I never saw children share so well."

Katie buried her face in Mama's apron. Mama held the hose at arm's length to keep them from getting wet. "What is it, Katie?"

It took her a long time to answer.

"Tell me, Katie."

"They cut down the redbud tree."

"What redbud tree?" Aunt Ethel asked.

"The redbud at Twenty-nine," Mama answered, turning off the water.

"The one Malcolm gave you?" Aunt Ethel asked.

Mama nodded.

"Humph. You mean the Judas tree, don't you?"

"Some may call it a Judas tree, but we don't," Mama said stoutly. "It's a redbud with heart-shaped leaves, and that tree was special to Katie and me." She stroked Katie's hair. "Come along, Katie, I have a wonderful surprise for you."

Katie was too upset to ask what it was.

"Brother's home. He came this morning. He's down at the bakery now, talking with Mr. Alexander."

When they reached the house, Brother was in the kitchen. "Oh, you're home," Mama said. Katie leaped into his arms. "You made it!"

"Sure, I did," he said, lifting her from the floor. "Once I got started, I finally made it. Where's Archer?" He set her down.

"He's coming. He wants a knife in the worst way to play mumblety-peg. He's itching for a knife."

"I reckon he needs britches more than he needs a knife."

"He's got britches. Mama made him a pair out of a pair of Uncle Helmut's. Mama sat up all night sewing for Archer so he could start school with me. Now she's sewing for Jane and Alice so they can start Monday."

Mama interrupted. "Brother, did you see Mr. Alexander?"

Brother gulped down a glass of water. "There's nothing now, but he'll let me know if there's anything soon." He changed the subject. "I saw the notice from Railway Express that our stuff has arrived. Did you write to Uncle Tom? He said he'd pay the freight."

"No, son, let's not do that."

"I certainly will. He promised!"

"It's forty dollars and—"

"Mama, forty dollars means nothing to Uncle Tom."

"I don't want to ask Tom for anything."

But Brother did write Uncle Tom, and Uncle Helmut drove him to the Post Office to mail the letter that night. Katie rode with them in the Studebaker.

The old coupe would not go very fast. It looked old-fashioned, but it was well kept, its brass polished and its leather oiled. Uncle Helmut had painted it himself, black with a thin red line trimming the hood and doors.

Uncle Tom's reply came in a few days. Mama read the letter and told Aunt Ethel, "Tom says Nora told him we don't have anything worth forty dollars."

Brother's eyes shot up from the sports page. "What? You mean he's not sending the money?"

Mama shook her head.

"Mama!" Brother reached for the letter but Mama didn't give it to him. "Our mattresses, the cedar chest, the sewing machine—what does Nora mean, 'not worth forty dollars'!"

"Stop gritting your teeth, son." There was a worried look on her face.

"Well, what in heaven's name are we going to do? If we don't get that stuff, they'll start charging us storage."

"You could ask Uncle Robert," Aunt Ethel injected.

"Never!" Mama answered sharply.

Brother was pacing the floor. "Worse than that, they'll sell it for salvage."

Mama was setting up the ironing board. "Stop worrying, son. Something will turn up. The Lord will provide."

"Poppycock!" Brother kicked the coal skuttle.

"Brother!" Aunt Ethel scolded. "You don't mean 'Poppycock'—that's blasphemous. The Lord *will* provide. Since I've been going to the Chapel, I've learned what it really means to trust God. All those years we sat in church, Becky, we never understood—"

"I understood," Mama said impatiently.

"Not really, Becky," Aunt Ethel argued. "So long as Mr. Schneider and I stayed in the Lutheran Church we did not learn anything. I wish you would ask Dr. Nelson to pray for you, Becky."

Katie remembered the Nelsons and the tent where they had preached. "What happened to the tent?" she asked.

"Oh, the tent's been gone for some time. They built a permanent building in the Mayesville section—a large wooden auditorium. Becky, go and have a talk with Dr. Nelson."

"No, Ethel, that will not be necessary."

"Why not?"

"Because I have a minister of my own."

"That's it, Mama," Brother said. "Why don't I go to see Dr. Hyatt this afternoon? Maybe I can borrow the money we need from the Presbyterian church."

Mama frowned. "Well, maybe a loan. But nothing more, do you understand?"

Brother was gone all afternoon. When he came home he had four ten-dollar bills and counted them into Mama's hand.

"A loan?" she asked.

"Yes'm. I'm to pay it back a dollar and a half a week as soon as I start working."

Mama went back to her sewing, whipstitching the last bit of a hem.

Alice and Jane tried on their dresses for the last time. "There," Mama said. "You can start school tomorrow."

The twins walked more than three miles to high school, morning and afternoon. When they came home it was suppertime and they were exhausted.

Every evening after supper Uncle Helmut led in family prayers. Sitting around the fireplace, they listened as he read the Bible. Archer, lying on his stomach on the floor, tickled Katie's neck with a straw. She was in torment trying not to giggle when a knock sounded at the door. It was Mr. Alexander. Brother stepped onto the porch to talk with him. In a few minutes he came inside, his face beaming. "I go to work at midnight in the wrapping department!" He was holding white clothes in his hand. "My uniform. Mr. Alexander said I can pay for the pants and shirt by the week."

"How much will you make?" Archer asked.

Mama tried to hush him. "Shhh." But all eyes were on Brother, waiting for an answer.

Brother leaned down and whispered in Mama's ear,

"Twelve-fifty a week and sometimes some loaves of day-old bread."

"Now we can find a place of our own," Mama said, and she was smiling happily. "Helmut, can you take me to look for a house tomorrow?"

The house Uncle Helmut found was in the Mayesville section, dangerously close to the mill village. It was the ugliest house Katie had ever seen—a duplex painted battleship gray with only four windows on its broad side. Mama said the stairs went up on that side. The only tree in the yard was a sturdy little ash beside the kitchen window.

On the front of the house hung a narrow porch with no banisters, bricks stacked for steps. Exactly the same kind of porch hung on the other side of the duplex, with a door, a window beside it, and two windows above, gaping like holes in a skeleton's skull.

They stood in the November chill, Uncle Helmut, Mama, Katie, and Mr. West who rented the property. Mr. West looked like an undertaker. A tall, spare man, his black suit draped his frame as if hanging on a rack; his collar was wrinkled and his string tie was frayed. Mr. West leaned with the wind—hat clamped down on his head, pockets sagging, knees bagging—his face so gaunt his mouth looked like a seam sewn shut.

Someone living in the other apartment was peeking out from behind a torn shade and their dog barked from the porch.

Mr. West led them up the steps, fumbled in his pocket for a skeleton key, dropped it in the lock, and turned it easily. As he opened the door, a piece of paper stirred on the floor.

One narrow room followed the other, an arch between the first two and a kitchen back of the staircase on the side. The staircase was against the outside wall. Three steps led to a landing with a window; ten more steps to the second floor. Handprints on the stairwell walls were telltale marks of dirty children who had gone before.

Upstairs, two bedrooms and a bathroom opened into a hallway. Empty light sockets hung from the ceilings in each of the rooms except the living room where there was a brass fixture.

Mama and Katie went through the house to the backyard. Mama wanted to examine the chimneys to see if they would draw well. They walked a distance from the house in a vacant lot where branch willows, honeysuckle, and broomstraw covered an acre. Mama was looking above the lot. "Look, Katie, look at the sunset!"

Satisfied that the chimneys were tall enough, they came back to the house. The woman living in the other side of the duplex came out to the fence that separated the two yards. "Good afternoon," Mama said. "I'm Mrs. MacLeod and this is my daughter Katie."

The woman was neat but nervous looking. "I'm Mrs. Cummings." She paused to hide her curiosity. "You're with Mr. West?"

"Yes."

"Well, Mr. West is a nice man." She glanced over her shoulder. "You might say he's the Mr. Lincoln of Mayesville. Folks respect him, make fun of him, and fear him, but he's one man everybody in Mayesville has to deal with."

Mama was looking over the yard. An unsightly shed marked the end of the property.

"They've never painted it," Mrs. Cummings said.

"Good place to keep chickens?"

"I suppose so."

"And back of the shed—did anyone ever plant a garden in back of there?"

"No, we never plant back there. My husband planted those collards over there." There were two rows on the other side of the house. "My daddy sent me to school to learn to play the piano and I never learned anything else. Don't know beans about gardening."

Mama smiled and turned toward the back porch. "It was nice meeting you, Mrs. Cummings. Good day."

Katie followed Mama through the house to the front porch. Across Thrift Street was the spring lot overgrown with brambles and trees. A path ran down an embankment to a ditch which channeled water to the spring house. Beyond the ditch lay Main Street, busy with traffic. On the corner was the ice plant.

Mr. West spoke. "Rent's twelve-fifty a month, cash in advance."

It was two weeks before they could move. The day before Thanksgiving, Mama told Katie to go to the new house when school was out.

In the brisk chill of November, Katie climbed the hill up Thrift Street. Going past the Chapel, she followed the street heading for the tall gray duplex at the end. A truck was backed up in the yard but it pulled away before Katie reached the house. A red shield was painted on the side of the truck and one of the men wore the uniform of the Salvation Army.

Standing on the porch of the other duplex was a boy Archer's age, only there was something wrong with him. He was grinning and drooling at the mouth.

Katie hurried inside. Furniture was stacked around the room and Brother was adjusting the pipe of a cast iron heater. "Lookit, Katie. We'll build a fire in this little devil and watch it burn through the isinglass." He called Archer from the kitchen. "Archer, run over to the ice house and get a bag of coal."

"I can't carry a sack of coal."

"The boy next door has a wagon. Ask him if you can borrow it." He fished in his pocket for the money.

Archer took the quarter and left.

"Brother, what's wrong with the boy next door?" Katie asked.

"That boy on the porch?" He wiped his hands, greasy and grimy, on his handkerchief. "He's feeble-minded. I don't think he'll hurt you. Be careful though."

Alice called downstairs. "Katie, don't you want to see where you'll sleep?"

Katie went upstairs. In the front bedroom was Granddaddy MacLeod's four-poster bed with feather mattress, and a cot. "This is our room," Alice explained. "We three will sleep in the big bed and Mama in the little one." She opened a door. "This is the closet and one of the drawers in the bureau is yours." On the bureau was Katie's picture of Daddy and herself in the lace frame. She picked it up and studied it.

"Your hem is turned up," Alice said. "Make a wish, Katie, kiss it, and it'll come true."

"I know," she said and kissed the turned-up place. Wishing would not help, she knew, but she wished all the same. If only Daddy would come, they wouldn't have to live in this tacky old house, she thought.

Alice looked out the window. "There's Uncle Helmut." They hurried downstairs to meet him.

He was carrying a box from the car. "I brought the girls' paintings and a few other things. Ethel says there are shades in the attic that belonged to your Grandmother MacLeod." He pulled an envelope from his jacket. "And a letter came to Katie." He handed it to her. "It's from your Aunt Angela."

"An answer to your thank-you," Mama said, pushing Grandmother MacLeod's platform rocker to one side. "Alice—Jane, where do you think the green rocker should go?"

Katie slipped upstairs to the bathroom to read the letter. "Dear Katie," the letter read. "To be a writer one must read prolifically. Under separate cover I am sending you three volumes by Sir Walter Scott, a biography of Milton, and essays by Chesterton."

Not a word about Daddy. Katie tore the letter to shreds.

By the time she came downstairs, the fire was burning in the stove. Uncle Helmut was gone. Mama and Jane were unpacking silverware. "This ladle came from your Grandmother MacLeod. It goes with her soup tureen, the one we use for ambrosia," Mama explained. "And these serving spoons came from an estate Malcolm bought when he had the furniture store in Bamberg. I'm glad Ethel kept these things in a safe place. . . . And here, Katie, here's the little place setting your daddy bought you when you were four years old. See, it's engraved with his pet name for you."

"'Pie,' did he call me 'Pie'?"

"Yes, when you were very small. Don't you remember?"

"No."

"Well, he gave you a little spanking one day and later on, he was resting on the couch. You climbed up on his chest and started loving him. It made him feel sorry. The next day he came home with this. He said you were 'sweet as pie.'"

Timothy wanted to see and crowded in between Katie and Mama. "Dear me," Mama said, "we need room to work here. Katie, take Timothy up on the landing and read him a story."

Katie carefully laid the little knife, fork, and spoon back in the box. "Am I too big to use it now?"

"Of course not."

Katie found the Bible story book and she and Timothy settled on the landing to read. As she opened the book, a letter fell to the floor. The handwriting looked like Daddy's.

Brother picked it up. "This is the letter from Uncle Tom," he said, unfolding it.

"Let me have that," Mama said, reaching for it.

Brother held the letter out of her reach. "Mama, you didn't tell me what Tom said about the children."

"It's nothing."

"I hope to tell you it *is* something!" He was angry.

"What did he say?" Jane demanded.

"He said the children should go to Boiling Springs Orphanage until Daddy comes home!"

"Oliver!" Mama took the letter and threw it in the fire.

"He's got his nerve," Brother fumed.

"We have nothing to fear from him." Mama grew pensive. "I think we must be on guard, however, that we do not tell our family business to outsiders."

"What do you mean, Mama?" Archer asked.

"Just that."

"Tell me why," he demanded.

"Son, if you must know, there are busybodies who like to pry into other people's affairs."

"I know that, Mama, but why must we all of a sudden be more careful than we've always been?"

"I don't mean anything more than that."

"Yes, you do, Mama. Something's worrying you."

"Well, son, the Public Welfare Department might question my ability to support a family this size."

"You mean they might try to take us away from you."

Brother clenched his teeth and ran his fingers through his hair nervously.

Mama was very serious. "I didn't say that, Archer. Another thing. I want you and Katie to be careful and not let Timothy out of your sight."

"Why?"

"Well, there are kidnappers these days and Timothy is such a beautiful child—"

"Kidnap? Who would do a thing like that?"

"I don't know. Just keep your eye on him."

In the silence that followed they could hear Mrs. Cummings playing the piano. Katie was so scared her heart was palpitating. Alice and Jane were pale as ghosts.

Archer drew himself up as straight and tall as he could and announced, "Don't worry, Mama—I'm going to find a job and take care of us."

Mama smiled. "Son, you're only twelve years old. What can you do?"

"I can deliver groceries."

"You don't have a bicycle," Brother reminded him.

"You can help me plant a garden," Mama told him.

When they finally went upstairs to bed, they undressed in the dark because there were no shades at the windows. Mama stayed downstairs to straighten up and the girls went to bed without her. They snuggled deep in the eiderdown of the mattress, and Katie felt a knot of fear in her stomach. She reached for Alice's nightgown to hold onto. Alice didn't complain; she was holding onto Jane's nightgown.

TWENTY
The Tiff with Ethel

Mama and Archer planted a garden in back of the shed—turnips, tendergreens, and onion sets. Then Archer built himself a wagon and found a job delivering groceries. Every afternoon and on Saturdays, he hauled groceries in the neighborhood, and at the end of the week he brought home a bill or two and some silver. Mama made him lay away a jacket at a store and pay on it each week. With the money left over he could do as he pleased. Usually he made enough to give Brother the dollar-fifty owed the church. On Saturday mornings, Brother walked the mile to town to make the loan payment at the church; on Sunday mornings he walked there again and worshiped God.

The rest of the family went to a small church across the spring lot and Main Street where people's clothes were not too fine. On Sunday evenings, when an unusually large crowd of mill people streamed down Thrift Street to the Chapel, Mama would let the girls and Archer go to the service there. A crowd of Chapel-goers meant there was special music or a play on the program. The plays were exciting. Archer boasted that he knew how they did the handwriting on the wall— how they had a woman's hand writing on the wall and her body not seen—but he wouldn't explain it to Katie.

Katie didn't care. There was a liveliness at the Chapel, a kind of joy that was contagious. She decided that people who carried Bibles were different.

Katie stayed with Aunt Ethel most school nights and in the mornings Aunt Ethel would either tell her to come home for lunch or she would pack sandwiches and fruit in a bag for her to take with her. Archer went home to Mama's for lunch.

Poor children ate free lunches, peanut butter sandwiches. Archer said, "Those sandwiches sure smell good."

"Yes," Katie replied, "but you would die before you'd take one." Archer ignored her.

Aunt Ethel gave Katie a nickel every week for notebook paper which Katie shared with Archer and the twins. Two rich sisters in Miss Byrd's class had their own individual pack of paper, a bottle of ink each, and long yellow pencils. One bottle of ink served the entire MacLeod family; their pencils weren't yellow, they were made of cedar, bought for a penny, and were sometimes broken in half to make two. The scent of cedar reminded Katie of Bull Creek and that made up for not having yellow pencils with erasers.

One morning when Katie had spent the night at home, she noticed the twins' lunch bag in the kitchen. Mama put coal in the heater and called to her, "Katie, you may go to Ethel's today for lunch. Just be careful crossing Main Street."

Katie fingered the twins' lunch bag. There didn't seem to be much in it. She peeked inside. Two cold pancakes!

Unexpectedly, Jane came in the kitchen. "What are you doing looking in our lunch?"

Katie's eyes were swimming.

Jane lowered her voice, "Yes, they're pancakes. Haven't you ever seen a pancake before?" She snatched the bag.

"But—"

"But aren't we ashamed? Of course we are, but we have the good sense to go over in a corner of the playground and eat where no one will see us." She was pulling on her coat. Alice was coming down the stairs. Jane stuffed the lunch into her coat pocket. "I'm coming, Alice!"

That day at lunch, Katie could not eat. Aunt Ethel's table was loaded with steaming food but all Katie could think about were the cold pancakes.

"What's the matter, Katie? Why aren't you eating?"

Another misery came to mind. "Aunt Ethel, who would want to kidnap Timothy?"

"Kidnap Timothy?"

"Mama said someone might."

"I don't know unless it would be your father. But you're his favorite child—you're the one he would snatch."

That's not true, Katie thought, *Timothy is everybody's favorite.*

"There's nothing that man wouldn't do."

"My Daddy? Why?"

"For spite." She got up to put dishes in the sink. Katie left the table. She didn't understand how Aunt Ethel could say such things about Daddy.

"Tell your mother I had a letter from Nora. I wrote Nora about those window shades in the attic that belonged to your Grandmother MacLeod. I thought you all might use them but Nora said no. Said they have good spring rollers in them and your Uncle Tom doesn't want to get rid of them. Don't forget to tell Becky."

But Katie didn't tell her. Not that day or the next or the next. Mama had enough misery.

Aunt Nora was not the only person Aunt Ethel wrote to. She wrote Uncle Robert, knowing Mama wouldn't want her to. Uncle Robert answered right away and the letter to Mama came to Aunt Ethel's address. Aunt Ethel lost no time taking it to Mama.

"A letter from Uncle Robert?" Mama frowned. "Ethel, you didn't by any chance write to him, did you?"

"Yes, I did. I knew you wouldn't like it so I didn't tell you. Go ahead, open it. Maybe the old skinflint sent you a check."

Clearly, Mama was upset.

"Read it," Aunt Ethel insisted.

"Dear Becky," Mama read, "Ethel has written me of your plight. I should think you would know me well enough not to expect me to respond to pleas for money. Your husband is responsible for your needs. Inasmuch as Malcolm has left you, I advise that you sue for alimony. Yours very truly, Robert McIntosh."

Mama's mouth was open. She looked at Aunt Ethel in total disbelief.

"Why the old miser!" Ethel was sputtering. "Becky, you know as well as I that all that money Uncle Robert has belongs to us. He stole it. There's no earthly reason why you shouldn't have your inheritance now."

Mama was furious. "Ethel, Uncle Robert is the last person on the face of the earth I would ask for *anything*. I can't believe you did this!"

"Becky, there's no reason to be upset."

"No reason to be upset?" Mama repeated. "Ethel, you have humiliated me and the children!"

Aunt Ethel wouldn't look at Mama and wouldn't speak. In a few minutes she jumped up and left.

"Ethel!" Mama called after her but she was gone.

Mama was so shaken she couldn't keep her mind on what she was doing. Going in the kitchen to begin supper, she turned the burner up too high and smoke poured into the dining room before she realized it. She opened the back door to let out the smoke and stood before the sink, staring out the window, her lips moving as she talked to herself.

Brother woke up and came downstairs. Mama told him what Aunt Ethel had done.

"You don't mean she told Uncle Robert! What right did she have to take matters in her own hands?"

"None. Ethel means well but she was in short, tending to our business. If she had told anyone except Uncle Robert! Of all people to tell!"

Archer scooped a spoonful of bread pudding. "Aw, Mama, forget it. Aunt Ethel was right. Uncle Robert ought to give you what's coming to you."

Mama didn't even hear him. "I feel so betrayed."

When Jane heard about it she said, "Just 'turn the other cheek.'"

"No. This is a serious matter."

"I agree, Mama," Alice said. "What are you going to do about it?"

"I'm going to try to get over it—try to heal the breach."

"How?"

"I don't know. It's a two-way street. You don't know your Aunt Ethel like I do. She finds it very hard to say she is sorry."

"Well, I'm not forgiving her until she apologizes," Brother said. "I would thank her to keep her nose out of our business."

"Brother, it's wrong to bear a grudge. The only way we can straighten this out is to be gentle with Ethel. I've told her how we feel and she understands. She's ashamed and that makes it hard for her to admit she's wrong. We have to have a forgiving spirit."

"Let's eat." Brother was in no mood to argue.

Katie was glad it was Friday. On Friday nights she stayed at home, and that was good because she didn't want to see Aunt Ethel right away.

Mr. West drove through the neighborhood every

Friday collecting rents. After supper, Katie and Timothy sat by the window on the landing watching him making his stops along the street. He drove a Model T that had to be cranked by hand, so he parked it and walked from one house to the next. Mr. West did not keep his car clean the way Uncle Helmut did. He was stingy and Archer said he only washed dirt from one side of the windshield so he wouldn't waste water.

When Mr. West was ready to come to the duplex, he cranked the Ford, and the old car chugged up the street, backfiring. It was hard to see in the dusk, but under the street lamp the Model T looked shiny as if it had been washed. Stopping before the house, he cut the motor and swung open the door.

Mr. West looked different—his suit looked new and his collar stood up like Uncle Helmut's detachable celluloid collar. The string tie was gone and a polka-dot bow tie rested at an angle below his chin. As he came in the yard, he stopped to examine the steps, drew out a writing pad, licked his pencil, and jotted down something on the paper.

When Mama answered the door, he said, "Good evenin', Ma'am," taking off his hat and looking the other way.

"Good evening, Mr. West. I'll get the rent for you." She kept it in the octagon can in the kitchen. She brought the money in an envelope and counted it out in his hand. Katie and Timothy squeezed beside Mama in the doorway to listen to Mr. West.

"I'll send a man up here next week to fix these steps," he said, still not looking their way.

"Thank you, Mr. West. That will be nice."

He did not make a move to leave. A gust of cold wind blew around the corner of the house. Mama stepped onto the porch and pulled the door behind them.

Mr. West cleared his throat and stood on the other foot. "Guess you know this house used to be a church?" His eyes made a fleeting glance toward Mama.

"So Mrs. Cummings tells me. A Methodist church, I believe."

He nodded. Mr. West didn't notice the cold. He was looking toward the ice plant where Archer was coming down the street pulling his wagon full of coal. "Fine boy," Mr. West mumbled.

"Thank you," Mama said, but Mr. West didn't hear her because a coal truck was emptying its load behind the ice house. When it was unloaded, Mama spoke again. "The coal dust is such a problem."

Mrs. Cummings came out on the porch to sweep. Her feeble-minded son, Lionel, stood in the doorway grinning. Mr. West paid no attention to them.

A flicker of a smile creased the old man's face. "Archer asked me about some rocks he found in the spring lot. Thought he had found gold." His eyes made another brief visit toward Mama. "Fool's gold, that's what it is—all over the spring lot."

Mama laughed. "Yes, Archer showed me those rocks. My son Oliver told him it was fool's gold. Incidentally, the neighbors say gold was mined in this part of Charlotte at one time."

"Ma'am, this house is just below the main shaft." He waved his hand toward the ice plant. "Down in the spring lot there's a stream runs right off that old mine shaft. As a boy I used to wade the creek looking for gold."

"Did you find any?" Mama asked, amused.

He shook his head. "All I got I earned with these two hands." He held up the palms of his hands. "I own four of the houses I collect rent on—not this duplex, of course." He motioned with his head. "I own some property back of here."

Another gust of wind came around the corner. "I'll have to get the children inside," Mama said. "It's too cold on the porch. Thank you for coming, Mr. West."

Then he looked directly at Mama, and it worried Katie because it was plain to see he liked Mama very much.

264

Archer crossed the yard as a shortcut to the coal bin. He hollered above the wagon's racket, "After I dump this, I'm going to look for pigeons!"

As soon as Mr. West's Ford turned the corner, Mrs. Cummings came over to borrow a cup of sugar. "Well, I never," she said, "I never saw Mr. West spruced up like that before! I wonder what's come over him?" She sat down at the table where Mama was folding towels. "Old man West's been a widower as long as I can remember. Never cared how he looked. Did I hear him say he's going to fix your steps?"

"I guess you did."

"Well, I'll never! I've been after him a year now to fix our steps and replace those rotten boards." Mrs. Cummings toyed with the cup of sugar and moved her tongue over her gums inside her cheek. "Mrs. McLeod." A funny little smile played at the corners of her mouth. "Is your husband living?"

Mama raised her eyes slowly and leveled a withering look at Mrs. Cummings. "Yes," Mama said, her blue eyes unrelenting. The woman was flustered. Right away she began folding towels.

After a while, Mama broke the silence. "These sheets are getting tattle-tale gray from all this coal dust."

Mr. Cummings was next door chopping steak. On payday the Cummingses always had steak.

"They look clean to me," Mrs. Cummings was saying. "How do you get them so white?"

"I wash them with bar soap on a board in the bathtub. Isn't that the way you do it?"

"No. My husband takes them to the laundry. Some day we'll buy a laundry heater and have plenty of hot water; then I'll have to wash them."

"I heat the water in a kettle on the kerosene stove," Mama said.

Katie heard Uncle Helmut's car horn and rushed to the door. Archer was in the Studebaker beside Uncle Helmut and yelled, "Come help me carry this stuff."

Katie ran to the car. Uncle Helmut told her, "There's

a parcel post package from the aunt in New York."
Archer handed her a big box, then reached behind the
seat and lifted out a croaker sack.

"Whatcha got?" Katie asked.

"Couple pigeons."

Mama came to the door. "Katie," she called, "ask
Uncle Helmut if they'll come to dinner Sunday."

Katie asked, but Uncle Helmut shook his head. He
turned off the motor. "I'll go in and talk to your
mother."

Katie followed Archer to the backyard. "Where'd
you get 'em?"

"Caught 'em down at the Chapel."

"What're you going to do with pigeons?"

"Sell 'em."

"Who you going to sell 'em to?"

"Niggers." He reached his hand in the bag and pulled
out a frightened bird. "See this one? I can get thirty-
five cents for her."

"How do you know?"

"I know." He put the pigeons in a wire cage he had
built and dropped a stick in the latch. "That's not all. I
can sell the same bird as many times as I want to."

"How's that?"

"Well, once you train a pigeon to come home to
roost, that pigeon will always come back to you. Those
dumb niggers don't know that. They'll buy a bird and
the first time they let it out, it'll come back here."

"I'm going to tell Mama."

"You do and I'll swat you one."

Of course, Katie would never tell. There were many
things Archer did that she never told. She never told
even the dangerous things he did, such as his exploring
the gold mine in the spring lot. He took Katie with him
but made her stay outside in case the shaft collapsed.
He didn't stay in it very long because a board fell on his
arm and nearly broke it. They never went there again.

The package from Aunt Angela contained two men's

overcoats and the books she had promised Katie. Mama rubbed the cloth against her cheek and pronounced it to be "all wool." Holding the coat at arm's length, she weighed it. "Nice and heavy."

Brother tried on the herringbone coat and then the Chesterfield. "I can alter this one for you," Mama said. "Maybe I can cut the other one down for myself."

"Oh, Mama," Archer said, "you can't wear a man's overcoat."

"You wait until I'm finished with it. You won't know it was ever a man's coat."

"Mama," Katie asked, "is Aunt Ethel coming for Sunday dinner?"

"No, I don't think so."

On Sunday, Aunt Ethel did not come, and she probably never would have visited Mama if it had not been for Sadie Allen.

Sadie Allen was a social worker from the Department of Public Welfare and she came to see Mama and asked a lot of questions. She came the day Mr. West's carpenter was building the steps and she had a hard time getting up on the porch because she was a large woman.

Mama sent Katie upstairs with Timothy, but Katie put Timothy on the bed to make a tent out of the bedcovers and she slipped back to the top step to listen.

"Mrs. MacLeod, Sycamore Elementary reported to our department that your husband is dead and that you might be in need of assistance."

Katie's mouth flew open. *Miss Byrd!* she thought. *Miss Byrd told them that!*

"Is this correct? Is your husband dead?"

Mama was indignant. "It is most certainly *not* correct!"

"Well, that's strange. It says right here he's dead. Where is he?"

"Mr. MacLeod is in Texas."

"Are you two separated?"

"I beg your pardon!"

"Mrs. MacLeod, this is my job. I'd thank you to answer my questions."

"And, Miss Allen, this is *my* family!"

"Mrs. MacLeod, since you have little visible means of support, I think you qualify for government relief."

"Miss Allen, I would thank you, the Department of Public Welfare, and the United States Government to stay out of our affairs!" The door opened. "Good day!"

The door shut so hard behind Miss Allen it rattled the windows and woke up Brother. He came in the hall buttoning his pants. "What's going on?"

Katie shook her head. They went downstairs together. Mama turned away from the window. "I'm livid! Absolutely livid! This is an outrage!" She turned to Katie. "Go back upstairs, Katie. Play with Timothy."

Upstairs in the big four-poster bed, Timothy had erected a tent, and Katie crawled inside with him. She could hear only the muffled voices of Mama and Brother talking downstairs.

When the twins came home, Mama didn't tell them anything. After supper she tried on one of the crepe dresses and asked Alice to help her with the fitting. "Mama, it's about time you made something for yourself," Alice said.

Alice pinned the dress under the arms and down the sides. "That watermelon color is perfect with your hair."

Mama basted the seams and tried on the dress again. "It's perfect," Alice said.

"Now you girls run along to bed. I'm going to stitch this up tonight."

Lying in bed, Katie listened to the sewing machine running hard. Mama was not making herself a dress for nothing—in her head was some sort of plan—Katie could tell by the way she drove the machine. The motor would run with a short burst of speed, then purr, and in a few seconds, go again. With her eyes closed, Katie could see Mama bending toward the light of the little bulb on back of the machine, see her lift the lever of the presser foot, fit the edges of a seam together, pulling the material with her right hand and guiding it toward the presser foot with the fingertips of her left hand.

The next day, Katie knew she shouldn't do it, but she went to Aunt Ethel's and spilled the beans about the Public Welfare lady. Aunt Ethel made Uncle Helmut get right in the car and drive them to Mama's. Mama was pressing the dress she had made.

Before Aunt Ethel opened her mouth, Mama held up her hand to stop her. "There's nothing to discuss," she said. "Helmut, I want you to take me to Judge Reynolds's office." She unplugged the iron and held up the dress, examining it. "Excuse me, I'll run upstairs and get dressed."

In a few minutes, Aunt Ethel stopped fidgeting and followed Mama. "Ethel, wash Timothy's face and comb his hair. Katie, you do the same. Pull up your socks."

"Becky," Ethel began, "I want you to know that I am sorry this happened."

"I know you are, Ethel."

"Is there anything I can do?"

"No. Just pray."

"Becky," her voice trembled. "I admit I have had a hard time praying lately. This thing between you and me has bothered me no end. I feel I did wrong in writing Uncle Robert. It was inconsiderate of me knowing how sensitive you and the children are about Malcolm."

"Ethel, we all make mistakes. I'm sure the children will forgive you and so do I."

When they came down the stairs, Mama looked beautiful. The dress was stylish and the heels she wore were an elegant pair Aunt Angela had sent. Uncle Helmut held Mama's coat for her. "Is my hat on right?" she asked, pulling nervously at the brim.

"You look stunning, Becky," Aunt Ethel assured her.

They squeezed into the coupe for the ride across town, the three grown-ups on the seat, Katie and

Timothy in the narrow space behind.

When Uncle Helmut drove, that is all he did. He didn't look this way or that or talk or even listen. They drove straight through town, past the square and down the hill on the other side. "There's the courthouse, Katie," Aunt Ethel said as they passed a stately looking building with a cannon in front. "Remember how your Daddy used to drive you children here to see the floodlights on the courthouse?"

Katie didn't remember.

Uncle Helmut pulled up to the curve before the Lawyers' Building. Mama let herself out. "Come along, Katie. You're going with me."

Inside the building, a uniformed elevator attendant called, "Going up?" Mama nodded, and he bowed as they entered.

"Fifth floor," Mama said as he closed the cage door. Katie's stomach lurched as the elevator zoomed upward. With her gloved hand Mama smoothed Katie's hair, and Katie got a whiff of Aunt Ethel's good powder. "Hold up your shoulders," Mama whispered, "and smile."

"Fifth floor," the operator called. "Watch your step."

"Thank you," Mama said and strode out of the elevator. The operator leaned his head out the door to watch Mama walking down the hallway.

They walked the length of the corridor to a heavy wooden door. "Judge Marcus Reynolds" was printed in gold with some other names. Mama hesitated, drew in her breath, and opened the door.

A man about Daddy's age was working behind a desk. He didn't look old enough to be a judge. He was tall, well dressed, and very busy. When he glanced up and saw Mama, he laid down his pen and stood to his feet. "Good afternoon." He paused. "My name is Zachary Kerr, attorney-at-law. May I be of some service?"

"Thank you. I am Mrs. Malcolm MacLeod and this is my daughter Katie. I wish to speak with Judge Reynolds if I may."

"To be sure. Please be seated."

He waited for them to sit in the leather chairs. Katie crossed her ankles the way Mama did and folded her hands. Mr. Kerr left the room, walking down a short hall to another office.

Katie looked about the room—the pendulum clock in its glass case on the wall, the leather-bound books, the filing cabinets, the frosted glass in the windows, the brass plate at the bottom of the door. Cigar smoke lingered in the air.

Mr. Kerr came back smiling. "Judge Reynolds will see you momentarily. May I take your coats?" He hung them on a coat rack and went back to his work, shuffling papers and stacking them. "Well, now, I don't have to do this just now." He laid the papers aside and glanced at Mama. Their eyes did not meet. The man looked at Katie. "So you are Katie," he said pleasantly. "What school do you go to?"

"Sycamore Elementary."

"What grade are you in?"

"Fifth."

"My, you look young for fifth grade. You must be very smart."

Mr. Kerr turned to Mama again. "Have you done business with us before?"

"My husband bought a house on Laurel Lane from Judge Reynolds."

"Malcolm MacLeod," he mused. "I've heard of him. He was in real estate here some time ago, wasn't he?"

Mama nodded. Their eyes met.

"He developed property up in the mountains five or six years ago, didn't he?"

"Yes. Do you know him?"

"I believe I do—rather tall man with sandy hair?"

"Yes."

A buzzer sounded. "You may go in now, Mrs. MacLeod." Mr. Kerr stood up and moved to escort her down the hall.

"I can find my way, thank you," she said politely.

Mr. Kerr went back to his work. He moved papers about, glanced down the hall a couple of times, stood up and walked about the office. He talked to Katie but she only said yes and no to him so he gave up. At last he slumped down in his chair, pulled out a desk drawer to prop his foot on, and waited.

Katie yawned and uncrossed her ankles.

It was five o'clock before the door opened down the hall. Mr. Kerr jerked himself erect, shut the drawer, and fastened the buttons on his double-breasted suit. A man's deep voice sounded in the hallway. "It's been a distinct pleasure seeing you again," the Judge was saying. "You are as lovely as always."

"Thank you, Judge Reynolds. You remember Katie?"

He reached down his hand to her, smiling. "Katie? Indeed I do. The question is, does Katie remember me?"

Katie smiled, and he straightened up like the courtly gentleman he was. "Have you met Mr. Kerr?"

Mama nodded.

Judge Reynolds laughed. "I'm afraid Mr. Kerr is a confirmed bachelor, married to the law."

Mama smiled. Mr. Kerr looked pleased. "May I?" He held Mama's coat. "I'll see Mrs. MacLeod to the elevator," he told Judge Reynolds.

Walking down the corridor, Mr. Kerr looked down at Mama and smiled again. "Where is your car parked?"

"My sister is waiting for me."

"Oh," he said and pressed the elevator button. They could hear the rickety cage coming up the shaft. The door opened and Mama stepped inside. Mr. Kerr made as if he would accompany them. Mama spoke quickly, "Thank you, Mr. Kerr. Good day."

"Please come again," he said and stepped aside. The door closed.

The Studebaker was waiting at the curb. They got in the car and Uncle Helmut started the motor. "Well?" Ethel asked.

"Perhaps later, Ethel," Mama said.

Mama held Timothy on her lap and squeezed him, kissing his hair and face. Katie wondered why she could not cry. *That's what I would do if I felt like that,* she thought.

TWENTY-ONE
He Touched Me!

Mama came in the house, took off her hat and coat, and went upstairs to change her clothes. When she came down, she went to the kitchen to start supper. "Tell me the minute you hear Brother awake," she told Katie.

It wasn't long before Katie heard Brother in the bathroom, but Mama heard him first and rushed upstairs. Katie waited a minute, then tiptoed up the steps to listen. Brother must have been shaving and Mama probably was sitting on the side of the tub. Katie could hear their voices through the door.

"Judge Reynolds said Miss Allen must be an overzealous bureaucrat. He said a woman like that could cause trouble, but he said he would do anything he can to help me."

Did he ask you about Dad?"

"Yes, and I felt I had to confide in him. He was discreet, but I could tell he does not think kindly of your father."

"That's because Dad defaulted on the house and then

made a fool of himself when Reynolds tried to help him. Judge Reynolds knows what a hard time you had at Twenty-nine."

"Well, your father made mistakes, but he loves us. He would never desert his children."

"Did Reynolds have any advice?"

"Nothing acceptable."

"What do you mean?"

"You won't like it any better than I. Judge Reynolds thought I would be wise to let Katie stay with Ethel, and Timothy with one of your father's relatives so that I can go to work."

"Who does he think we are? Does he think we're some kind of poor white trash?"

"No, he doesn't think we're trash. He was concerned that the Welfare people would consider our income insufficient. I'll have to find work that I can do at home until Timothy is in school.

"I want you to put a notice on the bulletin board at the bakery advertising my services in dressmaking and alterations."

"I will, Mama, but the girls who work at the bakery wear uniforms and they probably don't have many dresses."

They started to leave the bathroom, and Katie ran lickety-split down the stairs.

As usual, Mr. West came on Friday. He stood first on one foot, then the other, talking with Mama on the porch. After weather talk, he began talking about people. "Mrs. MacLeod, my carpenter told me Sadie Allen paid you a visit the other day."

Mama frowned.

"I've known that woman since the day she was born," Mr. West continued. "Born and bred on the mill hill. Not too good a reputation, if I may say so. Now that she's got this big job with the gov'ment, it swelled her head. Everybody in Mayesville is put out with her. Just let me know if she gives you any trouble."

"Thank you, Mr. West. Now if you'll excuse me, I must get supper on the table."

In February, Sadie Allen paid another call, but Mama did not invite her in the house. They stood in the freezing cold and talked on the porch. Katie sat on the landing with Timothy, holding him close, trying to hear what they were saying.

When Mama finally came inside, she was shivering. She stood close to the heater, rubbing her hands to get warm. After a while, she told them, "I've decided to take a course in home nursing." She drew Timothy close to her. "I'll be going to the Y. Timothy will go with me and stay in a nursery there, and you, Katie, will have to go to Aunt Ethel's after school each day."

Katie sensed a battle was over—an uneasy compromise had been made. Going to Aunt Ethel's in the afternoons was little enough price for Katie to pay.

In a few days, Jane was called to work as extra help at the dime store. "Mama, do you think I'll make enough, added to what Brother makes, to keep Miss Allen from bothering us?"

"Jane, don't you worry about that. I'll do the worrying in this family."

But Katie worried too. The best solution would be for Daddy to come home. Katie began to sit on the landing in the evenings, pretending to study while she looked down the street and prayed that the next car would be Daddy's or that he would come walking up from the Chapel. Steam on the glass fogged the view, so she took the roll of toilet paper from the bathroom and kept the window wiped clean. Sometimes she closed her eyes and prayed that when she opened them Daddy would be walking under the street lamp heading home.

Anyone going upstairs or down had to crawl over Katie, her books, and her papers. When Timothy fell asleep in the living room, Archer struggled to carry him upstairs to bed. He kicked Katie's books out of the way and grumbled as he squeezed by her on the narrow landing.

Katie didn't hear Brother getting up until he was in the bathroom yelling, "Katie, bring me that toilet paper!" Katie grabbed the paper and dashed up the steps two at a time.

When Brother came downstairs he was still fuming. "Katie, for Pete's sake, look at all the toilet paper you've wasted. There's hardly enough to last the week as it is, and, Mama, every night she sits there using it to wash the window so she can see out."

Mama was quick to reply. "Leave Katie alone, Brother. If she wants to look out the window it's because she has a good reason."

"It's wasteful, Mama. You shouldn't let her do that." In his white uniform Brother looked very pale.

"Shhh, son. You're tired and cross. Come, eat your supper."

Mama led the way to the kitchen and took his supper out of the oven. When she came back to the landing, she peered over Katie's shoulder. Mama's hand went around Katie's neck and caressed her cheek. Katie felt the wedding band on Mama's finger. "Never give up, Katie. Some day. . . ."

Jane came bouncing down the stairs. They moved to let her pass.

Brother called from the dining room. "Mama, when do you finish at the Y?"

"In May." She moved away from Katie and went back to the rag rug she was working on. "After that, when school is out, I want to find work."

"Remember that time you wanted to take bookkeeping and Daddy raised sand? No wife of his would ever do public work, he said."

Mama smiled. "That was a long time ago."

Brother finished his supper and came into the living-room.

"Your father always wanted to be the provider. When you children were small he always saw to it that I had a nurse as well as a cook and a yard man."

"That, too, was a long time ago, Mama."

"Your father hasn't changed. Only circumstances have changed."

"He's been gone a year. A lot of things can change in a year."

In April the violets bloomed in the meadow, and Katie had the bright idea of picking them and selling bunches of violets in Aunt Ethel's neighborhood. It worked! As shy as she was, pressing doorbells and facing strangers was no easy hurdle, but the nickels and dimes the violets brought were incentive enough. After violet season ended, Aunt Ethel's pansies began to bloom and Katie picked them to sell. Hyacinths, phlox, candytuft, jonquils, forsythia—everything was blooming at Aunt Ethel's, and good Aunt Ethel could not say no to Katie. Business boomed and the money was all profit. At ten years old, Katie was independent. Never again would she have to ask for a nickel for notebook paper. Until frost, there would be no end to the flowers—marigolds, zinnias, asters, wild ragged robins, and larkspur.

In the late spring, Brother paid off the loan at the Presbyterian church. That left him free on Saturdays to play ball with the bakery team. He was a good pitcher, but often he was put out of the game for cursing the umpire. When Brother wasn't sleeping, he was playing baseball or tennis or going out with girls.

Katie very much wanted to learn how to play tennis, but there was no one to play with. Using the side of the house and Brother's racket and ball, she practiced by herself. The clapboards made the ball bounce unpredictably and Katie ran her legs off chasing after the rebounds. But soon, tennis practice was stopped. Brother, who had a hard enough time sleeping in the daytime, could not stand the ball hitting against the house.

Katie wished Archer had time to play. He had bought a secondhand lawn mower, sharpened the blades and started a grass-cutting business. He had customers as far as a mile away, and he worked from dawn to dusk. He wanted to buy Mama an ice box and all his earnings went into the octagon can until he had enough money to go to the secondhand store.

Archer was also busy with pigeons; he traded breeds with other pigeon fanciers, built more cotes, trained tumblers and fantails. His knowledge of the birds and enthusiasm excited other boys and moved them to invest every nickel they could in pigeons. For a thirteen-year-old, Archer was, in Brother's words, "enterprising." "Entrepreneur," Mama called him.

Mama fussed about the pigeons ruining the wash on the line, but she could not deny Archer anything, so the pigeons stayed and multiplied. Mama added chickens to the backyard and Archer built hen nests.

With the close of school, Alice took care of Timothy so Mama could look for work. The job she found was on the other side of town in an awning factory. The owner of the shop, Mr. Rogers, hired Mama because he had known Malcolm MacLeod in South Carolina years before.

Awnings were bought in warm weather, which meant there would be layoffs in winter. Making awnings was hard, but repairing tarpaulins and tents was back-breaking. On the back side of the shop, high above the ground, a narrow deck extended the length of the building. There the canvasses were hung and repaired. Mama worked in the hot sun, struggling with the heavy canvas, finding the splits, patching them, sewing up rips. The work was so dirty, Mama carried a change of clothing to wear home on the bus.

As Mama began to earn money, things improved. Brother put up a laundry heater and water tank. Mama began paying weekly on insurance policies for herself and Brother.

In July Jane went to work full time, and it was at the ten-cent store that she met so many boys. Sunday afternoons the boys came from all over to visit Jane and

Alice. Some of them were from the country and walked for miles. They crowded into the little living room and sat on the stairs when there were not enough chairs. To relieve the situation, Jane bought a secondhand couch, and Mama recovered it. With bright pillows and potted plants, the living room was transformed into a cheerful little parlor.

Chuck Bundy, one of the boys the girls thought was particularly handsome because he had a cleft chin, played the ukulele. The girls taught the boys to sing, and they would sing far into the night until Mama called bedtime.

Although the twins were not allowed to go on single dates, they could pair up and go to the picture show. That's when they started playing pranks on the boys, switching partners, each pretending to be the other sister. The boys tried to bribe Katie to tell them which girl was which, but Katie wouldn't. Finally, Chuck discovered a way to tell them apart. Alice's earlobes sloped to her head and Jane's didn't.

When Mr. Cummings stole a chicken, Mama had a good idea for stopping his thievery. He came to the fence to talk and Mama told him about the missing hen. "Well," she said, " I guess that poor old chicken wandered off somewhere and died. It was real sick with the sore head."

Mr. Cummings turned pale. "The hen was sick?"

"Sick unto death with the sore head."

Money was too scarce to buy a garbage can. An oil drum served the purpose but when it was full, paper bags were used to hold the garbage. They were left on the back porch until Tuesday when the trucks came by.

Unfortunately, Brother brought his uniforms home in paper bags and this led to the fatal mistake. Katie set the uniforms on the street thinking they were bags of trash. Worse than that, she was sitting on the landing looking out the window when colored boys came looking in the cans lined along the street. When they peeked inside the bags, they carried them away. This puzzled Katie, but she didn't think about it again until they were searching the house for Brother's clothes. Mama even went out to the garbage can to see if they were thrown away by mistake, but the can was empty.

Katie never told anybody what happened. She was too ashamed. She tried to give Brother some of her flower money to buy more uniforms, but he wouldn't take it.

Katie felt terrible. The next morning she was stirring the oatmeal with the little spoon, wondering if anyone could ever again think she was "sweet as pie." She heard Brother coming home from work, as he bounced onto the porch and flung open the door. He was so excited he stuttered when he tried to talk. "Mama, wait'll you hear what I have to tell you! A new man came to work at the bakery last night. His name is Earl and he moved here from Aiken, South Carolina. In Aiken he was living in a boarding house and he met a man who told him that he has a son working at this bakery in Charlotte. The man told Earl that his son was twenty years old and that he worked in the mixing department at night! That can only be me, Mama; the other men are all older than I am."

Mama was wide-eyed. "You mean, that was Malcolm?"

"It's bound to be. And, Mama, I've only been in the mixing department three months. Dad must have been in Charlotte recently." He ran his fingers through his hair. "Of course, he could have gotten his information from Uncle Tom."

"How would Tom know you're in the mixing department?"

"Aunt Ethel writes to Nora."

"Did this Earl know the man's name or describe him?"

"No. He said this happened several weeks ago. He didn't know his name and couldn't remember what he looked like. Said the man was just passing through."

"Son, I think we should do something."

"What? Aiken might just as well be on the other side of the moon."

"You could borrow the Studebaker."

"Spend money for gas—take off from work on a wild goose chase? If that was Dad there wouldn't be a trace of him left."

"But, Son—"

"If you want to go after him, you can, but in my opinion if he wants to come home he knows where he can find us."

That ended the matter, but in the days that followed, Mama kept it on her mind. She would come home from work too tired to read the paper, and sit on the porch, staring straight ahead. She didn't talk much and she never sang any more, but, after a while she got over it.

It seemed to Katie that Mama realized how sad she was making them and that was why she began to do something about it. On Saturday afternoons, if there were no peaches to peel or beans to can, Katie would bring Timothy uptown, and Mama would meet them at the square. They would drink a cherry smash in the drugstore, visit Jane's ribbon counter, and then go to a cowboy picture show.

Katie was afraid to go uptown. The rushing traffic, the noise, the people were frightening. Once on the square, she backed Timothy against the wall of the drugstore and held his hand tightly. Keeping her eyes open lest some stranger try to talk to them, she prayed Mama's bus would be the first one up the hill, but it wasn't. Many buses came up the hill, and Mama was on none of them.

A man walked over and stood beside Timothy. Katie was afraid to look up.

"Well, hello, Katie," the man said, and Katie looked up to see Mr. Kerr looking down at her. "Fancy seeing you here."

"We're waiting for our mother."

"Oh?"

"She should be on the next bus."

But she wasn't.

"Is your mother working?"

Katie nodded. Mr. Kerr had a nice smile.

"May I ask where she is working?"

Katie didn't know if she should tell him or not. He was a very nice man. "Rogers's Tent and Awning Company."

"That's near the courthouse, isn't it?"

"I don't know."

He tucked his newspaper under his arm. "It's a warm day."

Katie didn't answer. *Maybe Mama had to work late,* Katie was thinking. Katie let go Timothy's hand long enough to wipe her palms on her handkerchief.

Mr. Kerr looked at his watch. "We've been waiting half an hour. Would you like me to drive you home?"

"No, thank you," she answered quickly. Another bus was coming up the hill. If Mama wasn't on that one, Katie was going to the dime store and tell Jane. But Mama was on the bus. She stepped onto the sidewalk weighed down with a purse and shopping bag. Her face brightened when she saw them.

Mr. Kerr hung back until the greetings were over, then he spoke. "Mrs. MacLeod—Zachary Kerr, remember me?"

Mama looked as if she did not recognize him; then she spoke. "Mr. Kerr, how do you do?" She turned her attention to Timothy. "Have you picked out the picture you want to see?"

"Yes'm."

Mama was ignoring Mr. Kerr. He cleared his throat and smiled. "Such a warm day, Mrs. MacLeod. Would you join me for a lemonade?"

Mama straightened up, her cheeks flushed. "Thank you, Mr. Kerr. No, we have shopping to do."

"Perhaps another time?"

"Oh, I think not, Mr. Kerr. Thank you just the same."

Mama took Timothy by the hand, and they stepped to the curb and waited for the light to change. Katie glanced back at Mr. Kerr who was watching Mama, a beautiful smile on his face.

While they visited Jane at the ribbon counter, she pretended to be straightening stock. Mama bought some grosgrain so the manager would not think she was only talking.

"Take Katie and Timothy by the toy counter," Jane suggested. "A couple of Filipinos are demonstrating yo-yo twirling. And, if you can wait a few minutes, the piano player will be back playing all the new sheet music."

They always went by the toy counter and let Timothy circle it until he decided on the little car he wanted. Katie bought a yo-yo out of her own money, and Mama bought one for Archer.

At the lunch counter they drank lemonade. Then it was time to go to the picture show.

The excitement of sitting in the dark theater, watching the lion growl and hearing the wonderful music, was indescribable. Katie's eyes were glued to the screen, taking in all the western scenery, the fast horses, and herds of cattle.

The story was about pioneers going across the country, fending off Indians and starvation. When they came to the part where men and women alike had to get out of the covered wagons, put their shoulders to the wheels and push the wagons, the music was slow and moving. The pioneers were singing, "Goin' Home." "That's the New World Symphony," Mama whispered. "A Bohemian wrote it."

Coming out of the movie, Katie was dazzled by the sun. The music was playing in her head. "Mama, would you like to be one of those pioneers?"

"Yes, Katie, I really would."

"I would, too."

There were so many people waiting for the bus that they blocked the sidewalk. Mama picked up Timothy together with her purse and shopping bag and told Katie to hang on, the bus was coming. But when the crowd surged forward, Katie couldn't hang on and they were separated. Katie's face was jammed against some woman's backside, and she was being pressed in on all sides. She could hardly breathe.

In the jostling, someone laid a hand on Katie's shoulder, touched her briefly, then touched her again. Someone was reaching for her! Katie twisted to see who it was but could see only the hand. It was a man's hand with a red ring and blond hairs showing in the sun. It was Daddy's hand! Daddy's hand! The crowd was lurching—then the hand was gone—Katie was being carried away bodily. "Mama!" she screamed, but Mama was already on the bus. Katie screamed as loud as she could! A passenger grabbed her, got her onto the first step of the bus, and pushed her inside.

"Mama! Mama! Mama!" she screamed, thrashing against the bodies that blocked her way.

"Let this child through," someone shouted, "she's hysterical!"

Katie clawed and kicked through the wedged-in people and packages.

"Katie, I'm over here!" Mama called.

Katie caught sight of her and lunged forward. Mama caught her and held her tightly. "Katie, Katie," she soothed rubbing her back, patting her. "It's all right— it's all right." She buried her face in Katie's hair, making soft sounds in her ear. Katie was trembling all over. "What is it, Katie?"

"Daddy! Mama, it was Daddy! He touched me."

Mama reached for the bell cord. "Tell the driver to let me off now!" Mama told a passenger and the word was relayed to the front. Mama and Katie moved toward the back door. As soon as it opened they stumbled down the steps to the street.

"We must hurry." Mama picked up Timothy. "You take the shopping bag and run!"

It had happened in the next block. Before they came

close they could see the sidewalk was deserted. They hurried across the street against the light and started looking. They looked in doorways, through windows, up an alley. Katie could see Mama's pulse beating in her neck. "Ah!" she said, spying a hotel. "Come, Katie." Mama marched in through the revolving door, across the lobby to the desk. "Is Mr. Malcolm MacLeod registered here?" she asked the clerk. He ran his finger down a page of names.

"No, ma'am. No MacLeod registered here. Try the Mecklenburg."

"May I use your telephone?" Mama called several hotels. It was no use.

When they were back on the street, looking up and down, a few people passed, but they were strangers. "Are you *sure*, Katie?"

Katie nodded.

"You *saw* him?"

"No, ma'am. I saw his hand."

"His *hand*?"

"The crowd had me all jammed in and this hand reached out and touched my shoulder right here. I couldn't turn around. Then it touched me again and I saw his hand—a man's hand—it was Daddy's hand. He had a ruby ring and the little yellow hairs stood up on his knuckles."

"You mean you didn't see his face?"

"No, ma'am. But I know it was him. I remember, Mama, I remember what his hands look like."

Mama's face was ashen. Timothy clung to her skirt as they waited a little longer looking at the passersby. None of them was Daddy.

When they told Brother what happened, at first he didn't think much of it. "Son, Katie was hysterical and that's not like her. What's more, she has a vivid memory. If she says she saw her father's hand, I'm inclined to believe her."

Then Brother decided to go over and ask Uncle

Helmut to drive him around town to look for Daddy. The rest of them sat in the house with the doors locked until it was time for Jane to get off the bus. Then Alice and Archer went to the bus stop to wait for her so she wouldn't have to walk around the ice plant in the dark. Once Jane was safe inside, they sat quietly, hugging their knees, listening and thinking.

"It's been a year and a half since Daddy left," Jane said. "If he's ever going to come back home, it's high time."

When Brother and Uncle Helmut finally returned, they told of all the places they had searched and all the questions they had asked. Uncle Helmut left, and Brother asked Katie to tell her story one more time. He ran his hand through his hair, shaking his head in despair. At last, Mama said they should go to bed. Daylight was showing over the spring lot.

TWENTY-TWO
Sadie Allen,
Resurrected

Perhaps it was the cowboy movies; perhaps it was the disappointment that Daddy had been so near yet did not come home. Katie began to lie. Day after day she thought of nothing but Bull Creek, the spring, the bluebonnets, the moon over Cat Mountain, and especially the armadillo. Then she began to weave tall tales of adventure and told them for the truth to children in Aunt Ethel's neighborhood. On those hot August days they congregated in Buddy Wilder's tree house and sat by the hour listening to the wild stories, never challenging the truth of what she said. Escapades on horseback—riding trails through the Texas hills, guns blazing—were never questioned. Wanting to believe made it easy to believe. For whatever reason, once she started, Katie could not stop lying.

Then Archer heard about it and came home and told Mama. "Katie's been telling lies, Mama—whoppers!" Then he laughed. "And Buddy Wilder and all those kids believed every one of them."

"Not lies, Archer. Stories," Mama said. "What kind of stories?"

"Lies about Texas. She told them that she and I had our own guns and holsters!"

Katie put her hands over her ears, humiliated.

"She told them we rounded up a gang of bandits in Johnson Hollow—!" Archer was laughing so hard he couldn't tell it. He thought it was so funny he was rolling on the floor.

Katie ran upstairs two at a time to get away from him. She smothered her head in a pillow to drown out the torment, but he wouldn't let her alone—he followed her upstairs. "Katie, did you really tell them Daddy was a U.S Marshal?"

Katie kicked the door, slamming it in his face. He ran back downstairs to tell Mama more.

Mama didn't pay much attention to what Archer said. Later, all she said was, "Katie, I've told you to stay away from those bad children and from that tree house." No more was said about the stories except when Archer wanted to get Katie upset. Archer made her feel like she was crazy. The shame of the lies was so great she wished Mama had punished her.

The summer heat was oppressive and Mama would come home too tired to talk. Alice would have the house cleaned and supper on the table. Nearly every day Mama was irritated. Finally it came out. "I wish Mr. Kerr would leave me alone."

"Oh?" Alice said. "What's he been doing?"

"Sometimes in the afternoon, he's waiting for me. Wants to drive me home."

"Why don't you let him?" Archer asked, "It would save you seven cents car fare."

Jane answered him, "You don't understand. Eat your supper."

He did understand, too. He was going on fourteen and beginning to notice girls.

After supper, Mama read the paper and did the crossword puzzle. Then they sat on the porch a while. Shielded from view by a kudzu vine trained to grow on strings across the front, they talked about things in general. When a car came down the street and slowed, they craned their necks to see who it was; not that they were curious, but they thought Daddy might drive by, keeping a watch on where they lived.

There were many suspicious automobiles. The ones that slowed, then speeded up when they were past the house, were always suspect.

They did not speak of Daddy on the porch for fear the Cummings would hear, but when mosquitoes drove them inside they talked about that morning he left home. They went over the details again and again, dredging their minds for some simple fact overlooked. When they disagreed about some detail, there were enough of them who remembered to determine the truth. Katie could not remember everything the other children could, but only Katie knew about Daddy calling Mama "Witch," and never in a million years would she tell them about that. As much as Katie loved him, she could never forgive him for that.

Katie knew something Mama would never be able to forget. It was something Mama came back to time and again. None of the others paid attention to it for it was such a trivial thing. Once you heard it, it became an echo. "Malcolm once told me I didn't know how to put on my face powder." Considering all that had happened, what he said didn't seem important, but it was important if you realized how much it hurt Mama.

Katie was glad when the conversation shifted to the funny things that had happened on Bull Creek—the polecat hunt and the bottle torch that exploded; the stump at the treasure site which scared the daylights out of them; the fish fry when big, fat Rosabelle Ziegler was showing off on the stallion and went sailing over the horse's head into the creek; the brush arbor meeting when the preacher ran through the bushes besieged by a hail of flying rock.

Everywhere they went they looked for Daddy, remembering a carbuncle scar Mama said was on his neck, remembering the way he pulled his ear, remembering the soft sound of his voice. And they prayed.

Somewhere along the way, a subtle change in viewpoint took place. Without realizing it, they no longer spoke of "when Daddy comes home," they began to say, "when we find him."

For Katie, using the place setting Daddy had given her became a painful reminder of him. She asked Mama to put the silverware in the cedar chest in the box with Daddy's watch.

Sunday night Katie sat on the stair landing watching the people rush in droves toward the Chapel. Clutching their Bibles, they walked fast like the five thousand must have moved when they were after the five loaves and two fishes. "Mama, may I go to the Chapel?" Katie asked.

"If the girls will go with you."

That they would go didn't seem likely; their boyfriends were visiting. Besides, the twins went to the Chapel only to see the Nelsons' son, Eric.

As it turned out, the boys thought it was a good idea to go to the Chapel, so Katie tagged along. The excitement began when they started walking down the street. The Chapel people were poor and workworn, but they looked like good people and they were enthusiastic. Inside the auditorium, the metal seats were filling up fast. Mrs. Nelson was already at the grand piano, her evangelistic music competing with the back-slapping, chatting people milling about. They greeted each other with "Brother this" and "Sister that" which even Katie admitted was tacky.

Mrs. Cummings had come early and Lionel was with her, sitting close to the stage. There was no telling how many times she had brought Lionel to the altar for healing, and he was no better. That was the reason Mr. Cummings gave for not going to church—God didn't answer his wife's prayers for Lionel.

When they first sat down there were empty seats around them, but soon the place was packed, and who should sit down beside Katie but Miss Sadie Allen. Her massive frame filled the chair and spilled onto Katie's. Being that near the hateful woman was uncomfortable.

The service began with rousing revival songs praising the Lamb and the Holy Ghost. Then a girl sat down at the piano, playing and singing with gusto, "On the Jericho Road." The words made no sense but the beat was exciting.

On the Jericho Road
There's room for just two;
No more and no less,
Just Jesus and you.

Each burden He'll bear,
Each sorrow He'll share.
There's never a care,
For Jesus is there!

On the last stanza, a phalanx of ushers marched down the center aisle to the front. Tin plates for receiving the offering were distributed among them and they stood with bowed heads before the gladioli, waiting for the blessing.

First, however, Dr. Nelson had to say a few words. Good-naturedly, he delighted the congregation with a funny story, told them how much a generous offering was needed, then prayed. As the plates moved up and down the aisles, someone played the piano, and now and then Dr. Nelson brought forth sounds on his trombone.

After the collection, there was more music with handsome Eric directing the choir and singing a solo himself. Dr. Nelson's sermon began jovially but it ended dead serious. It was all about Jesus loving sinners and you could feel the lighthearted crowd simmering down, getting serious, being moved.

At the close, the choir was singing one stanza after another of "Just As I Am" and every head was bowed or was supposed to be. Dr. Nelson spoke in hushed tones above the low moaning of praying people. He was asking people to come forward and they were coming. Some woman shouted, "Hallelujah! Praise God!" and that made Katie nervous.

Katie peeked through her fingers and saw Mrs. Cummings on her knees sobbing, Lionel beside her giggling. Katie felt a lump in her throat.

Sadie Allen scraped her feet on the floor and Katie looked her way. Sadie's big body was writhing as she gripped both sides of the chair with all her strength. For a fleeting moment, Katie thought she was sick but Sadie's face was contorted with absolute anguish of soul.

Above the hubub, in a booming voice, the preacher shouted, "Come, Sadie! Come to Jesus!" Katie looked and the preacher was weeping. "Come, Sadie, just as you are! Jesus loves you—just as you are!" he thundered. "Jesus died for you!"

And Sadie got up, weaving back and forth, and with a stifled cry, she stumbled toward the altar and fell down. She was on her knees, leaning all the way over, her head against the floor, her body heaving with one convulsive sob after another.

A rip beneath the placket of her skirt began to lengthen. With every violent jerk, the seam gaped a bit more exposing fat flesh. The preacher's wife, elegant in her long white gown, moved toward Sadie Allen. When she reached her, she put her arms around the big woman and hid the rip from view.

Sadie straightened up to rock back and forth on her heels. She was calmer and her groaning lessened.

The service drew to a close. Mrs. Nelson helped Sadie to her feet, turning her around to face the congregation. And what a face it was! Tear-streaked and flushed, there was a glow in her face like a light turned on!

"Sadie," Mrs. Nelson asked so all could hear, "what happened to you tonight?"

In a voice so soft few could hear, she answered, "Jesus saved my soul."

A burst of "Hallelujah!" "Glory to God!" "Thank you, Jesus!" sounded all over the auditorium.

Alice and Jane didn't like that, and the boys said, "Let's go." They quickly slipped out of the chapel into the night.

When they reached home, they had a lot to tell, and Mama listened with some amusement. She did not approve of commotion in church, but she did admit, "Dr. Nelson has cleaned up this end of town. If it weren't for the Chapel, Mayesville people would still be drinking and wasting their lives."

"Mama, what do you think happened to Sadie Allen?" Jane asked.

"Well, I suppose she repented of her sins, but I wasn't there. Besides, the Scripture says, 'By their fruits ye shall know them.' There's no other way to evaluate any spiritual experience."

The conversion of Sadie Allen did not go unnoticed in Mayesville. Some thought she should shout it all over town like the chief of sinners. Others thought she should change overnight and be like Dorcas, "full of good works." She was neither.

Mr. West told Mama, "They tell me all the meanness drained out of her." He shook his head dubiously.

One or another of the MacLeods saw Sadie at different times and places. She was the same Sadie Allen in the same size clothes, but she was a different Sadie. You could see it in her face—the burden was lifted. She was quiet. "If anything," Brother said, "she's like the Mary who sat at Jesus' feet—just listening and learning."

In some ways, Sadie was so different some people began going to the Chapel to see what was going on. Even Brother attended a few services. He and Eric became friends but the Chapel was not for him.

Sadie's impression on the community sparked in Katie the ambition to be noticed. There would come a day, after she wrote a famous book, that people would inquire about who she was and want to know all about her life. It would be important to leave behind a record of noble sentiments, something to explain her character. Things such as G. K. Chesterton used when he wrote about Charles Dickens. Katie spent one whole evening searching for a motto that she could use for a lifetime. The Bible seemed the logical source and she finally selected Proverbs 4:23. Carefully, she lettered the verse on a card and put it on the mirror in her room at Aunt Ethel's. "Keep thy heart with all diligence; for out of it are the issues of life," it read. Katie did not quite understand "issues of life," but no one would know that.

Katie felt that she was growing up now that she was going to Consolidated School. The school included grades seven through twelve, and although Katie was only eleven years old and small for her age, much had happened that year to make her feel older. For one thing, Timothy had started to school. The worst event was Uncle Helmut's death. He died suddenly, without warning, while watering the flowers.

Uncle Helmut's casket was put in the living room and people came for two days to view the body. Before, death had never seemed to Katie to be real, but when she touched Uncle Helmut's forehead and he felt cold like stone, there was never to be an escape from the reality again.

Death posed another question that she had never taken time to consider. Timothy had thought about it when he was six years old. He had asked Mama, "Where did I come from?" Mama smiled and answered, "The Salvation Army."

After Uncle Helmut's death, Katie had to spend the nights with Aunt Ethel, so she decided to ask Aunt Ethel what she wanted to know. "Aunt Ethel," she began, "where do babies come from?"

Aunt Ethel was so shocked she couldn't answer right away. At least she wasn't going to say, "From God," and leave it at that.

"Well, Katie. . . ." Aunt Ethel wouldn't look at her. "Well, let's see—I tell you what—er, no, not that." Then, in desperation, "Katie, you just read the Song of Solomon."

So, she did. There were parts that embarrassed Katie. Her own breasts were small and even if they were full grown, why would she want someone to "lie all night" between them?

Katie read all eight chapters twice and the embarrassing parts several times. She felt guilty, but how could anything in the Bible be wrong? Then she had an idea— she would get Mama to explain the Song of Solomon.

With the Bible in her hand, Katie lay on the floor beside the rocker. Mama was ripping up a dress, picking out the threads. "Mama, what does 'feed among the lilies' mean?"

"Oh," Mama said, happily surprised, "the Song of Solomon." She began quoting verses:

My beloved spake and said unto me,
Rise up, my love, my fair one, and come away.
For, lo, the winter is past,
The rain is over and gone;
The flowers appear on the earth;
The time of the singing of birds is come,
And the voice of the turtle is heard in our land;
The fig tree putteth forth her green figs,
And the vines with the tender grape give a good smell.
Arise, my love, my fair one, and come away."

Katie smiled up at her, encouraged that she knew the book so well. "Well?" she asked.

"Oh—'he feedeth among the lilies.' That refers to the bride's husband who was a shepherd. The lovers were separated and he was feeding his sheep where the lilies bloomed. Would you like to hear the whole story?"

"Yes."

"Well, the shepherd in the poem loves a young girl who works in a vineyard. Because she is sunburned, her brothers do not think much of her and she works very hard. When she marries the shepherd, their first bed is among the cedars in some glen or lovely secluded place—"

Archer came bursting in the door. "Mama! I got a job! I got a job in the grocery store!" Excited, he hopped up and touched the ceiling.

Archer was fourteen, tall, and good-looking, big enough for the long white apron he would wear.

"I'll be waiting on customers and everything— putting up stock. I'm going to learn the whole grocery business!"

Katie did not bring up the Song of Solomon again. If Aunt Ethel thought it told where babies came from, then it was plain as day that babies came from people loving each other. Katie figured that it was people who brought babies into the world, and that Mama thought it was beautiful. That was good enough for Katie. She wouldn't worry about it anymore.

Katie wondered why they did not teach important things in school like where you came from and where you were going. School was drudgery, except for the walk across the meadow every morning. Consolidated School was back in the woods near the cemetery, and getting to run the path beside the creek was slightly like running the trail alongside Bull Creek.

Another bright spot concerning school was Miss Packer, the English teacher. She liked Katie and seemed to understand how she just couldn't face school some days. Especially on gym days. Most girls hated the blouses and bloomers—what Katie hated was changing clothes in front of everybody. The other girls were big bosomed and proud of their shapes while Katie was still growing. On gym days, Katie made excuses to see the nurse and faked an illness as often as she dared.

Christmas holidays seemed so long in coming. Mama had laid away coats for the twins and there was no money to spare for Saturday movies. Archer was using every spare minute to repair a secondhand tricycle for Timothy's Christmas present, so he had no time for Katie.

But, when Christmas morning came, it was worth it. Alice and Jane wept when they saw the coats. "Oh, Mama!" Alice cried, holding up a coat, "Swagger coats— oh, they're beautiful!"

Mama beamed. "Try them on. See if they fit."

Jane blew her nose. Feeling the soft fur trim, she could hardly talk, "Mama, you shouldn't have—" Both girls put their arms around Mama's neck and kissed her.

When Archer brought in the tricycle, Timothy's eyes sparkled. Laying his hand on the handlebar, he asked, "Mama, is it really mine?"

After the holidays, even school seemed better. Miss Packer assigned Katie to write the gossip column for the school newspaper. "Miss Packer, what can I do to become a real writer?"

"Observe, Katie, observe."

Miss Packer was never wrong, so Katie began observing—listening to people talk, watching their mannerisms, the way they moved—and soon, Katie's column was the most popular feature in the paper.

Yet Katie was not popular. In her heart she was sure everybody knew more and had more than she. There was only one person she felt really comfortable with— Peggy Shuler. Peggy was in Katie's homeroom, and she was a lot of things Katie wasn't. She was small with dark, naturally curly hair and the boys liked her. What's more, she was very neat, did her homework, and made all A's. But there was a quality about Peggy that was hard to describe—soft-spoken and kind, Peggy loved Katie. She was the kind of person who wouldn't tell secrets or look down on another person.

Katie and Peggy laughed a lot together because Katie could make anyone laugh. And, one warm spring afternoon, Katie persuaded Peggy to skip school and pick pansies at Aunt Ethel's.

Even though they were not missed at school and were never reprimanded. Katie wondered if Peggy felt guilty. Peggy loved going to church—twice on Sundays and to prayer meeting Wednesday nights. Her church was behind Consolidated, a distance away. It couldn't be another Chapel because it was a Presbyterian Church; yet Peggy had the same light in her face people at the Chapel had.

When Easter was approaching, Katie was wishing Peggy would invite her to church. She was helping Aunt Ethel make floral designs for the cemeteries, wiring galax leaves to sticks. Out of the clear blue sky, Aunt Ethel asked, "Katie, are you saved?"

Katie didn't look up. Being "saved" was tacky. It was for people like Sadie Allen. Aunt Ethel was waiting for an answer. "Aunt Ethel," Katie said, "if you do the best that you can, that is all that God can ask."

But the words boomeranged. Right away Katie knew that she had not always done the best that she could.

That started it—the troubling. Lying in bed, Katie would think about the lies she had told, the sneaky sins of going to the tree house knowing she was disobeying or staying home from school pretending to be sick.

Aunt Ethel was to be in the Easter play at the Chapel and the MacLeods went to view her performance. Eric Nelson was the Christ and when they stretched his half naked body on the cross, they nailed real nails and one nail was hit wrong and went zinging over the heads of the people. It had a shocking effect. Suddenly, Jesus on the cross was no longer a Sunday school picture card; he was a real man with real nails in his hands and feet. How awful! Katie was so disturbed she didn't notice

Aunt Ethel dressed in a costume with a lot of other people at the foot of the cross. Ringing in her ears was what they were shouting, "If you are the Son of God, come down from the cross and we will believe in you!" Katie thought in her heart, *Yes, why didn't he come down? Then everyone would have believed in him.*

At Easter all the twelve-year-olds in the Sunday school on Main Street were joining the church. Katie decided she would join, too.

"Well, Katie," Mama said, "if you're going to join the church, you should go over and have a talk with the minister. Tell him who you are, and ask Mr. Burton any questions you have."

Going to see Mr. Burton was not easy, but Katie went to his study to talk with him. He was a fat man with thick glasses and he sat smoking his pipe while they talked. There was only one question Katie wanted to ask. "Mr Burton, what does it mean to 'be saved'?"

Mr. Burton took a long draw on the pipe and leaned back in the swivel chair. He talked for a long time but Katie didn't understand what he was saying. He laced his fingers across the top of his head and droned on and on. When he was finished, Katie thanked him and got up to leave. "Come early, Sunday," he told her. "The children joining the church will meet here in the study and go through that door to the sanctuary." He was pointing with his pipe so she would know the right door.

Katie joined the church, but it didn't make her feel any better inside.

Only Miss Packer seemed able to cheer Katie. There was something wonderful about being special to Miss Packer. After Katie made a speech in history class, Miss Packer told her she did so well she wanted her to recite a poem in the next assembly.

Katie memorized the poem right away and practiced it over and over. But on the day of the program she lost her nerve. Just before the curtain was raised, Katie remembered a hole in the heel of her sock. Panic-stricken for fear someone would see the hole, her mind went blank.

Miss Packer never said a word.

That afternoon, Katie found Mama picking the early garden lettuce.

"Don't think about it, Katie, No use crying over spilled milk," Mama said. "You should have darned the sock before you went to school."

"I don't like to darn socks."

"Neither do I but you have to take the bull by the horns and do those things you don't like. You can't procrastinate. Now don't look back, Katie—never look back—look forward."

Mama kept a pace that left no time for looking back—even the present was a blur to her. Before daylight she was up and at the awning shop. When she came home, there was cooking and cleaning. "Never pay anyone to do something you can do for yourself," she said. There was little else for her but work, work, work. Occasionally, Archer or Brother could persuade her to go to a movie if it was a Jeannette MacDonald picture.

For Mama to stay home from work, she would have to be dying. But dying she thought she was when green bile poured from her mouth and perspiration drenched her clothing. Brother begged her to let him call a doctor but she wouldn't. The best they could do was sit by her bedside until the crisis passed. The illness forced her to stay home one day, but the next day she went back to work.

That evening when she came home from the shop, Mama had something to tell them. As soon as Brother got up for supper, she called the twins. "Stop what you're doing, girls, and come to the living room."

Katie and Timothy were sitting on the stair landing. Mama began carefully. "Children, when I went into work this morning, Mr. Rogers told me that Malcolm came into the shop yesterday."

"Daddy?" the twins chorused.

"Yes. You know Mr. Rogers knew Malcolm in Greenwood. When this man came in and asked for me, Mr. Rogers recognized him."

"What did he say, Mama? What did Daddy say?" Jane urged.

"Well, according to Mr. Rogers, he came in about two o'clock in the afternoon. He asked where I was and why I wasn't at work. Mr. Rogers told him I was sick and he left."

"Is that all?" Brother asked. "He didn't ask where we live or anything?"

Mama shook her head.

"Did Rogers say whether or not Dad was drinking?"

"I wish you had not asked me that," Mama said and said nothing more.

On Saturday of the same week, Katie and Timothy met Mama on the square and Mr. Kerr came up. Mama was annoyed that he was there.

"Oh, by the way," he said, "I saw your husband at the train station Thursday."

Mama's face changed. "Pardon me?"

"I said I saw Mr. MacLeod at the depot Thursday. Was he coming or going?" Mr. Kerr had a twinkle in his eye.

"Which track was he on?"

"Hm'm," he pondered. "Southbound."

"Well, Mr. Kerr," Mama said, "coming or going is Mr. MacLeod's business. If you will please excuse me." She took Timothy by the hand and they left Mr. Kerr standing on the corner.

They hurried to the five and dime to Jane's counter. Mama beckoned nervously and Jane slipped from behind the counter so Mama could whisper.

"Oh, Mama! What do you think?"

"I don't know what to think. We'll talk about it when you get home."

"Is that all he said?"

"That's all."

"Why didn't you ask him more questions?"

"That would have told Mr. Kerr more than it would have told me. I'm about fed up with that man."

Mama sat through the movie but her mind was not on it. As soon as the cartoon was over, they rushed home. Mama changed clothes and went into the yard to work. With the swing blade she began attacking honeysuckle and brambles growing in the field. She worked with ferocious energy—hacking, pulling, uprooting relentlessly.

Katie tried to stop her. "Mama, you've been sick—please, don't work so hard!"

"I have to Katie. I have to."

"Mama, stop—look at the sunset."

Mama only glanced at the sky and went right on working.

There were no more reports of Daddy's being seen in town. In the next year, Katie began praying all the harder that he would come home because something was happening in the MacLeod family. It was well along before Katie realized it. That Christmas, the twins were eighteen, in their last year of high school. Alice was in love with Chuck Bundy. They were talking about getting married.

Jane was making plans to go to business college. Aunt Claire in Greenville had offered to send her if Jane would come and live with her.

Brother, at twenty-four, was getting serious with a girl in Christian Young People's Club, and he was changing in many ways.

Even Archer was going out every night with girls. At sixteen, he was ambitious and smart—there would be no holding him back once he took a notion to go higher than a grocery clerk.

Plainly, the family circle would not be intact for long—the MacLeod children would separate, each going his own way, leaving Mama, Katie, and Timothy at home. Mama kept trying to find a full-time job because the seasonal work at the awning company wouldn't bring in enough money to live on when they were gone.

Katie mustered enough courage to ask Mr. Avery for a job in the hardware store next to the bakery. Mr. Avery ran an electrical business and the store was a sideline. "Thirteen?" he mused.

"Going on fourteen," she added. "I'm in the ninth grade."

She got the job temporarily. Katie worked hard, praying Mr. Avery would keep her on after Christmas. He did, and for three dollars a week she worked afternoons and Saturdays.

A small furniture factory was opening on the other side of town and Mama applied. Some gentleman she had known years before owned the business; he hired her right away. She was to be a jack-of-all trades—the cutter, seamstress, decorator, and sometimes even the bookkeeper.

In the spring, Aunt Claire came for a visit and brought Granddaddy MacLeod with her. He looked the same—a wiry little man, jaunty, dressed to the hilt. He had left Texas and was living in a residential hotel in Greenville, enjoying the attention of widow ladies. At seventy-five he was as keen as ever.

No, he didn't know Malcolm's whereabouts, he said. "None of the MacLeod's have heard anything about him, Becky. Steve and Benjamin are still in Tyler and keep on the lookout but so far, nothing. The boys are doing well—they'll make their million before they're forty."

Aunt Claire said nothing about Daddy. She sat in the platform rocker and seemed disturbed by the conversation. There was something nice about her—she didn't make Katie feel uncomfortable. Aunt Claire taught school, was still single, and could laugh easily. She told Jane about the college and what the arrangements would be.

When they were ready to leave, Granddaddy fished in his pocket and found a half dollar which he pressed in Katie's hand. "There you are, girlie," he said and patted her head.

After the twins' graduation, Alice and Chuck set their date to be married. Mama liked Chuck and gave her blessing to the marriage but, as the wedding date drew closer, she became fretful. Chuck came for Sunday dinner and after he left, she found fault. "Alice, you're not going to marry a man who points with his fork, are you?"

Everybody laughed except Alice—she fled upstairs in tears. Mama followed her and after they talked a while, they made up. Then Mama tried to persuade Alice to have a real wedding. "It doesn't have to cost a lot of money. You can have a simple ceremony in Mr. Burton's study."

"No, Mama. We don't have money for a trousseau much less money to pay a preacher."

"But it's just not done in our circles, Alice."

"Our circles, Mama? Maybe the MacLeods don't get married by a justice of the peace but—"

"Oh, Alice, you are a MacLeod. Your poor father wouldn't want this."

Alice kissed her. "Oh, Mama, lots of people nowadays get married this way. I don't mind."

Katie knew that she did mind—there was no denying that Alice wanted a church wedding in the worst way.

The night Alice and Chuck were going to be married was no different from any other night when she and Jane double-dated. The girls were dressed in their best and they were nervous. Alice kissed the boys and Katie, but when she kissed Mama she began to cry, and Mama had to say something funny or everybody in the room would have cried. "Take good care of her, Chuck," Mama said.

Later that night, when Jane came home, she was alone. As Katie crawled into the big bed beside Jane, she had the same feeling she had when Uncle Helmut died. For the first time in her life, she heard Jane sniffling in her pillow.

The next one to leave would be Brother. He was rapidly pulling away. He had always gone to the Presbyterian Church uptown, but now he was interested in the Christian Young People's Club that met at the Public Library. The teacher of the Bible class was pastor of the church Peggy Shuler attended. Brother was so involved in the Club he started going to the church were Mr. Powell preached.

Katie knew something unusual was taking place in Brother when he came home bringing a little motto to hang in the kitchen. He waited until Mama came home to hang it. He drove a tack in the wall, hung the motto, then stood back and read it, "The Lord will provide." Then he turned and kissed Mama. She smiled and patted his cheek.

The change in Brother was disconcerting and revived Katie's worry about her own spiritual misgivings. When Brother began to talk about such things as "justification," Katie asked him, "Brother, why are you so interested in the Bible?"

"Well, Katie, you remember how I always went to church? Remember how I used to invite boys from the bakery to go with me? Well, one day I was in the drugstore and I asked a fellow to go to church with me. Now this man played ball with me and knew how I cussed, so he turned on the stool and faced me with it. 'Why should I go to church with you?' he said. 'I don't see that it does you any good.'" Brother ran his fingers through his hair. "That hit me like a line drive in the stomach! I came straight home, went up to my room, and told the Lord I was a sinner and needed a Savior. He forgave me and accepted me as his child, and, Katie, I haven't cussed since."

"You mean you weren't a Christian before?"

"No, Katie, I wasn't; I only thought I was."

The conversation disturbed Katie.

306

A few weeks later, Brother invited the whole family to the Presbyterian church uptown to hear an evangelist. Katie sat between Jane and Alice with Archer beside Chuck. The elegant stone church was as wonderful as ever with its pipe organ and vaulted ceilings. The service was dignified, but the evangelist told interesting stories from his own life when he had been a drunkard—quite unlike Dr. Hyatt's sermons. When the invitation was given, first Chuck, then Archer rose and went forward. Katie couldn't believe her eyes! Not in a million years would she get up in front of all those people and say she was a sinner! That's exactly what they were doing—telling everybody they were sinners!

Katie wondered if Mama had ever done anything like that. "Yes," she said, "when I was eleven years old—in the Williamsburg Presbyterian Church. It didn't set well with my elegant aunts, but I knew what I was doing."

Katie didn't have the nerve to ask Alice or Jane. They were so perfect they had to be Christians.

In August, Jane left for Greenville and business college. "And, Mama," she said, "I'm going to find out everything I can from the MacLeods about Daddy. I'm sure they know where he is."

"If anyone can find him, you can, Jane."

When school started, there was no one to look after Timothy in the afternoons. Alice and Chuck were living in the country; Archer was working in the grocery store, Katie in the hardware, and Brother was sleeping days.

Katie would not be able to spend weeknights with Aunt Ethel because she needed to come home as soon as possible to look after Timothy. But one Saturday night she went to Aunt Ethel's.

"Dr. Nelson is coming tonight for a home Bible study. Won't you join us, Katie?"

"Have to study," Katie said, making an excuse. In the bedroom she spread her books on the library table, opened a notebook, and looked as if she were studying. The doorbell kept ringing until all the people had come.

Above all their voices, Katie could hear Dr. Nelson's big voice.

The troubling, which she had not thought about until Brother told her his experience, was weighing her down. Katie didn't know if she was a Christian or not. If a person must be saved, she wasn't sure she understood what that meant. Whatever Brother had must be right, but to get up in front of everybody and walk down an aisle the way Chuck and Archer had done was something she could never do. Katie thought about Peggy and wondered if she had ever walked down an aisle.

Dr. Nelson was teaching in the living room and there was a transom opening in the bedroom. Katie could hear everything he said. She did not listen, but she did hear his text repeated over and over: "The blood of Jesus Christ, God's Son, cleanseth us from all sin."

Katie was tired after the long day at the store and laid her head on her arm. The words drummed in her head. Katie tried to remember a time when she did not believe in Jesus but she couldn't. She thought about the time on Bull Creek when she was so sick and asked the Lord for strength to tell Mama to pray, and she remembered how she was healed.

On the other hand, if she were a Christian, why did her sins weigh so heavily now? Katie thought of the dream when Jesus invited her to come to him and she refused. Was that an invitation to be saved?

Wearily, Katie heard Dr. Nelson quoting the Bible again: "The blood of Jesus Christ, God's Son, cleanseth us from all sin." Finally, Katie spoke to God in her heart. "All right, Lord, if I've never been saved before, save me now."

Katie fell asleep at the table. When the Bible class was over, Aunt Ethel woke her up, and Katie climbed into bed.

Two weeks passed before Katie thought about her prayer. When she realized that she was no longer troubled about her sins, she knew she had been heard. "He saved me!" she said. It didn't occur to her to tell anyone, not even Peggy Shuler, but when Peggy invited her to church, Katie went.

One look and Katie knew Mr. Powell was a man of God. When he was preaching, there was no acquired Scotch accent, nor was there any Bible thumping or forceful actions. His stance suggested that he stood for something, and Katie was soon to find out what it was. His kind blue eyes looked from beneath shaggy blond brows, and when he spoke there was a lift to his chin that made you trust him. He spoke clearly and with conviction and what he stood for was the truth of God's Word.

The word Mr. Powell used over and over was "grace" and his only gesture was the sweep of his hand upward, as if he would lift up the Lord and the Word of God.

Katie knew she was where she belonged.

TWENTY-THREE
Archer
Seeks His
Fortune

When Brother joined Mr. Powell's church, Katie moved her membership there.

Brother was in love with Rebekah, a pretty, quiet girl who sang in the choir. Their marriage was only a matter of time, but Brother agonized over leaving Mama with all the responsibility. In prayer meetings he often mentioned an "unspoken request," but Katie knew it was about his getting married.

Finally, Brother wrote a letter to Mama and left it beside her thermos on the kitchen table. He told her their plans and how much he hated to leave her, how much he loved her and would always stand by her.

That evening when Mama came home, Brother, rumpled from sleep, stood waiting for her at the door, fighting back tears. When Mama came inside, she put down her things, reached up, and kissed him. "Son, you're doing the right thing."

Then Brother cried.

After Brother's marriage in October, the house seemed empty. Coming home after dark, Katie would first make sure Timothy was all right. Even if Timothy was too sick to go to school, neither Mama nor Katie could afford to stay home with him. Mama would bundle him up and leave his medicine where he could find it and ask Mrs. Cummings to look in on him.

After starting supper, Katie and Timothy would go upstairs and lie across the bed in the front room, watching for a bus on Main Street.

The spring lot across Thrift Street became an ominous hole after dark, and the ice plant cast black shadows from the street light. Katie and Timothy would listen to the motor of a bus straining to scale the hill and try to hear if it stopped at the top. To hear it stop was not enough to be sure Mama got off it; they had to wait and see who came around the ice house.

Katie could sense that Timothy had a nagging fear that some night the bus would not stop, that Mama would not come home. She could tell it by the way he put away his toys and did nothing but wait until he saw her coming. Katie had the same uneasiness, and in her mind she had planned what she would do if sometime Mama did not come home. First, she would take Timothy to Mrs. Cummings. Then she would go down to the corner where a lady had a phone and she would call Archer at the store.

As they concentrated on the vigil, Katie often prayed. Somehow prayer didn't seem to speed the buses, but it seemed right to let God know they were scared. At first glimpse of Mama coming around the corner, Katie and Archer would fling on their coats and run to meet her. That caused supper to burn sometimes, and, worse than that, there were times when the burners on the kerosene stove were turned up too high and the house filled with smoke. Poor Mama. Smoke meant dirty curtains, walls, everything.

Mama said people had to be patient with Katie—that she was careless or absentminded, or both.

Melvin Avery was a good and patient man. He let Katie do what she wanted to do with the hardware store. Fortunately, he had a sense of humor. Even when Katie made a window display of long johns hanging on a clothesline, and Mrs. Avery thought it indecent, Melvin Avery smiled and went about his office work.

Katie's enthusiasm knew no bounds. Everything she could learn from Archer about "massive display," "volume business," and salesmanship, she put to her own use in the hardware business.

There was much to learn about the merchandise because the store stocked everything from plow points to ladies' notions. Customers were few and far between, which gave Katie time to study the differences between stow, carriage, and machine bolts. When there was nothing else to do, Katie poured up bulk turpentine and alcohol in bottles and labeled them. Turpentine was mixed with paint, alcohol with shellac.

Katie didn't always label the bottles correctly, and a customer, an ordinarily soft-spoken gentleman, came in the store screaming, "I mixed this with my paint, and when I put it on the walls, it curdled! Do you hear? It curdled!" The man thrust his head forward wildly and beat his fist against the counter.

Mrs. Avery was always puttering around in the store trying to keep things spic and span. The shellac cans were on a top shelf, and for some reason Katie had left the cap loose on one of the cans. When Mrs. Avery moved it to dust, it tipped over and shellac poured on her head, her glasses, and the front of her dress. Mr. Avery had to take the afternoon off to drive his wife home and try to clean her up.

But what Katie cost Mr. Avery in carelessness, she made up for in sales.

"You're like Malcolm," Mama said. "He could sell snake oil to a surgeon."

One of the reasons sales shot up in garden tools, chicken wire, and seeds was that Katie learned all about gardening from Aunt Ethel and Mama. They told her what she needed to know about planting at the right time, the kind of fertilizers needed for different vegetables, and what to do about insects and compost.

Mr. Avery was pleased with Katie's work and, in time, Mrs. Avery was friendly again.

When business was slack, Katie scribbled stories or typed them on Mr. Avery's typewriter. After school, Roger Napier, the boy who worked in the drugstore next door, would come over to hear the latest installment in a saga. Roger wanted to be a newspaper reporter, so he was a good critic of Katie's writing. He also wanted her to marry him and proved his love with double-dip ice cream cones.

From Europe, news of Hitler's advances were filtering down to the high school students. Katie wrote a story about young people in Nazi Germany, and Miss Packer had it published in the city newspaper.

That was when Roger stopped bringing her ice cream and telling her how much he loved her. When Katie told Archer about it, he explained, "Didn't you say Roger wants to be a reporter? Well, don't you see—girls shouldn't try to out-do boys. Men have to win."

Money was in such short supply, Mama often divided the nickels and pennies between herself and Timothy for lunch money and car fare. She carried a sandwich and a thermos of coffee for herself, counted fourteen cents for car fare, and gave the rest to Timothy.

When it came to appearances, Mama sewed up runs in her stockings, but saw to it that the boys had good socks and polish for their shoes.

She understood the differences in her sons. "Archer is aggressive—Timothy is passive—Brother is a combination of them both. Their strengths are their weaknesses and, Katie, I pray to God they know that."

Archer was restless. He talked about how he had mastered the grocery business.

"At seventeen?" Mama raised her eyebrows. "Hardly."

"I have, Mama. I'm head of the produce department, I can cut meat. I make all the signs and the displays. I can order stuff, and I know how to sell. Mama, I know all there is to know about merchandising."

Katie believed him.

When Archer brought a friend, Rodney, for supper, no one thought anything about it; he often brought a friend for a meal. When he dressed to go out in his brown suit and hat, there was nothing unusual about him except his pockets. As he kissed Mama good-bye, she looked up from the crossword puzzle and smiled. "My, your pockets look like squirrel nests." They laughed. "Have a good time, boys."

That night, Archer didn't come home. Mama wakened Katie at midnight. "Archer isn't home yet. He never stays out this late."

Katie got up and they went downstairs. Mama rekindled the fire and put on more coal. She went into the kitchen for something and Katie heard her gasp. Katie flew to the kitchen. Mama was standing in the middle of the floor, her eyes pressed shut holding back tears. In her hand was a letter. Katie took it from her.

Dearest Mama,

I'm going to California to seek my fortune. Rodney is going with me. When we make a lot of money I'll be back and I'll buy you everything you ever needed or wanted. You won't ever have to work hard again. Please don't worry. I will be all right.

All my love,
Your Archer

Tears were sliding down Mama's cheeks. Great racking sobs shook her body. Katie didn't know what to do. She put her arms around her, but Mama was not to be comforted.

Mama made her way back into the living room and sat on the couch. "There's no earthly way to find him, Katie," she sobbed.

In respect for her grief, Katie said nothing.

"Oh, my poor child," Mama said, "he'll freeze to death in that thin suit." Mama walked to the door and looked outside, then to the landing to look down the street. "Oh, Lord," she prayed aloud, "send him home. Some how, some way, make him turn around and come home!"

A flood of tears followed, and until she spent herself there was nothing Katie could do.

All night long they waited in the living room, for the most part huddled on either side of the stove, trying to keep warm.

"Katie," Mama said, "Archer has worked like a grown man since he was twelve years old. Remember that little wagon he made with the wobbly wheels? He was too small a boy to pull those loads of groceries up hills but he was determined."

"And the lawnmower, Mama."

"Nothing but a piece of junk, but he kept it going. He wore the life out of it, and it wore the life out of him."

"But he bought you that ice box."

Mama nodded and blew her nose again. "Even on Bull Creek when he was a little fellow, if it hadn't been for Archer we would have gone hungry. How I worried about him with that gun. Katie, do you remember the time he had only one shell left and he went out and killed a jackrabbit?"

Of course she did. It was an experience they were fond of repeating. "It was a big rabbit."

"Oh, yes. He always got what he went after. And, Katie, he'll get what he's gone after now. He won't come home until he does." She was crying again.

"Mama," Katie said softly. "Do you remember that day we were standing on the boardwalk watching a motorboat come up the river?"

Mama nodded.

"You told me then that no matter how small I might feel, I would change history. Well, Mama, I'm wondering if one of the ways we change things is by prayer?" She waited. "We've asked God to bring Archer home. No matter how determined he is, can't God turn him around, like you asked him to, and bring him home?"

"Katie, I hope so. Sometimes I wonder if God will

override a person's stubborn will."

Katie put more coal on the fire and thought about what Mama had said. Perhaps what she said had a bearing on their prayers for Daddy. Maybe Daddy didn't want to come home.

When the sun came up over the spring lot, Katie moved to the front window to watch the pink sky behind the lace of bare branches. White frost stood above the clay ground, spewed up by the cold.

Mama went to the kitchen to put on the coffee. Katie followed. They moved woodenly, without words. Katie lit the burner and turned down the wick while Mama made the oatmeal. Katie opened the thermos and set out the lunch bag. Mama walked to the kitchen door, threw bread to the pigeons, stood watching them on the ridge of the roof, their feathers fluffed, cooing. Did they know he was gone?

Katie fed the chickens, and when she came back inside, Mama was leaning on the sink. "This is Malcom's forty-fifth birthday," she said sadly. "He will soon have been gone six years." She was looking out the kitchen window, her eyes full of hopelessness.

Katie spoke softly, "See where Archer carved his initials on the ash tree?"

"They carve their names on your heart, Katie, that's where they carve them and they never, ever go away."

Two days passed and Mama would not let Katie tell Brother or Alice that Archer was gone. On the third day, Archer came home. Mama was at work.

"We nearly froze," Rodney said. "We caught a ride in an open-bed truck, and once we were in it, we found out that Tennessee driver was never going to stop! Archer's lips turned blue!"

The boys were laughing and stuffing themselves with food at the same time.

"Once that truck stopped," Archer continued, "I knew what I was going to do. I crossed the road and started thumbing the other way."

Archer went back to school and back to the grocery store. In a few days he brought home an old LaSalle and began working on it in the front yard. Mama was so glad to have him home she didn't insist that he take it behind the house.

Jane came home for the weekend, and Archer met her at the depot in the car. The house was alive again with Alice and Chuck, Brother and Rebekah.

The first thing Katie wanted to know was whether Jane had learned anything from Aunt Claire about Daddy, but Brother beat her to the question. "Jane, have you found out anything?"

She shook her head. "Not a thing. . . . Well, I think a couple of suspicious things happened. You won't like this, Mama, but I have even gone through Aunt Claire's mail and read letters from the family hoping I would find a clue. Nothing. I've listened to telephone conversations and I've asked all kinds of questions but I haven't come up with anything concrete."

"You said you've seen a couple of suspicious things?" Brother asked.

"Well, one day Aunt Claire took me to visit Granddaddy. She told me not to pay any attention to anything he might say, that he was getting senile."

"Did he say anything?" Alice asked.

"He said Aunt Angela knows where Daddy is, but she lives in Europe now."

"If your grandfather is senile, he may be confused about his facts. Does *Claire* say Angela lives in Europe?"

"Aunt Claire said the last time she heard from her she was in Canada."

"Do you think Granddaddy is senile?" Brother asked.

"Probably. I wrote to Aunt Angela at the address in Canada but I haven't heard anything."

"What was the other suspicious thing?" Archer wanted to know.

"Well, I finally broke down and told Aunt Claire all

the things I have done to try to find a clue—how I read her letters and eavesdropped. I was pretty upset and Aunt Claire was understanding. But right after that, she put on her coat and went over to visit Uncle Tom. It made me think they knew something and Aunt Claire was wondering if they should tell me."

"What happened?"

"Nothing. When she came home she didn't mention the subject again."

Archer graduated in June and started business college. Alice's baby girl, Betty, was born just before Katie went to Camp Lookover with Peggy and other young people from church. The week in the mountains had a profound effect on Katie.

The camp was hidden in a little hollow in the Blue Ridge Mountains. The log lodge where the campers ate and slept overlooked Boone Fork Creek. Standing extended over the creek was an old mill where meetings were held downstairs and boy campers slept upstairs.

There were hikes and horseshoes, softball and swimming in the "Blue Hole," but nothing was more fun than sunning atop the huge boulders lying midstream in the creek. Peggy and one or two of her boyfriends were serious students of the Bible. After singing and laughing a while, something serious would be said and they would open a Bible and start discussing a passage. Katie loved it.

At Lookover there was time to be alone, and Katie found a place higher on the mountain where she could sit on a flat outcropping of stone among the mountain laurel and read or pray to her heart's content. Sun and shade dappled the ferns in the glade, and in the still retreat birds came close enough to touch. Katie's heart was warmed toward God.

She began to wonder what God wanted to do with her life. Financially, it was out of the question to consider college; yet, if others went to school on faith alone, Katie knew she could too. Of course, Mama needed her at home—that was the big thing. Mr. Powell said a Christian most often finds God's will in the path of duty. That troubled Katie. She really wanted to go to school; there was nothing she wanted more. If only she could know for sure what God's will was.

Mr. Powell recommended a school in New York City. That was one thing Katie was positively sure about— she would never live in a city! She wrote for a catalog from a school in Texas, a Christian college that trained missionaries.

When she came home from camp, there was a funeral wreath on the Cummings' door. Inside the house, she found Timothy lying on the couch, his leg bandaged and his face white as cotton. "What happened?"

"I cut my leg."

Mama came from the kitchen.

"Who died?" Katie asked.

"Lionel, Katie. Lionel is dead."

"Lionel? How? What happened?"

They sat down. Mama explained. "Timothy was in the backyard chopping a stick with the butcher knife and somehow cut his leg. Mrs. Cummings saw it— rushed outside—saw the blood spurting profusely and tried to stop it by wrapping a towel around his leg. Then she called a taxi and rushed him to the hospital. She had told Lionel to stay inside the house, but he didn't. He wandered down in the spring lot. When she came home, he was nowhere to be found. Some men formed a search party and they found his body in the old gold mine shaft."

"Oh, Mama! What happened? Did the shaft cave in on him?"

"No. Apparently a large timber fell and hit him on the head. They think he died instantly."

"When's the funeral?"

"They buried him yesterday."

Timothy spoke up. "The city is going to do something about the shaft now."

"Katie, I want you to go over and speak to the Cummingses," Mama said.

"Oh, Mama, I don't know what to say."

Katie tried to remember Scriptures from camp that would be helpful to the Cummingses. Now would be a good time to try to tell Mr. Cummings about Jesus, she thought.

But Mr. Cummings wanted no part of it. "What kind of a God is it who would let a thing like this happen?" he bellowed.

Katie didn't know what to say to him. She turned to Mrs. Cummings. "Thank you for saving my brother's life. Mama said he would have bled to death."

Mr. Cummings was angry. "Oh, yes. If she had been looking after our boy instead of your brother, this wouldn't have happened."

Katie went back to work and, in the fall, back to school, but the accident and its aftermath were not forgotten. It served to show her how she needed to know the answers if she were to help people. Katie learned everything she could in church but it wasn't enough. She couldn't wait to go to Bible college. By the time Katie graduated, her mind was made up—she was going to Texas Bible College.

It was the spring of 1941. Katie was seventeen, full of confidence and faith.

"Why don't you go to Metropolitan Bible Institute in New York?" Peggy asked.

"Not on your life. I hate cities."

There was another reason for choosing Texas Bible College: it was cheap—no tuition and only seventy-five dollars a month for room and board. Katie didn't have any money, and seventy-five dollars a month would be easier to trust the Lord for than the higher cost at Metropolitan.

In the fall, when it was time to leave if she were going to school, Katie sat on the church steps with the other young people and stated with boldness, "Wednesday is the last day I can leave and get to Texas in time for the opening. So I'm telling you, the money will come by Wednesday. I won't be here next Sunday."

Peggy and the others were polite, but Katie knew they thought she was slightly crazy. That was all right, too, Katie reasoned. People thought George Mueller was crazy, but he fed thousands of orphans by faith, and God never let him down.

The money did not arrive, and Katie was in church the next Sunday. She told her friends, "I'm going to work and save my money, then next year I'll go."

In December, war was declared. The boys and Katie were sitting with Mama at the table eating Sunday dinner when President Roosevelt came on the radio with the news. Pearl Harbor had been attacked.

In a few weeks, Archer was drafted into the army. "It's something we can't help," Mama said. The last morning he was home, Archer appeared to be in good spirits. He gobbled his oatmeal as usual and started to the kitchen with his dish, but Katie took it to the sink for him. He zipped his jacket and kissed Timothy and Katie, keeping up a banter, trying to make the parting easier. But after he kissed Mama, he couldn't say anything more. He grabbed his little satchel and bounded out the door.

They stood on the porch watching him run through the spring lot to catch the bus to the Greyhound station. The lump in Katie's throat was unbearable. She wondered if she would ever see Archer again.

In another month, Brother was also drafted. After basic training, he was shipped to a base on Canada's west coast to serve as a baker. Mama breathed a sigh of relief. "At least if he stays there, he won't be in combat."

"Why don't you go to work in a defense plant, Becky?" Aunt Ethel urged. "The pay is very good."

"After the war defense plants will be closed; furniture plants won't be."

Katie stayed on at the hardware store. Getting merchandise was difficult. When there was a roll of chicken wire or a keg of nails to sell, Mr. Avery asked black market prices. It was the only way he could stay in business, but Katie didn't feel good about it.

The war complicated everything. Chuck had taken a civilian job with the Navy and moved Alice and the baby to Quantico. Jane was working for Uncle Tom in the insurance office and he did not pay her enough to live on, much less send anything home. There was no way Katie could leave Mama with all the financial responsibility and the uncertainties of wartime.

Archer trained in Florida, Tennessee, Kansas, and the desert of California. With each move, Mama tried to prepare herself for the inevitable—his going overseas.

Archer's letters were full of lighthearted news about fellow GI's, K-rations, girls, field maneuvers. He described sunsets on the desert and the night sky, kangaroo rats, and furlough hopes. He also began sending a monthly allotment to Mama. She spent as little of the money as she could and deposited the rest of it in a savings account for him.

The next summer, Archer came home on leave. He was filled out, broad-chested, and tanned—handsome in uniform. "So like your father," Mama said wistfully.

Before his furlough was over, Archer took Katie outside to look at the pigeons. "Katie," he said, "I know you want to go to school, but please wait until I come home. Mama needs you like never before."

Katie sighed. "It's okay, Archer. I'm not going anyplace."

Soon after Archer returned to the base, Katie went to Camp Lookover. The week's vacation there brought Katie back to all the promises she had ever made to God. In the bower on the mountainside, with the same sweet breezes sweeping through the leaves as birds twittered in the branches, Katie prayed again.

"Lord," she said, "I really don't know if you are calling me into Christian work—whether or not I should go to school—you must show me."

Katie flipped through the Bible hoping for an answer. None came. She lay back on the rock, her arm covering her eyes. Tears slid from the corners of her eyes down her temples. If God would not answer, there was nothing she could do. She knew of no sin that would keep him from answering her. The dinner bell was ringing. Wearily, Katie gathered her pencil, paper, and Bible together and walked back to camp.

Perhaps it was God's will for her to stay at home and look after Mama and Timothy. "No," Peggy said, "you mustn't give up. Something will work out. Maybe your sister Jane will come home."

But in the fall, Jane wrote that she was going to marry an Air Force captain. He was stationed in Florida and couldn't get enough leave to come to Charlotte for the wedding. Jane was going to Florida to marry him. Florida might as well have been China—none of the family could attend.

Katie and Mama spent the winter with a gloomy round of daily duties. To work and home again. Write letters to the boys, read the news from the front and the names of war casualties, then work in the garden, clean the pigeon pens, take care of the house and meals. Going to church was a bright spot and Brother's letters helped. Filled with praise to God, he talked about witnessing and fellowshipping with other Christians. He described what life was like for him and it made his world seem nearer.

"It doesn't take everybody long to get out of the mess hall after the work is finished," he wrote. "I often like to listen to the sounds of escaping steam or a dripping water faucet or the odd noises that we hear in stillness that would never be heard in the turmoil of a day's operation."

Mama seemed to have dismissed from her mind Katie's dream of going to school. She never spoke of it, and Katie didn't bring it up. She wondered why God allowed the yearning to grow stronger.

Timothy grew into a spindly boy of fourteen. Archer sent him combat boots and he easily filled them. He was no longer their "little brother"—he was coming into his own with a job in a department store after school hours. Yet he did not make enough to take over the electric bill and fuel bill that Katie paid. On her salary of eighteen dollars a week, Katie had no hope of saving for school.

It was childish to cling to the hope that Daddy would come home and make the way easy. She had given up hoping for that. Jane still expected to find him; she was like a dog with a bone—persistent. For Katie, it was hard not to feel a certain resentment that things were as they were.

She was sweeping the floor in the hardware store, the boards as familiar to her as the palm of her hand, when she stopped, leaned on the broom and thought, "Is this it, Lord? Is this what you want me to do the rest of my life?"

In the summer of '43 Katie was despondent. At Camp Lookover, she tried again for a showdown with the Lord. Before anyone else was awake, she went to her retreat and poured out her soul to God. On the third morning it came to her almost by chance—what the problem might be, if there was a problem. Wrestling with the idea for a while, Katie finally prayed, "If you want me to go to Metropolitan Bible Institute in New York City, I'll go." She spoke the words deliberately and meant what she said even though she didn't like it.

Knowing she had done everything she knew to do, she continued. "Now, Lord, if you want me in Christian service, tell me through the Bible."

Katie opened her eyes and her Bible at the same time. The chapter was Isaiah six. She read slowly, taking it personally to see if it applied to her request. When she came to the verse, "Whom shall I send and who will go for us?" her heart leaped to respond, "Here am I, send me!"

"You will have to *send* me," Katie prayed. After all,

she had no money and no prospect of having any.

Katie hugged her knees, feeling that God had answered but not daring to say for sure. "Lord," she prayed, "if you want me to go to Metropolitan, have Mama suggest it to me."

Perhaps it was an unfair test. There was no way Mama would suggest such a thing. She didn't even know Katie still wanted to go.

Before the week was over, Katie received a letter from Timothy. Archer was in England. Katie's heart sank. In the next meeting, she asked for prayer for Archer, now so much nearer the enemy. The news put going to school out of Katie's mind.

Saturday night, Katie arrived home in time for supper. Mama was putting the tea on the table. Katie kissed her and they sat down. Timothy asked the blessing and they began eating. Before either of them asked her about camp or anything else, Mama passed the rice and said, "Katie, if you want to go to Metropolitan Bible Institute, why don't you go?"

Katie didn't know what to say! God had made his will clear.

NEW YORK CITY

TWENTY-FOUR
Chris, Tony,
and David

The night train was packed with servicemen heading north. Katie stood on the platform, bulging suitcase at her knee, ticket in hand. That morning, Mr. Powell had presented the Sunday school offering to Katie. The seventy-five dollars bought the railroad ticket, and the money left over was in a sock pinned inside Katie's blouse. Except for a few dollars in her purse, it was all she had.

No one came to the station to see her off. That was the way she wanted it. Leaving Mama and Timothy was hard enough without saying good-bye in public.

Katie had never ridden a train before; the uncertainties made her so nervous she shook. People were streaming onto the train. The noise was unbearable— shrieking whistles, rumbling engine, clanging cars. Katie felt her stockings bagging at the knees. Peggy always laughed at the way Katie's stockings bagged. She picked up the suitcase and lugged it alongside the train. A sailor took it out of her hand and carried it for her. He forced his way through the crowd and pulled Katie behind him. He pried the people apart so they could squeeze through, then shoved the bag onto the platform between the cars. There was no chance of finding a seat or even standing room inside. The sailor propped up the suitcase and motioned for her to sit down. When she was settled as comfortably as she could be, he yelled in her ear, "You okay?"

She smiled and nodded. He winked, gave a quick salute, and turned to make his way through the passengers.

As the train moved slowly, Katie leaned over to see the depot they were leaving. It was no use. The suitcase rocked beneath her. In it and in the trunk in the baggage car were pretty dresses Mama and Aunt Ethel had made or bought for her. They had sacrificed grocery money in order to clothe her, and that made leaving home all the harder. If either of them had come to the station to see her off, Katie's courage might have failed at the last minute. "Trouble with you," Archer had said, "you hesitate. . . ." They were swinging buckets of spring water over their heads in an arc, and Katie had soused herself. "The way to be brave is to know what you have to do and do it. Don't hesitate. . . I know in my head the water won't spill. . . ."

Katie thought about that morning Archer had left for the service, how he must have felt as he ran through the spring lot and didn't look back. There was no way he could "know in his head" that all would be well.

Katie worried about changing trains in Washington. Surprisingly, Mama had not cautioned her about changing trains. They had wired the school to have someone meet her in New York, but there was no guarantee anyone would be there.

Katie thought again of Archer. He wouldn't like her leaving Mama, not when she had told him that she wouldn't. What else could she do? Everything had happened so fast, falling into place at the proper time. There was no doubt that it was God's will.

The conductor squeezed his way through the mob to punch tickets, but he didn't come through to call stations. The clatter of the wheels on the rails was hypnotic, but Katie was wide awake, scared. When the train stopped, she would try to see the name of the town printed on the station house. Steam shot out from beneath the wheels, conductors swung down to the platform, luggage carts piled high were pulled to the rear to the baggage car. When the train was loaded, the conductors looked up and down the track and swung their lanterns, calling, "All a-boarr-d." As the train was pulling out, they swung aboard again.

The hours to Washington were endless, what with the stopping and waiting, lurching forward, jolting— the slow, creeping pace as the engine strained to pull its load. In the misty light of railway stations, all depots looked alike. Katie wondered if she would recognize the Washington terminal.

But by the time the train reached Washington, there was no mistaking that this was it. The train screeched at a snail's pace around bends and turns seeking a slot among the many tracks. Katie's pulse quickened. The conductor stood on the lower step, gripping both hand-holds to keep passengers from jumping off while the train was still moving. The train finally creaked to a standstill. As the conductor stood aside, the stampede began. Katie was pushed from the train by the surge and stood bewildered on the platform. The rushing crowd knocked her about. A sergeant saw her plight, swooped up her bag, and ran interference as she followed him.

In the terminal he set down the bag and smiled. "End of the line?"

"No."

"Where to?"

"New York."

"Follow me." He pushed his way through the crowd and Katie followed in his wake. When they reached the gate, he handed her the bag. "It's right down there. Just follow these people. It's on the north track."

"Thank you so much!" she said, and he was gone.

So far, so good, she thought as she bumped down the steps with the bag. *Now to worry about somebody meeting me in New York.* The trains were all running late.

As the locomotive pulled out of Union Station, daylight pushed back the cover of night. Gathering speed slowly, the train creaked and strained its way out of the yards. Katie looked down on tenements for the first time, row houses with steps painted white, and sad-looking people sitting on stoops, waiting to start the day. Dirty clothes were strung on rooftops, paper littered the sidewalks, trucks and cars jammed the streets—it was not a pretty view.

In a few hours, the train crossed the Jersey meadows; oil tanks and flat grassland shared the same vast space. Rivers and ships and docks loomed in the dreary drizzle of a foggy rain like a surrealist painting; the sun was blotted from view.

But this dismal scene was lost when the train plunged underground, burrowing its way beneath the Hudson. The darkness, the stale air of the tunnel was oppressive. The approach to the station was slow and painstaking. At last the train pulled to a stop, and Katie wearily made her way to the ground.

Emerging from the escalator into the vast building, people dwarfed by the high vaulted ceiling, Katie was overwhelmed. Penn Station looked and sounded magnificent. Above the bustle of rushing passengers, the haze of smoke hung like some wafting spirit. Great shafts of sunlight beamed through the haze. Sounds were muted in the enormous space and above them all was the drone of the stationmaster's voice calling first one train, then another.

Katie spied the information booth, picked up the suitcase, and struggled across the floor. She scouted the counter area for a person who looked as if he were looking for someone. For half an hour she waited; people came and went, met each other and glanced at their watches, but there was no one who looked as if he came from the Institute. Katie mustered the courage to ask the clerk.

"No, Miss," the uniformed woman answered curtly. "No one has asked for a Katie MacLeod."

"Excuse me," she asked timidly, "where can I get a taxicab?"

"Which direction?"

Katie didn't know and mumbled.

"Speak up, Miss."

"Three-forty, West Fifty-fifth Street."

"Over there, Miss. Right through that door."

As Katie stepped into the sunlight of Eighth Avenue, traffic noises blasted her ear drums: taxis racing the street, bus motors wheezing, horns blaring, brakes squealing, voices shouting, and over and above them all, the staccato of pneumatic drills ripping up concrete. The greasy smell of exhaust and oil covered Katie like a film.

Across the street was the United States Post Office with its impressive columns and broad steps. Above the crown of the building hung the flag, and beneath it, across the length of the crown, were inscribed the words: "Neither snow nor rain nor heat nor gloom of night stays these couriers from the swift completion of their appointed rounds."

A flock of pigeons swooped onto the sidewalk, so many she had to walk around them. Their presence in this alien place was welcome.

Katie watched other people getting into cabs, and in a while she realized they were standing beneath a "Taxi" sign. She picked up the bag and moved up the block. In a few minutes she was in the back seat of one of the yellow monsters, heading up Eighth Avenue, the meter clicking at a terrifying rate.

In the stops and starts, the mad spurts, the wild weaving in and out of traffic, Katie's senses were bombarded with sights, sounds, and smells. Trash cans over-flowing with garbage, steam rising from sidewalk grills, police on horseback, newsstands, steel grates across store fronts, garish signs, bars, gyms markets, cheap shops, pretzel vendors, fruit stands and, towering above the street, walls that stretched up to the sky. The only familiar building she saw was Madison Square Garden. Brother would be interested to know that she had seen Madison Square Garden.

Dumped on the sidewalk before the 340 building, Katie surveyed the scene. Beautiful wrought iron gates marked the entrance, and above them there was an elegant sign—"Metropolitan Bible Institute." At eye level on the stone facing of the door, was another sign, "Air Raid Shelter" and above that, impressive polished brass numbers, "340." A mailbox, bolted to the sidewalk, stood to the side—the one link to home.

Katie took a deep breath, picked up her suitcase, and entered. "I'm Katie MacLeod," she told the student at the desk. He plugged in the switchboard to an unseen authority and spoke a few words. Returning to the desk, he pointed Katie toward the elevator. "Get off on the fourth floor. Miss English, the Dean of Women, will meet you there."

Miss English was a plain woman who wore sensible shoes and had a cultivated voice. She led Katie down the hall to her room. The small room was furnished with a bunk bed, bureau, desk, sink, medicine chest, and closet. Katie noticed the black shades at the windows. "Here in New York," Miss English explained, "we have air raid drills and brownouts." She opened the closet door. "Your roommate will be here shortly. She's Christine Burwell from Pennsylvania."

Katie liked Chris immediately. She was reserved and she spoke, as Katie learned later, the way Pennsylvanians around Lancaster speak. "I'm not Dutch," Chris said. "There's some mystery about my Dad's origins, but it's plain he's from southern Europe. In Lancaster, southern Europeans are not fully appreciated."

Chris did not think of herself as charming, but she

was. And she was funny. In her dry way, humor was as natural with her as breathing.

Chris agreed to go with Katie to get her trunk. The cabdriver took one look at them, heard the southern accent, and decided to be accommodating. He drove as far as he could through the Penn Station labyrinth, took the baggage check, disappeared for a while, then came back with the trunk on a dolly.

In all, the trip took more than an hour. Back at school, the cabby lifted the trunk onto the sidewalk, reached out his hand for the fare and Katie paid him. Then she gave him a ten cents tip. The man glared at her, spat at her feet. Flinging himself behind the wheel, he threw the car in gear and roared away.

"Why'd he do that?"

"Katie, you don't give a cab driver a dime!"

"But—"

Chris was patient. "Get a hold of the other side of this trunk. You see, Katie, up here you don't accept service unless you are willing to pay for it."

"But he was such a nice man."

"In New York you pay for 'nice.'"

On registration day, Katie had forty dollars. The catalog plainly stated that the first semester expenses must be in hand on registration day. "Well," Katie said to herself, "I'll go as far as I can and if they throw me out, they throw me out."

They didn't throw her out. A nice Spanish professor, Mr. Vincent Rinaldo, signed Katie up for courses, took her money, and asked where she would like to work. When she had no preference, he assigned her to the library.

A reception was held the next evening for new students. Katie tried on several dresses and let Chris decide which one she should wear. "You've got a good figure, Katie," Chris said. "With your small waist the princess style looks great, and the beige color is good with your hair." Katie brushed her hair, pulling it up on top and letting the rest hang soft about her face.

Going to a reception was something new. She dreaded it. "Do we have to go?"

"We have to go," Chris said. "Just think of the martyrs going into the arena and it won't be so bad."

The president, Dr. John Paul Ramsey, was a robust man with ruddy complexion and a hearty laugh. Chris said he was the smartest man she had ever known. He did not walk but plunged forward, his mind busy while his heavy body thrust him straight ahead. He looked more like a discus thrower than a scholar. Chris said he was reared in the lumber camps of Wisconsin, that he chopped wood for exercise and hiked across the George Washington Bridge reading the Greek Testament.

Professor Rinaldo was Katie's favorite from the start, probably because he accepted her forty dollars matter-of-factly and relieved Katie of considerable concern. But Chris told Katie more about the olive-skinned Rinaldo. "An Italian from Brazil, a Latin gentleman with a Latin temper. Brought up in the City, he loves it with a passion; particularly he loves the arts. Some of his dearest pleasures were denied him when he left the Catholic church to embrace the faith of the fundamentalists. We frown on movies, plays, and the dance, you know."

Professor Rinaldo was soft-spoken and kind, but the thrust of his chin and his piercing brown eyes did not tolerate pretense. His wife, a pretty Englishwoman, adored him, bore their sacrifices well, and kept up appearances as he would have her do. They were people of prayer and submission to God, and their lives harmonized.

Katie adored "the Duchess," Mrs. Smithwick, who taught classics and speech. "The age of the Duchess will not be revealed," Chris said, "until she is well inside the Pearly Gates, but it is commonly rumored that she was well acquainted with Ulysses Simpson Grant."

The Duchess held her four feet eleven inches as erect as possible, but the years weighed heavily on her shoulders and the stoop could not be totally corrected. The Duchess was a patrician, with a nose and chin fit for any dowager. The pince nez glasses strung from a tiny chain were on and off repeatedly, and Katie suspected that her dark and powerful eyes were her secret vanity. A lovely pile of white hair, coiffured in waves and French twist, set off her elegance. As if that were not enough, long strands of beads graced her ample bosom. The resonant voice, precise in its diction and rich in its vocabulary, made conversation with the Duchess a cultural experience.

"In case you don't know," Chris said, "Professor Arthur Steinberg is a Jew. He escaped Czechoslovakia hours before Hitler's advance. Steinberg told our class he grew up in Prague where marching boots were heard in the streets every day of his life. Left his mother and brothers when he escaped. He's tough, Katie. Watch out for Steinberg."

Professor Steinberg was a short man with an immaculate military bearing; the cut of his suit was European, his manner courtly. All this insinuated disapproval of high-spirited American youth, but Professor Steinberg could laugh and laugh most heartily at himself. Katie admired him.

There were other faculty members too—earnest young seminarians teaching between calls to the mission field or pastorate, opinionated spinsters, dull and dogmatic middle-aged men, librarians, and deans. "All living on subsistence pay," Chris said, "and saying nothing about it."

"How long have you been at Metropolitan?" Katie asked Chris.

"This is my second year. At the rate I'm going, I should finish the three-year course in five."

There were courses in English, languages, philosophy, theology, archaeology, history, Bible, and all the skill courses for teaching and preaching. Katie knew she was where she belonged.

But there was too much to see and do to plunge into

studies right away. First of all, there was Tony, a good-looking fellow Chris said came "straight out of Little Italy."

Tony gave Katie a rushing good time. He introduced her to pizza pie, the Staten Island ferry, and took her to the Statue of Liberty, which he, as a native New Yorker, had never seen. A walk in Central Park was not Tony's idea of a good time. He always headed for Fifth Avenue via Fifty-seventh Street to window shop at Tiffany's, Cartier's, Bonwit Teller, Bergdorf Goodman, and the rest.

The excitement of the city began to take hold of Katie. Riding the subway, swinging from the straps, studying all the foreign faces, listening to so many languages—it all was fascinating. Katie was blissfully aware of the anonymity to be enjoyed.

Tony kept buying Katie things: candy bars ("something sweet and nutty for someone sweet and nutty"); a music box that played, "I'll Be Loving You Always"; a museum doll; a leather notebook. And he was always asking her to marry him.

"He likes money," Chris said.

"How do you know?"

"I can smell it." Chris was cryptic, to say the least, but this time she supplied evidence. "He wouldn't work nights at the Post Office if he didn't love money."

It seemed like a poor argument to Katie. "What does his liking money have to do with me?"

"He thinks you're rich."

Katie rolled on the bed in a fit of laughing. "Chris, don't be ridiculous!"

Chris was sitting on the sink, peeling an orange. She was a pretty girl, but, of all her features, her short, slender fingers were the prettiest.

"You have clothes, Katie." She held the peeling poised over the waste basket. "You also have pretty ankles. Men go for ankles." She dropped the peeling.

"You're too funny for words, Chris. Tell me, all that

nonsense he gives me about wanting to marry me—doesn't the 'love' part come first?"

Chris deftly separated the orange sections.

"How would I know? People marry for all sorts of reasons—to get in out of the cold—stuff like that."

"There you go, being philosophical."

Chris ignored her. "You also have the southern charm. Men are suckers for the way you talk. You sound so helpless."

"Helpless!" Katie shrieked.

Chris handed Katie a slice of orange. "*I* know you're not helpless. I know you're made of stainless steel, but even you don't know that yet. When you look in the mirror, you see those soft brown eyes, and you think you're a marshmallow; what you think you are is all you can be."

"Good grief!"

Chris was looking out the window. "What do you see?" Katie asked.

"There's a guy in the apartment across the street who's a writer. All day long he sits there in his underwear typing away."

Katie got up off the bed and looked over Chris's shoulder. "How do you know he's a writer?"

"I've been watching him a year. He gets stuck on a word and he sits there with that gismo in his hand—it looks like a short ruler—slapping his leg as he agonizes."

Katie watched the man for a minute and agreed.

Chris's gaze drifted. "You can see a lot out this window," she said. "There's a lady who walks her dog every morning at seven o'clock. She lives in that same building—comes out in a mink and satin pajamas. With snow on the ground she'll wear opera pumps. That's what you call a classy outfit."

"What else?"

"See that little girl on that tiny balcony? That balcony can't be three feet wide—it was built for flower pots. Well, that little girl has played there nearly every day for as long as I have been here. She must be four years old now. I suppose by the time I graduate, she'll be seven or eight and still playing there. I don't know why people want to raise children in the city when they could raise children in Pennsylvania."

"I've got to get ready. Tony's sister has invited us for an authentic Italian meal tonight."

Tony's sister lived in Brooklyn in a walk-up flat. There were as yet no children, but one was on the way. Tony's brother-in-law was a merchant seaman and had the tattoos to prove it. He spoke no English, but kept a conversation in Italian going with his wife.

Katie sipped claret for the first time and disliked it. A plate of olives, cheeses, celery, and peppers was passed and Katie wondered if it might be the meal.

That plate was followed by spaghetti and meatballs and Katie ate with relish. Unwittingly, she left no room for the courses that followed: chicken cacciatore, veal scallopini, eggplant parmesan, and ravioli.

The tortino at the end of the meal was the finishing touch. Katie excused herself to the bathroom.

There was no denying the authenticity of Tony's Italian heritage, and for the first time Katie reflected upon her own heritage.

Home seemed far away and she was not homesick. Every letter from Mama contained a dollar or two and that struck a feeling of guilt in Katie's heart. She was having such a good time while Mama was slaving to keep body and soul together.

Even the war seemed far removed. Air raids were frequent enough to become routine, like fire drills, and although there were boys Katie had known in high school who were missing in action, they were not personal friends. Archer was still in England, his letters entertaining. Although he felt serious about a girl in Kansas, he was spending more time with WAC's than with military duties.

Brother's letters related his spiritual experiences in helping wounded men returning from war in the Pacific.

Then came word from Aunt Ethel that Roger Napier had been killed in action. Katie had not thought of him for a long time. The clipping said his plane was shot down by the Japanese. His death had an unsettling effect. By Christmas, Katie was ready to go home, and Tony wanted to go with her.

In Charlotte they took the bus from the depot and Tony carried Katie's suitcase and his own around the ice plant and down Thrift Street. The Cummings' dog met them at the corner and barked at their heels embarrassingly. Mama had the porch light on and the servicemen flags in the window added to the forlorn look of the old house. But, whatever it might look like to Tony, to Katie it was home, and she was glad to be there.

When Mama opened the door, she had a dustpan in her hand. As Katie hugged her, she could see what had happened. Above the heater the plaster had fallen— Mama was in the process of cleaning it up. The slats above the stove hung with shreds of plaster, and the hole gaped mockingly.

Mama greeted Tony and took his coat upstairs. Tony perched on the edge of the sofa uncomfortably. Mr. Powell had invited him to stay at their house during the holidays, and when Mama came back downstairs, Tony asked her to call him.

"When did you get a phone?" Katie asked.

"Recently."

When Mr. Powell came, Tony was ready to leave.

Jane made a twenty-four-hour bus trip to come home for Christmas. Her husband Scott was overseas and she had decided to move to Atlanta for a better job. Finding a place to live in wartime was difficult.

"Katie, I can't wait to get settled. In a big city like that there must be plenty of organizations that can help me find Daddy."

"Like what?"

"The Missing Persons Bureau."

Mama frowned. "No, not that."

"Why not?" But Mama didn't answer. "Well, there are other ways. I check phone books. Don't you, Katie?"

"Not really. Every time we pass a phone booth Tony checks for coins in the change box. I keep thinking I'll look through the directories, but I haven't done it yet."

Timothy came into the room, ready to go to work. He was growing slender and was good-looking, with Mama's eyes and hair.

"What do you think of Katie's boyfriend?" Jane asked him.

"I like the way he talks. He thinks Katie is 'beyootee-ful.' Told me he once lived on the 'fi-teent flaw' of an apartment house. Calls New Jersey 'Joisey.' I guess that's what they mean by the Brooklyn accent."

"He's from Brooklyn all right," Katie said. "He calls a park a 'pock' and anybody named Smith he calls 'Smit,' but I like him because he's different."

"He's also very nice-looking," Jane added.

Mama frowned but didn't say anything. Katie knew what she was thinking. Christmas dinner at their house had been different for Tony—baked hen and dressing, fruit cake and ambrosia—but it meant nothing to him; he hardly ate. As far as Mama was concerned, Tony was all right to have as a friend, but she wouldn't want Katie to get serious about him.

Mama needn't have worried. When they arrived back in New York, Tony never dated Katie again.

"What happened?" Chris asked.

"You were right."

"How'd you find out?"

"The ceiling fell in."

"The ceiling fell in?"

"Literally." Katie took a deep breath. "Tony saw our little home and the trashy street, the space heater and the hole in the ceiling, and it changed his mind."

"A bittersweet lesson, Katie."

They were looking out the window. The man across the street was typing furiously. He was at it morning, noon, and night. No doubt about it, being a writer was a grueling job. "I'm going to be a writer," Katie told Chris.

"Well, don't tell the Foreign Missionary Volunteers—they have prayer meetings for everybody who isn't committed to headhunters and monkey meat."

Katie began studying in earnest for exams. She wouldn't think about boys for a while, she told herself. But she did. In every class she looked them over. The cute ones were taken; the others were married, draft dodgers, or misfits.

"You know who's good-looking," Chris said. "That Norwegian day student, Nels Jensen."

"Looks don't count. I'd say he's a 4-F."

Katie made good grades on exams, then concentrated on getting as many hours work as possible in the library. Semester bills were due.

In February, Jane wrote that she had found a room in Atlanta and was working in an office. She was already looking for Daddy, and she wanted to know if Katie had done anything about finding him.

Katie borrowed the telephone books from the desk and looked up all the MacLeod listings in the five boroughs. Some of the numbers she called, but they were all dead-ends. She wrote Jane and told her.

If Katie had any idea about looking further, she forgot it when David Dudko came along. David was a day student who had his own car. Born in the Ukraine, the son of a pastor, he had traveled all over Europe and planned to return to Russia as a missionary.

David was blond like Brother, with broad shoulders. He had a good, Slavic face, and his accent sounded romantic.

David's appeal was unlike anything Katie had ever known before. "Cosmopolitan," Chris said. "He's the next thing to Park Avenue."

David took Katie to the Don Cossack Chorus, introduced her to Chinese food in Lee's at Mott and Pell

Streets in Chinatown, and took her to Luchow's, the restaurant that Caruso, Lillian Russell, and Diamond Jim Brady had frequented.

There was something strangely incongruous about David. He told stories of privation and persecution in Russia—stories he heard at home but did not remember first hand. Because his father was a pastor, David spoke as if their poverty knew no limits. But of all the students at Metropolitan, David had the most money. It was not a purposeful lie but the kind of lie one believes because it is expected. David did not know he was affluent.

On her twentieth birthday, he took Katie to dinner at Stouffer's overlooking the city, then to the ballet at New York City Center. Dancers performed magic on the stage—they became toys, toys wound up, marching toys winding down, arms and legs, stiff and still. The theater was exciting with its music, the lighting, the velvet and posh sets.

Walking home after the ballet, Katie was cold and shaking. David put her hand in his overcoat pocket, wrapped his arm around her and hugged her close. In Schraft's they ordered coffee, and while they waited, David reached for her hand. "I love you, Katie," he said. She met his eyes and smiled.

By the time they reached the Institute, the gates were locked shut. David tapped on the window and attracted the student at the desk. Sleepily he came and unlocked the door. David pressed a bill in his hand.

When the boy went back to the desk, they still stood in the vestibule waiting to say good-night. David took Katie in his arms and kissed her. In the dimly lit foyer, the lobby deserted, they were safe. "Goodnight, David," Katie said, fingering his lapel, but he would not let her go. He kissed her again, then released her. If David had looked in her eyes, he would have seen that she didn't want him to let her go. Katie thanked him for the evening, pressed the elevator button and stood looking back at him. When the door opened, she smiled, leaned toward him, kissed him again quickly, then stepped into the elevator, and closed the door.

Katie didn't take the elevator all the way to the fourth floor but stopped on three and walked up. In that way, she was not likely to be heard coming onto the floor after hours.

When she reached the room, she woke up Chris.

Chris listened to the account of the evening from beginning to end. Then she rolled over on her side and declared, "David doesn't love you, Katie. He only wants to make love. There is a difference, you know." With that she rolled over and went back to sleep.

Just in case Chris was right, Katie tried to discourage David. She succeeded. A month later, Katie turned a corner in the library stacks and there was David kissing a senior girl.

TWENTY-FIVE
Moling
in
Manhattan

In June, the Allied Forces launched the assault across the Channel. After D-Day there was no news from Archer. Katie was at home, working in the hardware store for the summer. It was hard to concentrate on anything except the war news. Mr. Avery kept the radio going all the time, and the overseas broadcasts were so garbled by static he had to lean close to the speaker to hear. Maps appeared in the paper every day showing beach head positions. Telegrams were arriving all over town from the War Department: "We regret to inform you. . . ." Casualty lists lengthened.

Katie wondered if she should stay home from school in the fall. If Mama received a telegram about Archer, Katie wanted to be there with her. The memory of the night Archer left home to seek his fortune was proof that if anything serious happened to him, Mama would need help.

In less than three weeks after the Normandy invasion, news came that the Fighting Seventy-ninth had reached Cherbourg and taken it. Archer's letters were censored but even so, their move on St. Lo and Cherbourg were described in some detail. Archer's praise for the Eighty-second Airborne and Ninth Divisions, his admiration for General Omar Bradley, was genuine, but between the lines it was clear that the horrors of combat were nothing to glory in. He was a soldier weary of war and there was a long way to go.

"Katie," he wrote. "I'm point man for our squad and that calls for a woodsman who can sneak about. All our hunting on Bull Creek stands me in good stead now. Yesterday, my entire platoon was captured in a ravine because they didn't know how to stay put and be still."

From France, Archer sent Mama pressed rose petals given him by a grateful woman. "Mom," he wrote. "A peasant woman gave me a rose and these are the petals. It was all she had to give me but the rose expressed the joy these people feel at our coming. They are people like us. Let the petals remind you that what we're doing is worth it all."

Mama brought a glass paperweight to preserve the faded pink petals.

In July, Alice gave birth to a baby boy. They named him Malcolm because Mama asked them to. Katie gave Mama the fare to ride the bus to Quantico to see her new grandchild.

Apart from that expense, Katie was able to save eight dollars a week so that by the end of the summer she had a hundred dollars. Archer sent money home to buy her a warm coat and Mama insisted that she take it.

The week before school opened, Mama became sick, sick enough to go to the doctor. "Stay in bed a week," he told her. "Then let me check you again." Katie was to leave for New York the middle of the week. Mama insisted that she go, but Katie could not bring herself to leave her while she was in bed.

Aunt Ethel came over. "Now, you go right ahead, Katie. I'll look after Becky." It was a comfort to have her there but Aunt Ethel had her own responsibilities. Mama looked up at Katie and for a passing moment her blue eyes said, "I wish you would stay."

It was hard.

Katie went back downstairs where Timothy was waiting to take her to the depot. At fifteen he was trying to be the man in the family that Archer had admonished him to be. Katie sat on the couch, unwilling to leave.

"Katie," Timothy said, "what does the Bible say about 'loving father or mother more than him'?"

It was not the first time the Lord had brought that verse to Katie's mind when she was wavering. She tried to smile at Timothy. "I'll go up and say good-bye."

Soon, Katie boarded the train, pushing against the press of bodies jammed inside. Timothy handed her the suitcase and stood aside for the train to pull out. Women were kissing their soldier sons and husbands, weeping and clinging to them. Katie looked down at Timothy, standing in the misty light. He was nearly grown. If the war lasted forever, how soon would it be before he would be in uniform?

The train was moving past him. She waved but he could not see her in the crowd. For a few minutes she leaned against the bodies, straining to glimpse the familiar sights slipping past. Rain began pelting down. The train lurched and threw them about. Katie began to push her way to the ladies' room where there was sometimes a vacant bench.

The room was crowded and stuffy, but there was room for her to sit down. Pressed into a corner, heart aching, she could not control the tears coursing down her cheeks. She closed her eyes, leaned her head back, enduring the noise of the train on the tracks. Her thoughts roamed about for a long time, but came to rest on Twenty-nine. Floating in her consciousness was the dream she had had at Twenty-nine—that mysterious childhood dream about Jesus, his hand outreached.

The wheels of the train were clacking at a fast clip. The whistle blew shrilly and long but through it all, Katie came to understand. Leaving Mama to follow Jesus was no small thing.

348

Katie took the Eighth Avenue bus from Penn Station, got off at Fifty-fourth Street, and walked up the block to the corner. Nels Jensen was coming down Fifty-fifth.

"Hi, Katie," he greeted her and took the bag.

"Hello, Nels."

"It's good to see you. Have a good trip?"

"Well, you know how it is. Every train is like a troop train these days, packed and jammed and always late."

They were crossing Eighth Avenue and Nels took her arm to steer her. He was a quiet sort; he was probably lazy, maybe even dodging the draft under the guise of being a ministerial student.

"The war's heating up. I saw a fleet of ships coming up the Hudson this morning. Well, they were in the Bay as I was coming over on the ferry, and we couldn't see them until they were almost on us. They loomed up out of the fog like phantoms and moved steadily toward us without making a sound."

Katie glanced up at him, struck by the way he spoke. "Oh?" she said.

"It'll get worse before it gets better."

They had reached the Institute. He held the doors for her and brought the bag inside. Returning students were congregated before the elevators with stacks of luggage piled all over. Every arrival brought forth squeals of delight and hugs all around. But Katie was not in the mood for ecstasy. The only person she wanted to see was Chris.

There was nothing demonstrative about Chris. When Katie came in the room, Chris was brushing her teeth and hardly looked up. "H'llo, Katie."

"Good to see you, Chris." She unstrapped the suitcase and took out a robe. "I'm going to take a bath. We'll talk later."

The bathroom was at the end of the hall. As the water poured, she slipped out of her clothes and eased her slender body into the tub. She lay there soaking in the warm water, listening as the girls ran up and down the halls greeting each other.

If it weren't so expensive, she would call home to see how Mama was feeling. But then, a long distance call would be a dead giveaway that she was worried, and Aunt Ethel would get alarmed.

Whatever would they do if Mama died? The dream surfaced in her mind again—Jesus with his hand outstretched; the platform with the babies in the jars; the rushing stream and the first step. . . . Well, she had made the step, taken Jesus' hand, and left Mama for him. "No man having put his hand to the plough and turneth back is worthy. . . ."

Girls had stopped running in the halls. Maybe they had gone to lunch. Katie reviewed the dream, turning it over in her mind for the comfort it gave. After a while, she stepped out of the tub, dried herself, and brushed her hair. Putting on the chenille robe, she gathered up her dirty clothes and went back to the room.

Chris was tying her shoes. Katie flopped on her lower bunk.

Chris caught her mood immediately.

"Chris," she began, "I want a job in the kitchen."

Chris waited.

Katie explained, "In the kitchen you work around mealtime, the time you ordinarily waste."

"Waste?"

"Yes, waste—hanging around talking."

"To boys?"

"Right." Katie sat up. "This year I'm knuckling down. My money situation is worse than ever, so I've got to put in the hours. Besides, there's a war going on. These birds around here seem to forget that."

"True. But we do 'pray for the chaplains and the boys in the service.'" she said, tongue-in-cheek.

"What's the news about your brother in the Pacific?"

"Not much."

"Aren't you worried about him?"

"Sure, but I figure with your brother Archer fighting the war in Europe and my brother Richard fighting the war in the Pacific, it'll be over in no time."

Katie smiled. "Come on, Chris, tell me how I'm going to get a job in the kitchen."

"Only one way. Go down and sweet-talk the chef."

It worked. Katie went to work before breakfast the next morning and worked three meal times a day. Time passed quickly as she tended the steam table or the coffee urn. After the meal, scraping or drying dishes, the student helpers sang as they worked, and that was fun.

From the kitchen Katie rushed to class or to the library. On Sundays, she went to Spanish Harlem to teach in a mission school. Every minute had to count and coffee became important as a stimulant to keep her going. Katie lost weight and even Chris worried about her. "You look owl-eyed. I'm going to write your Mother if you don't take better care of yourself."

"You wouldn't!"

"Naw. How is your Mom?"

"Better. She's back at work. The doctor will probably dismiss her soon."

One day, Katie was at her usual place in the library, studying a commentary for Old Testament history, trying to ignore the rain pouring down outside. Rain had been falling all week, and she felt depressed. Chris slipped up behind her, closed the book, turned off the lamp and whispered, "Come on. I brought your coat. You're going with us."

In the hall was the gang Chris ran with—Steven O'Brian, Mark Seville, the Lowell twins, Gretchen and Greta, Nels Jensen, and a new boy, Todd Beecham.

"Where're we going?" Katie asked, tying a kerchief around her head.

They were on the street before they told her. "Moling. We're going moling," Gretchen said, laughing.

Rain was thundering down; they were huddled together under umbrellas.

"What's moling?"

"You'll see."

They took the Eighth Avenue subway, and automatically the "Moles" as they called themselves, began speaking Brooklynese. Each of them had a separate identity when they were Brooklynites. Nels introduced them, "I'm Joey, Chris is Mabel, Steven is Hoimon... you can be Moitle, Katie."

The Moles unloaded at Penn Station, and Nels proceeded to explain moling to Katie. "What we do, Katie, is try to see how far we can prowl around underground without surfacing to the street or paying a token to ride the subway. The game is over when we have to come up. You lose if you use a token."

"Swell, Joey."

They were coming up on the second level of the station. Once on the second level, they walked past the Long Island Railroad Information booth and the Seventh Avenue I.R.T. turnstiles. Under Gimbel's sign they huddled. "Okay," Nels announced, "Let's see if we can get to the Public Library at Forty-second Street and Fifth Avenue."

Nels grabbed Katie's hand, and they were off running. They ran past Gimbel's underground windows, then turned left and walked briskly past Saks-34th's windows. They practiced their Brooklynese. "Youse is a great spo't, Moitle, leavin' de books 'n all."

She laughed. "I t'ink youah swell, Joey."

Reaching the signs "30th and Sixth" they were faced with a maze of turnstiles. Nels looked all around trying to get his bearings. The rest of the Moles had scattered, going separate ways.

"Theah it is, Moitle!" Nels shouted pointing to the sign "To 35th Street." Turning left, Nels and Katie rounded a circle. "This heah is de only way, Moitle."

Nels slowed down, confident they were on the right course. Soon they were looking for another sign. "Wha-da we lookin' foah?" Katie asked.

"West Side Sixt' Avenoo and Toity-fift' Street."

"Ovah deah, Joey!"

Taking the wide, well-lighted tunnel, moling did not seem as much like burrowing as it sounded.

"Moitle, d'ya know wheah we are?"

"No, Joey, wheah are we?"

"Weah right benea' Six' Avenoo an' Fo'tiet' Street."

"Fasta', Joey. On to dem lions!"

They broke into a run, heading for the steps. Nels announced triumphantly, "Up dese heah stai's is yer New Yawk Public Liberry."

They were laughing, trying to get the umbrella open. "Twenty-two minutes flat. This has got to be a woild record," Nels said.

Surfacing, they leaned into the wind against the rain. The street was ablaze with lights. Red, yellow, green, blue reflections shimmered like streamers on the pavement. Automobile tires sang on the wet surface.

Katie and Nels waited half an hour on the steps beside one of the lion statues before the others began straggling up the steps. Mark, as spokesman for the group, declared them winners. Standing at the head of the lion, he pretended to read a proclamation: "On beha'f o' de Moles' Society o' the gre-at city of New Yawk, I pronounce Joey and Moitle, de winnahs! An' on beha'f of de Soci'ty, I pre-sent dem wid dis beyootaful silvah trophy!"

Nels, with mock pride, bowed and received the trophy, a tin can Mark had retrieved from the trash.

Then they made a dash for Chock Full O' Nuts for cream cheese sandwiches and coffee.

Back at the Institute, Nels gave Katie the trophy. "Can't take it all the way to Staten Island," he said.

"T'anks, Joey, g'night."

"See yer aroun', Moitle."

Katie admitted molin' was fun but that was the end of fun and games for a while. Determinedly, she returned to the books and Chris could not bring her out again. Katie, you're the worst Mole I know!" she complained. "Stephen would like to date you. Why don't you give him a chance?"

But Katie turned a deaf ear. She did well in classes,

and even in morning chapel she took notes on Dr. Ramsey's exegesis of Romans. No one enjoyed chapel more than Dr. Ramsey. He led the singing with gusto, prayed a short prayer, then expounded the Greek for twenty minutes. He was in his glory, and although he put some students to sleep, he inspired others, particularly the young seminarians who aspired to become scholars.

Katie was coming into her own intellectually. In philosophic discussions she could hold her ground and male students chafed under her attacks.

"Not good," Chris said, shaking her head. "Men don't like a smart woman."

That reminded Katie of Archer when he told her men must win. Katie shrugged her shoulders, "So what? Who cares?"

Girls came to Katie's room to argue predestination and free will until the dawn. Chris was not happy about the bull sessions, but she was nice about it. She could always find a Mole to sit with her in the lobby or play ping-pong in the recreation room.

"This thing of being bent on an education is a bore," Chris told Katie.

"Chris, it pays to sharpen the axe."

"My 'skin of the teeth' philosophy is a two-edged sword." They were walking out of the Institute before breakfast. "True, there are panic times, but with the help of my friends I pull through. On the other hand, 'skin of the teeth' allows free time for the important things in life. By the way, you know 'skin of the teeth' is in the Bible?" Chris was proud that she knew that.

Katie laughed. "Okay, what are the important things in life?"

"Important things like worrying about Joey. Here lately he's been straining his brain over Plato. Nothing worse for ruining a fine mind. First thing you know, he'll become a real mole like you, Katie, burrowing in a book all the time, drop out of the Society. . . . And you're important, Katie. If they didn't make us take thirty minutes exercise every day, you would stay in the mausoleum twenty-four hours straight, seven days a week."

They were going to Central Park. Chris was the only friend Katie had who would get up early enough to make the Central Park trip before Katie had to be in the kitchen to serve breakfast. At the end of Fifty-fifth Street, toward the East River, the sun was coming up like a great orange ball. The dark spire of the Fifth Avenue Presbyterian Church was etched in gold, and along the street, window panes were gilded.

Chris was grumbling. "You're neurotic, that's what you are, Katie. Work, work, work. If I had any sense I wouldn't encourage you—I'd be in my warm bed right now."

"Chris, you are probably right. I probably am neurotic but do you know why I'm up, doing my duty?"

"There is no reason for insanity," she said exasperated.

"At this early hour of every day, my mother is already at work. She's running a sewing machine at full tilt and she'll run it until late this afternoon. She'll come home to a cold house so tired she can't put one foot ahead of the other one. Then she'll read the mail, glance at the headlines, build a fire, cook supper, wash dishes. She'll read the paper, nap on the couch ten minutes, the paper over her face. Later she'll get up, write letters, clean house, and wash or iron before she goes to bed."

They were crossing Columbus Circle to enter the Park. "Why does she work like that?" Chris asked.

"It's necessary."

"Necessary? Necessary for what?"

"For money, Chris, what else?"

"For grief, maybe, but not for money."

"Grief? What in the world are you talking about?"

"Work is an escape, Katie. Look at you. You work your head off because you don't want to think about the war or about home or whatever. Some people thrive on work, some just bury themselves."

Katie was not ready to accept Chris' psychological analysis. "I guess you're going to tell me I should trust the Lord more about my financial needs."

"Not a bad idea, you being a Christian and all." Chris jumped up on the bench, ran along it, jumped to the next bench, and plopped down on it.

They sat looking back at the Plaza Hotel rising above the bare trees, its white front beautiful in the morning sun. Pigeons fluttered about, making their gargling noises, looking for a handout. Katie teased a squirrel with a stick. *Chris is probably right* she thought. She tossed the stick toward a big rock jutting out from the ground. The rocks didn't belong in a city, but neither did the squirrel, or, for that matter, Katie herself.

"The Mole Society is going to Fulton Street Fish Market today. Wanna go?"

Katie shook her head. She wouldn't tell Chris, but she didn't have any money. "Come on, we've gotta' leave," Katie said.

At breakfast, the Duchess led in the morning hymn and Professor Steinberg led in prayer. As he prayed, Katie asked the Lord to send her some money. If she were to teach Sunday school the next day, there had to be a letter from home or somewhere with enough money in it for carfare.

When Katie came up from the dining room, the mail had just come in. She went in the lobby to wait until they put the mail in the boxes. Standing at the window, she watched students playing volleyball for a minute, then sat on the couch. Sun streamed through the tall casement windows onto the Oriental rug. The grand-father clock at the end of the room chimed the half hour, and the happy voices of people chatting at the desk carried into the lobby.

Katie studied the statuette of Benjamin Franklin resting on a marble table, the gift of some socialite to the school. The seated Franklin was cast as a thoughtful figure smiling benignly. Franklin had been enjoyed and maligned by students for several generations and survived them all. For the wealthy donor of the piece, Franklin had been no sacrifice; the Gould or Schwab benefactor scarcely missed him. Ironic that she, Katie MacLeod, called of God, could sit in such luxury without ten cents carfare necessary to teach a Sunday school class.

People were getting quiet. The mail was up. Katie went to look in her box. One letter, a V-mail from Archer. No money.

Dear Katie,

The Bible Mom sent me really had an exciting experience recently. As you know, we put roofs on our foxholes and slit trenches for protection against the rain. Well, this night I went to bed and the Bible in my pocket was uncomfortable so I put it in a crack in the roof of my foxhole and went to sleep. The next morning we moved back a few hundred yards to more favorable positions and I forgot the Bible.

We stayed in the second position several days and during that time the Jerries occupied our old position and I could not retrieve my Bible. During the time that I was mourning my Bible, our artillery was constantly pounding at these positions. The Air Corps was strafing and bombing and from my position I gave up hope of ever seeing the Bible again. Even if it escaped the shells and bombs, some Jerry would take it as a souvenir.

Several days later I got permission to go back to the area. I found my foxhole pretty well in shambles with a shattered tree lying across it. I dug into the hole and sure enough, there was my Bible and billfold, safe and sound. Apparently the Jerry who used my hole was too scared to look around for souvenirs. . . .

Thank you for praying. Twice recently, I was saved from sure death. Once, my platoon made it to a bomb shelter but I didn't. The shelter suffered a direct hit and every man was lost.

The other time, the Jerry had pity on me. I was

looking straight up the barrel of his gun. Then he ran without shooting. Of course, you are not to tell Mom these things.

Love,
Archer

Katie folded the V-letter carefully, ashamed that she had grumbled about money.

The Mole Society was congregating in front of the elevators. "Better come along, Moitle," Nels coaxed.

She smiled. "Not this time."

Chris came over to persuade her. "Come on, Katie. You'll have fun with Joey."

"Not today."

"You don't like him?"

"It's not that."

"He reminds me of Ashley in *Gone with the Wind.*"

"Sounds like you have a crush on him, Chris."

Chris shook her head. "Not my type. I go for Rhett Butler."

After they left, Katie went into the chapel to be alone. She reread Archer's letter and felt ashamed for feeling sorry for herself. She asked forgiveness and thanked God for sparing Archer's life.

One of the hymnals was on the seat; she thumbed through its pages. There was Daddy's hymn, "Will There Be Any Stars in My Crown?" She had never seen it in a hymnbook before.

"Well," she said to herself, closing the book and getting up, "guess I'll have to be a good Christian like Chris says, and trust the Lord for carfare."

On Sunday morning, when no money had appeared, trusting wasn't easy. Dressed and waiting in the lobby for the other students, Katie ran over in her mind exactly what she was doing. To walk out the door without money was really kind of foolish. What would the others think when she had to ask them for a loan at the turnstile? Knowing them, they might not have a dime to spare.

Then she had an idea—*sometimes loose change falls*

out of pockets behind sofa cushions. Katie slipped into the
lobby to search. But the Duchess was in there admiring
the Lord's Day, and you couldn't very well take the
lobby apart while the Duchess was there rejoicing in
the resurrection.

Students were spilling off the elevators with their
Bibles, flannelboard, trumpets—a tacky-looking lot.
"Coming, Katie?" someone called. Professor Rinaldo
was with them, going somewhere to preach. Katie was
nervous. If there was any person she did not want to be
embarrassed in front of, it was Professor Rinaldo.

Dirty snow piled high along the curb and slush in the
street splashed with every passing car. Katie tried to
think of an excuse to go back to the school. While she
was thinking, they reached the subway and were troop-
ing down to the tunnel. The professor, with his usual
charm, directed her to go ahead of him. At the turnstile,
he stepped ahead and held up a handful of nickels. "My
pleasure," he said and dropped money in the slot for
each of them as they passed through.

As the train screamed underground to Harlem, Katie
thanked God for the remarkable answer to prayer. Still,
confidence did not soar that carfare would be forth-
coming for the return trip. She nudged the girl next to
her. "How far's the mission from school?"

"Fifty blocks or more."

I could walk it, Katie thought.

That Sunday, for the first time in all the months they
had taught, the superintendent presented each of the
student teachers an envelope. Inside were three one-
dollar bills for carfare!

Katie promised that she would never again doubt
that the Lord would provide.

Before Christmas, Archer wrote that he was sending
a ring to the girl, Eleanor, in Kansas.

*I asked Mom to take money out of my account and buy
the ring. Don't get me wrong; Eleanor knows I will
never leave Charlotte. I plan to take care of Mom.*

359

Katie folded the letter and put it back in the envelope. If Archer did make it through the war, he would never be home again. He would be like all the others—Alice, Jane, Brother—scattered to the four winds once they married. In two years Timothy would finish high school and go off to college. It didn't take a prophet to read the handwriting on the wall—someone would have to stay single to send him to school.

Chris interrupted Katie's thoughts. "The Moles are going to the Planetarium Saturday. Wanna go?"

"If I can get somebody to work for me."

"Have them work lunch and dinner. We'll spend the day."

The Moles not only went to the planetarium, they traipsed all over the Museum of Natural History, bought hot dogs from a vendor, and walked through the Park to the Metropolitan Museum of Art. Nels regaled them with limericks and puns, and in the Park he got so carried away he mimicked Maurice Evans playing the lead in the *Taming of the Shrew*. He used the pavement beneath the statues and busts of the greats as his stage. Passersby stopped, intrigued by his performance. It was a wild day!

Coming home, they stopped at Nedick's, and Nels convened a conclave. Heads close together, he spoke in a clandestine whisper. "Not a word of this back at the Institute. Never let it be said that the Moles are getting cultured!"

"Not a word," they swore, shaking their heads with mock gravity.

To ensure their reputation, their next excursion was strictly frivolous. Mom and Pop Ellison lived in Flushing and their home was open to Institute students day or night. Nels and Mark carried keys to the Ellison house. "We'll go skating at the old World's Fair grounds," Chris said. "Then we'll go over to Ellisons and eat."

Ellisons weren't home when they arrived, so they used Mark's key. Furniture was stacked in the center of the room and rugs were rolled up. "They've refinished the floors," Mark observed. "Step over."

By stepping from rug to rug, they reached the refrigerator without mishap. Mom and Pop would consider it a compliment that they felt so free. They gorged on leftovers and wrote a note stating that they had obligingly "cleaned out the refrigerator." "Face it, Katie," Nels said, with a flourish of the pen, "the Moles can say, 'I love you' as no one else can."

The excursion was the last one before Christmas. Bing Crosby's *White Christmas* played over the radio in every dormitory room, and the nostalgia of it made her sad. Archer had sung it constantly when he was home on his last furlough. Another Christmas without him would be dismal. No one was coming home except Katie.

She was late getting home—trains were so packed she couldn't get aboard. By the time Katie arrived, the tree was up in the living room. It was a cedar tree and its fragrance brought a rush of Bull Creek memories. The same bells and angels that had adorned the tree back then, decorated it again.

She and Timothy sat watching the lights blinking as they waited for Mama to come home from work.

"Timothy, do you remember Christmas on Bull Creek?"

"I remember my teddy bear." He hesitated. "Katie, do you remember the day Daddy left home?"

"Yes. Do you?"

"I remember having the measles. Katie, what was he like?" Timothy's blue eyes bore an innocence that was hard to bear.

"Oh, Timothy—it's hard to say. He and Mama are a lot alike and a lot different. They both love cows and children and they're both sentimental."

"How are they different?"

"Well, Daddy can make money but he can't keep it. Mama, on the other hand, can manage money. I guess you would say Daddy is a plunger—he'll take risks—

but Mama is conservative—she looks for security."

"Did they get on well together?"

"Yes. They had their differences, but they never quarreled in front of us or let on that anything was wrong." Katie thought of the day in the doorway when Daddy muttered, "Witch." "What a great team they would have made if either of them could have said, 'I'm sorry.'"

"You mean you think there was trouble between them?"

"Nothing they had not lived with a long time. Daddy was acting all out of character the day he left. I'm only saying that if they had differences, neither of them could ever apologize."

"Was it me, Katie? Did I cause all this?"

"What! Whatever would make you think that? Timothy, I know Daddy's poor heart aches that he has not known you. You are a son who would make any father proud." She walked to the window. "I can't conceive of what keeps him away from us."

"Maybe he's dead."

"No. Brother says it's unusual for a body not to be identified and the next of kin notified."

"You know what I think?"

"No, what?"

"I think he's in prison."

"Don't ever say that around Mama."

They heard a bus stop. Timothy put on his coat to go meet Mama, and Katie started putting supper on the table.

When Mama and Timothy came in the door, Timothy took the packages upstairs and Mama took off her coat and gloves. Removing her hat, she fluffed her hair. She was wearing it shorter, in waves, and she was as pretty as ever, but her hair was gray and the sadness of her eyes showed through at times.

They knew what was uppermost in their minds and without preliminary, Katie asked, "Has Jane found any clues?"

362

"No, but she's turning the world upside down in her search."

"I know. She tells me in every letter to keep looking." She handed Mama the mail.

"It's been nearly twelve years, Katie. Sometimes I despair of ever finding him." The sadness came in Mama's eyes and did not go away. Katie determined to renew her efforts to find Daddy.

Katie decided that life was too serious to run around the city with children playing games. She dropped out of the Mole Society. At best she had a year and a half before graduating with a three-year diploma. She had to make the most of it.

The Bible Society colporteur needed a helper for hospital visitation and Katie volunteered. Miss Ramseur, an indefatigable worker, took her on rounds at Bellevue, St. Vincent's, the Lying-in Hospital, and Roosevelt.

Katie carried scripture portions in twenty-five different languages or dialects. The problem was in finding the correct language portion for the patient who spoke no English. When totally baffled, Katie held up each of the portions until the patient recognized his own language.

The horrible illnesses, sick people in isolation, the mentally distraught, the terminal cases—all weighed heavily on Katie's heart. She came back to the Institute and tried to pray for them. She suffered nightmares— Daddy in an isolation ward; Daddy dying.

When male students were going to the docks to preach to the longshoremen, Katie wanted to go with them, but the Moles told her it was no place for a girl.

"Tell you what, Katie," Steven said. "if you'll go to the St. Patrick's Day parade with us, I'll take you to Jerry McAuley's Mission Saturday night."

In Steven O'Brian's honor, the Moles never missed a St. Patrick's Day parade. Katie had never been to one, so they struck a bargain.

In the mission, Katie sat on the platform with Steven

and the rest of the gospel team from the Institute. Studying the faces of derelicts seated in the audience, Katie discerned traces of something from their former lives. The slack contours did not mask the fine intelligence of the brow; the listless limbs did not hide sensitive hands.

Later the mission superintendent confirmed her observations. "That man was a concert pianist—that one a banker. We even have preachers, surgeons, artists."

As they left the mission, Katie was thinking that even a man like Malcolm MacLeod could wind up in a mission.

After that night, she volunteered for every rescue mission assignment in the city. Wherever they sent her, she searched the audience, thinking she might find him. She even told the superintendents what he looked like, his business, his habits, and although none of them had seen him, they promised to keep an eye out for him.

Men in rescue missions became very special to Katie. They burdened her, and one night at the Bowery Mission, the burden became too much. Asked to speak a few words, she told the men about her father and how she searched their faces hoping she might find him.

When the invitation was given, thirteen men came forward, tears streaming down their faces. No doubt each of them had left a wife and children somewhere. Perhaps now they would have what it would take to go home to them. Katie felt good about what she had done.

"Katie," Chris asked, "what's with you going to all these skid row missions? Sure you're not getting superspiritual?"

Katie laughed. "Not a chance. Just collecting material to write about someday."

"Then go with me and Mark to the newsreel theater tonight. We're going to the Embassy. I keep thinking I'll see my brother in one of those films from the front."

"Don't you know you'll never find anybody by looking for them?" Katie said wearily. "If they don't come back to you, you'll never see them again."

"Katie—" Chris looked worried. "Are you sure you feel okay?"

"Oh, I'm just tired."

"Katie, what you need is a good love affair."

"Affair?" Katie raised her eyebrows.

"You know what I mean. One day it will come to you. With all your defenses intact, love will come to you—quickly, unexpectedly and—boom!—you'll be swept off your feet."

Katie smiled. "Run along, Chris. Have a good time."

Victory in Europe seemed imminent during the last days of April. At least school would soon be out and Katie would be heading home.

The news broke on May 7. German troops had surrendered to General Eisenhower.

Katie ran up the steps two at a time and burst onto the fourth floor yelling, "He won the War! He won the War! Archer won the War!"

Everybody was hysterical—shouting, screaming, crying!

"Come on, Katie," yelled Chris. "Let's get the Moles and go to Times Square!"

A sea of people jammed the Square, a blitz of paper filled the canyon walls, servicemen climbed lamp posts, car horns blew, church bells rang. There was pandemonium! People were drinking, dancing, weeping, laughing, kissing in the streets. The city was wild with joy!

TWENTY-SIX
Brahms
and
Lilacs

It was not until later that the horrors of Dachau,
Buchenwald, and Auschwitz filled the newsreels with
pictures and stories that shocked the civilized world.
The day Professor Steinberg learned that his mother
and brother had died in the gas chamber of Dachau, no
one else knew. He stood alone in the lobby at the
casement window, his face lifted toward the stars. The
room was full of young people laughing and talking.
Katie sensed a strangeness about him, despite his strict
military bearing. When she spoke, he acknowledged
her presence with a courtly bow of his head. "Miss
MacLeod, I was wondering if some of the students
would care to go with me for a street meeting?"

Katie shied away from street meetings but an over-
whelming compassion for the little man made her say,
"Professor Steinberg, I'd be delighted to go."

A few days later Chris told Katie about his tragedy.
"Another brother is dying with tuberculosis."

Katie thought of her own good fortune in having
Archer come through the war without a scratch. Archer
came home on one of the first troop ships and lost no

time in going to Kansas to marry Eleanor.

Brother would not be home until Japan surrendered, but he wasn't in any danger—he wasn't even overseas.

That summer, Katie worked in the hardware store and helped Mama with the gardening and canning. The next year was to be her third and last at the Institute, but Katie knew she needed more education. An additional two years with some work at the university would give her a degree.

Mama was bending over the pea vines picking peas when she asked, "Katie, when you graduate next year, exactly what are you prepared to do?"

"I don't know, Mama. Work in a church. Something like that."

"Don't you think you should get some courses and qualify for a teaching certificate?"

"What about Timothy? How are we going to send him to college?"

"We'll manage. The Lord provides, doesn't he?"

"It'll take me three years—counting next year."

"That will be three years well spent." Mama picked up the pan and headed for the house. Mama had just turned fifty-two, and she was as shapely as ever with ankles Chris would admire. Her smooth skin kept her youthful looking.

"Mama, do you ever see Mr. Kerr now?"

"Oh, occasionally."

"Mama—" Katie hesitated. "Why don't you go out with him?"

"Katie, I'm a married woman."

"It's been thirteen years."

"And it may be thirteen more but that doesn't change the fact."

They sat in the kitchen to shell peas.

"Mama, don't you ever get lonely?"

Mama's blue eyes told her she had pressed too close. Katie kissed her cheek.

"Mama, I've seen too many broken men—too many wasted lives—I wonder if we should look for Daddy any longer. Timothy is nearly grown—I wonder if anything would be accomplished by finding him now?"

"What do you mean 'accomplished'? If he is broken— if his life is being wasted, that is all the more reason for finding him."

The bombs were dropped on Hiroshima and Nagasaki, and in August Japan surrendered. By September, ex-GI's were flocking to the Institute. They had thrown away their guns and bottles and came to the Institute for spiritual weapons. They were eager to return as missionaries to Africa, Europe, Japan.

They were a breed apart. None was unscathed by the war they did not want to talk about. They were nervous, critical, tough, and they wanted to get married *now*. They had a profound effect on the student body.

The Mole Society felt their spirits dampened by the no-nonsense attitude of the GI's. When George Truesdale, ex-Army corporal, spotted Katie, he never suspected she was a Mole. "Where do you want to go?" he asked on their first date.

"The New York Stock Exchange."

"Are you serious?"

"I've never been there. I'd like to see it."

Reluctantly, he took her, but his cynicism made the visit less than enjoyable. They looked down on the brokers' frantic scramble, the big board signaling the rise and decline of their fortunes, and George had a lot to say about it. "Worshiping the god Mammon," he said. "Gambling—that's what it is. I gambled three straight years in the Army. Didn't win a dime—and I'm a shark."

George had also been an alcoholic and who knows what else. Reacting to his bitter past, he never let up. George knew what was wrong with the world and he gave it short shrift. Katie decided he needed her to settle him down, give him perspective.

Unfortunately, George did not see her attention as that at all. Writing from White Plains on a Friday, he told Katie he could not live without her. He would see her Monday for her answer.

Katie received the letter Monday, read it in the lobby, and rushed upstairs to get ready for the day.

"Chris, what do I do? I want to keep going with George for a while."

"Until he gets his feet on the ground, right?"

"Right."

"Well, Katie, let his *mother* do that."

George came to spend the day. They went first to Prospect Park and he rented a boat to row them out on the lake. Katie did not agree with Chris—she was not mothering George—she was befriending him. That was an important role to play even if marriage was out of the question.

No doubt this rowing on the lake was George's idea of being romantic, and when he got tired rowing he would pop the question.

He rowed across the lake and back but he did not pop the question. Surely George didn't lack nerve—this man who had killed Japs, afraid to propose?

From Prospect Park they went back to Manhattan and with part of the afternoon left, decided to take the ferry over to Staten Island. George was quiet and that was all right with Katie. He held her hand and whistled through his teeth the way he always did. Leaning on the rail, watching the white spray and the gulls flocking alongside, Katie decided George was waiting for night to come.

On the other side, he paid the return fare and they sat watching the sun go down over Jersey. Night came on quickly, a full moon rising over Brooklyn and the New York Bay. If a romantic setting was what he wanted, the star studded sky and the lights of Manhattan's skyscrapers reflecting in the broad water, were hard to beat.

But nothing was said. Katie was perplexed. By the time they reached the Institute she knew he was not going to say anything about the letter. Going up in the elevator, she felt relieved, but she felt let down as well.

Katie saw George in classes, and they chatted afterward. With some of the Moles they went to Chock Full O' Nuts for doughnuts, but it wasn't until two weeks later that Katie learned what had happened.

"Katie, I found out what happened," Chris announced. "Between the time George wrote that letter and the time he saw you on Monday, a gorgeous redhead crossed his path!"

"A gorgeous *redhead*?" Katie rolled over on the bed, laughing. "Who can compete with a redhead, much less a *gorgeous* redhead!"

"Touché!"

During Christmas vacation, George married the redhead. By that time, Katie had forgotten about George and everything else that was not work or study. Instead of working in the kitchen, she ran the elevator and worked nights on the switchboard.

Early Sunday mornings on the train to Tuckahoe, where Katie taught Sunday school, she began thinking about writing. The train followed the Bronx River, not too far from Hawthorne's Sleepy Hollow locale. To write well would require a background in English, and Katie was considering N.Y.U. Graduate School.

Professor Rinaldo advised, "Stay at the Institute until you get your degree, then go to graduate school."

Such a plan would make a grand total of six years— out of the question. The Moles had encouraged her. "You can do it," Nels Jensen said. "I'm doing it, Moitle. When I graduate this year, I have three more years in seminary."

"How are you going to do it?"

"Work nights, I *have* to do it—my church won't ordain me without seminary."

Mark spoke up, "Joey, if you get any more theology there'll be no living with you!"

True, Nels Jensen had turned into a serious student. From a boy burrowing around in subterranean corridors, he had grown into a promising scholar. With Nels there could be enlightening conversation; he taught the Moles interesting insights into Kant, Hume, and Barth. There were long discussions in the lobby. Ben Franklin would have been proud of them.

Chris sought out Nels when tests were due. If Nels tutored her she could pass. The entire Mole Society was called in when she had a paper to write. Chris went to pieces over papers. Every Mole went through the agony of ethical temptation because it would be so much easier to write the paper for her than to help her. But all in all, they owed Chris a lot. Chris kept them together, sewed up their personal rifts when they argued too heatedly, mended their souls when they were tired or broke. Of them all, Chris was the one with the understanding heart.

"You mess with Katie," Chris vowed, "and she'll write you in a story and spread you coast to coast! I'm the affectionate, lovable kind—I care about you Moles!"

It was Chris, on that beautiful April Sunday, who insisted that Katie come away to celebrate her birthday. The two of them rode out on the train to Flushing to Mom and Pop Ellison's, and when they arrived, the Moles were there with a surprise party already in progress.

Lilacs filled the house with a heady fragrance. Greta was playing the piano and they were singing. Pop Ellison's cherubic face brightened the party. Katie was glad she came.

The Moles were in such high spirits, they exhausted themselves. After dinner the Ellisons left to visit with friends, so the Moles had the house to themselves.

Mark and Chris lay on the living room floor listening to Brahms; Steven and Greta went for a walk; Todd and Gretchen played chess.

Katie sat on one end of the couch, thumbing a *Life* magazine. Nels looked down at her and smiled. His face looked different to her. "May I?" he asked and his voice was soft.

"Sure." She made room for him.

"Mind if I stretch out?" He lay on his side on the couch, his head in Katie's lap. It was innocent enough, yet she felt herself strangely stirred.

Katie was seeing Nels Jensen with an unexpected joy; the kind of joy she felt when first glimpsing the bluebonnets—a rush of feeling.

How was it that she had never looked at him, truly looked at him to see him as he was? The strong Nordic bones of his face were beautiful—she wanted to trace his brow with her finger, his nose, his lips, his chin—but she didn't.

Strands of gold showed in his dark hair. She touched his hair with her fingers, smoothed the waves back from his brow. Like a child, he lay content, loving to be touched. When Katie's fingers stopped, Nels turned on his back, looked up at her into her eyes. She was irresistibly drawn to him, leaned down, and kissed him unashamedly.

He reached for her and the passion she felt for him was unlike anything she had ever known. Nels kissed her gently, again and again, caressing her, stroking her hair. She trembled in his arms for the pleasure she felt.

That night, lying in the upper bunk, Katie could hear the deep-throated sound of the *Queen Mary* coming up the Hudson. Chris, in the bunk below, was breathing soundly, dead to the world. Katie could not stop thinking about Nels and went over and over in her mind every detail of the day. She had not known desire could be so strong. Maybe it was the Brahms and lilacs . . . what they call "a fit of passion." *Oh, Lord, let it be more than that—let it be real.* She turned over to go to sleep.

Sleep wouldn't come. Overhead was the little wall lamp she read by. Feeling for it, she found the switch and turned it on. Reaching down to the bureau, she picked up the Bible. Settling back on the pillow, Katie found the *Song of Solomon* and began to read.

In the clear light of day, Katie still felt exhilarated despite the restless night. There were no lilacs or

Brahms and yet the strong steady waves of joy passed over her. In the shower at the end of the hall, she made her decision—she would avoid Nels. She had to. She turned her face to the shower head and let the water stream down over her. There would have to be distance between them because whatever this was, it could get out of hand.

Toweling herself dry, praying she would have the strength, Katie's confidence was weak. "Please, Lord," she prayed. "Help me."

She did not see Nels until noon. He tried to be casual—threw up his hand and called, "Hi, Moitle," but the name sounded wrong. He never called her Moitle again.

She was standing on the stairs ready to go up to the dorm floor. He stood below her, a deep earnestness in his eyes. He had not slept—his whole appearance was disheveled. The corduroy jacket, the gray slacks, were rumpled; his collar was open.

"Katie," he began again, "could we go some place to talk?"

He was pleading. She wanted to reach down and touch his dear face. "Not now," she said, smiling, trying to control her voice. "Let's wait a while."

She stood gripping the railing as he literally backed away—out of touch—putting distance between them. He held her eyes until he turned the corner out of sight.

Sometime later, Nels came to understand. He said so, the only way he knew how. "After Metropolitan, there's seminary for me, Katie—three long years of seminary." The pain in his voice told her plainly that in his mind theirs was no "fit of passion"—no passing thing. They would have to be careful; they had a long time to wait if ever they were meant to be.

Nels did his part. He took care not to allow their lives to melt into one mold of familiarity, going to classes together, eating together, studying together. He planned their dates as separate and distinct events, and made them as elegant as he could afford them to be.

Somehow he finagled tickets for the last of the season's operas, Verdi's *Aida,* and Chris helped Katie dress for the occasion. Nels knew about opera. A native New Yorker, he had grown up with concerts and theater.

He knew the Village and steered Katie down Bleeker Street to view a sidewalk art show. They lunched in a clam bar and fed pigeons in Washington Square. A flower vendor in the Square had violets for sale and Katie could not resist them. With his last dollar, Nels purchased a bunch for her. There was nothing he wouldn't do for her, and Katie took pleasure in knowing that she was the one who made him so radiantly happy. There was no suppressing his exuberance.

The New York Philharmonic was playing its last concert and Nels took Katie to hear it at Carnegie Hall. When the orchestra began playing, Katie felt uneasy. The uneasiness mounted to an irrational sense of fear. She had been holding Nels's arm—now she was clutching it.

"What's the matter, Katie?"

"I don't know—" Her voice was hardly audible. Slowly something was taking shape in her mind. "Nels, what are they playing?"

"*The New World Symphony.*"

"Wagon Wheels?"

He nodded. "The same."

The New World Symphony, she remembered. *That's what Mama called the music in the movie the day Daddy touched me!*

Katie tried to get hold of herself, but as the slow, powerful strains mounted, the trauma of that terrible day would not be stilled.

"Nels, please, could we leave?"

"Of course."

In a corner of Schraft's, Katie tried to explain. "I've never told anyone about this, Nels."

"You don't have to talk."

"But I want to." For the first time in her life Katie

did indeed want to talk about it. At first, the words trickled forth like a slow leak in a dam, but then they flowed easily. She told him everything.

Back at the Institute, Nels pressed the elevator button for the eleventh floor. They were alone in the elevator and when they reached the top floor, he led her to the service stairs that went up to the roof. When they stepped onto the roof, wind whipped over the parapet, bringing with it the sooty smell of the city. The din of traffic below was a constant drone and above the drone sounded the tugboats' plaintive horns. The night sky was clear and studded with stars. Nels took Katie in his arms and held her close.

TWENTY-SEVEN
Myths Must Die

The summer at home without Nels was a long one. He was working in a camp in New England, and although he wrote every day, it was not the same as being with him. Lying in the hot upstairs room, Katie wondered how she could survive three years' separation when he went to seminary.

Mama was in the other bed, her labored breathing battling exhaustion. An oscillating fan on the floor swept the air back and forth, its blade and guard rattling predictably.

Chris was right about Mama—work was escape, a drowning out of pain. Katie propped herself up on her elbow and watched her mother sleeping. Mama had been alone fourteen years, and in that time she had not stopped loving. Perhaps, somewhere out there, Daddy was loving back, sick with the same pain of separation.

Katie rolled back on the bed. She loved like Mama—she knew she did. There was one man for her and no other—one commitment never to change, never to waver.

If loving Nels turned out to cause pain such as Mama endured, there was no question in Katie's mind that she could survive as Mama had. But if, like Daddy, after twenty-two years of marriage, Nels disappeared, Katie wondered if she could bear the suffering brought to their children. For a boy like Timothy never to know his father, for Archer to assume the responsibilities of a man when yet a child—could she stand that? Could she support them as Mama had done and make the best of life's cruelties? If the separation had been caused by death, there would not have been the shame, the terrible shame that even now as adults, haunted them.

Maybe Nels and I won't have children, she thought, but then rejected the idea. *I want to bear his children and make a family for us.*

Mama murmured in her sleep, "Malcolm...Malcolm."

Sometime in the wee hours, Katie fell asleep. A nightmare tormented her—Daddy behind bars, insane. Over and over again. She woke up drenched with perspiration, too afraid to go back to sleep.

In July, Jane wrote home that she was pregnant and couldn't come. Alice and Chuck came for a week with Betty and little Malcolm. Brother and Rebekah joined them as they visited in the backyard. They reminisced about Daddy, laughing about the day they came up from the schoolhouse and found him making cigarettes out of toilet paper. They talked about Maas and Mr. Frady; the box supper and the fish fry. They joked about coasting in the Cadillac and they sang all the stanzas of "Redwing." They grew wistful as they described to each other the moon coming up over Cat Mountain; the exquisite beauty of the ice storm; the long view from the boardwalk.

Chuck and Rebekah sat silent, respectful of the emotion Bull Creek stirred in the MacLeods. "Honey," Brother said to his wife, "when we lived on Bull Creek we had less than we have ever had, but we were the happiest. Life was so simple—if we had enough to eat, we had nothing else to worry about."

Brother was heavier than before the War. At thirty-three, his hair was receding from his forehead. He still bore a striking resemblance to Daddy. His mannerisms were the same—the pulling of the ear, the way he pulled at the crease in his pants to prevent wrinkles. But Brother did not think like Daddy. Thrifty and cautious, he was like Mama. "Never pay anyone to do something you can do yourself." He lived by that.

Archer wrote that he and Eleanor could not find a place to live and he had decided to re-enlist. They were going back to Germany.

Jane couldn't find a place to live, either. She was still living in one room. With the baby coming, they were desperate. Mama invited them to come home, but Jane wrote, "I want to stay in Atlanta because I have another idea for finding Daddy. I'm sure he's alive. I hate to tell you this, but Aunt Claire wrote me that Granddaddy MacLeod died a month ago. There's only one reason they did not tell us—so that we wouldn't attend the funeral. I believe Daddy was there."

Mama pondered the letter for a while. "What do you think, Katie?"

Katie shook her head. "I don't know."

Nels wrote that he had a surprise for Katie, and in August she left early for New York. He met her at the station, tanned and fit from the summer sun and air. He teased her as long as he could, then told her while they waited for the bus. "I've been accepted at New York Seminary. I'll be staying here!"

New York Seminary was in Manhattan and although Nels would be busy at school, commuting and working, they would see each other.

Back at school, she rushed to tell Chris. "Chris!"

"I know," she answered. "He's staying in New York. What's more, I have another surprise for you."

"What is it?"

"President Ramsey wants you to work in the Admissions Office—not as a flunky but as one of the big brass!"

"You're kidding me!"

"If I'm kidding, I married the pope."

"Oh, Chris. They'll pay me enough to save money for N.Y.U."

"You'll need it if you go to N.Y.U. Tuition is twenty dollars a credit point."

"The Lord is answering prayer, Chris."

"Apparently. The timetable is perfect. Nels will be in seminary three years, you will get your degree in two years and your Master's the third year. Then you can waltz down the aisle."

"He hasn't asked me yet."

"Nothing to worry about."

Katie had never been happier. She plunged into the office work and school, and saw Nels at least once a week. They talked on the phone and scribbled poems to each other. Chris said that Katie was again tolerable to live with.

With the coming of finals, Katie assumed Nels's duty of tutoring Chris. This was Chris's second trip through Old Testament History, and if Katie didn't drill her thoroughly, it wouldn't be her last.

"What's Shekinah glory?" Chris asked.

"It's the cloud that came down on the holiest of holies in the tabernacle."

"Where's that in the Bible?"

"It's not in the Bible."

"What do you mean it's not in the Bible? Professor Steinberg is always talking about the 'Shekinah glory.'"

"Well, that's what the Jews called it. When the cloud lifted off the tabernacle, the Children of Israel knew it was time to move."

"The cloud was the 'Shekinah glory'?"

"That's what I said, Chris." Katie tried to be patient. "The Shekinah glory represented the presence of God with his people."

"Is that the same as the pillar of fire by night and the cloud by day?"

"The same."

"How come it wasn't a pillar of fire in the day-time?"

"I don't know. Maybe they needed a shade from the desert sun."

"Why was it a pillar of fire at night?"

"So they could see it. By the way, you know when the Children of Israel crossed the Red Sea, the cloud went behind them."

"How come?"

"Well, they crossed the sea at night, and the cloud was a light to the Children of Israel, but on its other side, the side toward the Egyptians, the cloud was dark."

"How come?"

"To confuse the enemy, I guess. Come on, Chris, we can't spend all night on this."

Chris passed her finals and the Moles treated her to an evening out. They went crosstown to Park Avenue and wormed their way through tunnels for an hour. They moled all the way to Grand Central Station. There they bought Chris supper in the Oyster Bar and played the "Whispering Gallery" game. Outside the Oyster Bar was the gallery, a low ceilinged, tiled rotunda which produced mysterious acoustics. One Mole would stand in a corner of the rotunda, facing the wall. Another one would stand against the wall in the corner diagonally opposite, twenty feet away. Whatever they whispered was clearly heard by the Mole in the opposite corner.

Nels waited until the others had had their turns, then he placed Katie in the corner opposite his and whispered, "I love you, Katie." Katie whispered back, "I love you, too."

With the coming of Spring, the inevitable began to press in on the consciousness of the Moles. Graduation would mean the society would lose half its members. They met to draw up plans for reunions, but they were grasping at straws; there was no way to prevent the end. The realization caused them to plunge into a feverish round of activities in the closing months of school. At

Easter, on Palm Sunday, they went to St. Bartholomew's to hear St. Matthew's Passion. The concert had a wonderfully moving effect on them as if the body and blood of Christ had been shared. Mystically, they felt themselves bonded together and to Christ so strongly they could not speak.

On the street, Chris broke the silence. "Whatever must heaven be if we can feel this close now?"

"Until we get to heaven, let's make the most of what we have here," Mark said. "Katie's birthday is next on the calendar—let's make it a big one at Ellison's."

Nels voted him down. "Katie's birthday is for Katie and me."

Arranging time to be together was difficult because of Katie's admissions duties and Nels' hectic schedule, but they saved up their free time in order to have the entire day together.

Nels came dressed in gray slacks and pullover sweater, trench coat slung over his arm. "Pessimist," she said, smiling.

"New York doesn't yet know it's April. And if it did, the month qualifies for showers."

He stopped in a grocery for picnic food; then they took the train to Pelham Bay Park.

Orchard Beach was deserted. Wind coming across the sound was chilly and Nels put his arm around Katie. Little white caps played on the water roughened by the wind and a sailboat was bucking the channel. Water birds skimmed near shore and ran ahead of them on the sand.

Katie asked Nels something about soteriology, partly because she knew the subject interested him and partly to keep the distance. He followed her lead. They both knew that on that beautiful shore alone they could succumb to each other too easily and complicate everything.

"Katie, I stumbled onto something interesting in Paul's letters to Timothy. It's about Demas and Alexander. Paul said, 'Demas has forsaken me,' and 'Alexander, the coppersmith, has done me wrong,' or something like that."

"So?"

"Well, I wonder why Paul didn't forgive them and patch things up." There was a twinkle in his eye. "Aren't we supposed to forgive everyone who ever does us harm?"

"Until 'seventy times seven.'"

"Yes, but that isn't all Jesus said about forgiving." He spoke carefully, with some hesitancy. "Jesus said, 'If thy brother trespass against thee, rebuke him; and if he repent, forgive him.' We can't overlook the 'repent' part." He picked up a stick and tossed it playfully at the birds.

"Well, what if the offender doesn't repent?"

"Don't you think that's what Paul ran into? Neither Demas nor Alexander repented and their relationship with Paul was broken."

"Think Paul carried a grudge?"

Nels smiled, "Hardly. If Paul had an unforgiving spirit, he too, would have been essentially unrepentant."

Katie thought on the problem. Out where the sailboat battled, the sunlight on a broad sweep of water was dazzling. "Well, Jesus asked forgiveness for the men who were crucifying him, and they didn't repent."

"True. Jesus said, 'Father, forgive them, they know not what they do.' Perhaps they were sinning ignorantly. Perhaps that is another category like the minor offenses we're told to bear. The slap on the cheek is a small injustice which we can turn to an opportunity to show grace. 'Turn the other cheek.' 'Go the second mile.'"

His eyes were following a gull flapping inland over the trees. Nels had the build of a swimmer, his strength in his shoulders. His hair, touseled by the wind, was flecked with golden tints and his young face, lifted to the sky, seemed seasoned and strong.

"Nels, no matter what you did to me, I would automatically forgive you."

He turned back to her and caressed her cheek. "If you love me, you would grieve over my sin and pray for me, Katie. You would talk with me and try to lead me to repentance. You would be gentle and kind and loving but you should hold me to the truth. God forgives on the basis of repentance; we can't set ourselves up as somehow more loving, more forgiving than God."

"Have you thought through all of this?"

"I'm in the process. That's why I needed to talk with you."

They stopped to throw pebbles in the water. The white sail of the boat bobbing in the distance was nearly out of sight. "Are you hungry?" she asked.

"Starved!"

They found some large boulders to shield them from the wind, and Nels built a fire. Katie unpacked the lunch.

They huddled beside the fire to roast the franks and for warmth. The heat swelled the plump weiners, and split their skins so that oil dripped in the flames with a hissing sound.

"Katie," Nels said, his voice so relaxed as to be almost guttural. "I once vowed I would never tell a girl I loved her until I was in a position to marry her."

"But you broke your vow in the Whispering Gallery. Or was that only a game?"

"I broke my vow."

"Does it matter a great deal to you?"

"It matters that I cannot marry you today." They were fitting franks into rolls. "Katie, I want to spend the rest of my life with you." He reached for the relish. "Do you want to spend the rest of your life with me?"

She laid down the roll, put her arms around his neck and looked into his eyes. "Need you ask?" She kissed him.

"Oh, Katie," he murmured, pulling her to himself.

Katie went soft in his arms.

Nels loved her in his gentle, sensitive way until Katie knew she had to pull away. She whispered, "I'm sorry," and, reluctantly, he released her.

The hot dogs were cold. She began preparing more. Nels leaned back on the rock smiling, his eyes following her. "I love you, Katie MacLeod," he said, "with the wind in your hair and your soft, sweet face lit by the sun. Won't it be Paradise when we can take our fill of love?"

Katie looked back at him. "Nels, it's Paradise just being here with you. I can't imagine what it'll be like to be married."

"Katie, were you ever in love before?"

She shook her head. "Were you?"

He smiled. "At fifteen."

"Who was she?"

"My history teacher." They laughed. "Katie, how many boys have you kissed?"

"Only David."

"What was it like?"

"Like kissing the back of my hand."

After they had eaten and put out the fire, Nels and Katie strolled along the beach, their arms around each other. There was a tenderness about him in the way he spoke. "Loving enough to be strong, each for the other's sake, has kept us safe, Katie, and it has done more.

"Our love, like a spring running over dry ground in rivulets, seeks courses in which to flow. . . . The little streams join each other here and there until at last they come together in one channel. . . . Like the spring, our love seeks ways of touching one another at many junctures until we can finally merge and our lives become one."

She leaned against him and his cheek rested on her head. "It's been a wonderful day, Nels."

"Happy birthday, Katie."

When they reached the Institute, a long distance call was waiting for Katie. It was from Mama!

"Katie, there's nothing you can do about this except pray, but I wanted you to know that the duplex has been sold and we must vacate within a month."

"Oh, Mama, whatever will you do?"

"We're looking for a house to rent or even to buy, but there's nothing. Ethel has offered to have us live with her, but we don't want that."

"Mama, if you find a place and it costs more, I can help you with the rent. I'll be working year round in Admissions and I can do it on my salary."

"Just pray, Katie."

What Katie did not tell Mama was that any money she sent home would be the money she was saving for N.Y.U.

The next day another call came. Mr. West had offered to sell Mama the house next door for a five-hundred-dollar down payment and monthly payments of forty-five dollars.

"Archer would want me to use the allotment money he sent home from service for the down payment. I don't want to, but it seems the only way."

"Do that, Mama, and I'll send twenty-five dollars a month on the payments."

In committing the N.Y.U. money to house payments, there was one favorable prospect. Perhaps this meant that she was not to go to Graduate school but marry Nels. Maybe a background in literature wasn't necessary. Nels wrote well without it; his papers, letters, and his poetry had literary merit.

At least, it seemed to be time to begin writing home about Nels. When school was out and she was working full time in Admissions, she began writing regularly about him. By Christmas time, Mama was prepared. Katie invited Nels home for the holidays.

The house Mama had bought had six large rooms and

an acre of ground. The backyard was covered with branch willows, honeysuckle vines, and broomstraw. "The property goes to the walnut tree," Mama said. "When I get to it, I'll make this field into a lovely little park and there's room for a big garden."

"Mama, you don't need to undertake all that." At fifty-four, Mama would not slow down.

Jane and Scott arrived with the baby for the holidays. When Timothy took Nels Christmas shopping, Jane began to talk about her new plan. "Katie, I have this friend who told me about a room in the Atlanta Public Library filled with city directories. I'm going there and check every one of those directories for Daddy's name."

"Boy, that's really like looking for a needle in a haystack."

"It's worth a try," Mama said.

"I like your Nels Jensen," Jane said, and she was on the verge of asking Katie something when Mama stopped her.

"Katie is a very private person, Jane," Mama said and that was that.

Katie wondered about Mama's quick defense. Was she only concerned about Katie's privacy or was she trying to postpone the inevitable news that Katie was going to marry Nels? Katie had planned to talk to Mama about getting married in June after graduation, but she decided against it.

Back in New York it was snowing. Snow fell for most of the month of January. For once, Katie wished there was someone to go moling. She called Nels, but he couldn't get away because he was making up for time lost at Christmas.

On the way to chapel, Katie stopped by the mailbox. There was a letter from Jane. She slipped into one of the back seats of the auditorium and read the letter while people were filing in:

Dear Katie,
I went to the library and found a room filled with city

*directories. My friend and I spent several lunch hours
looking. I was ready to leave but decided to stay fifteen
more minutes. That's when I found a "Malcolm Mac-
Leod, Real Estate Broker," listed in the New Orleans
directory.*

*I called Mama and she told me to write a registered
letter on Scott's railroad stationery.*

*When Daddy signed for that letter, the receipt was
returned to me but before I received it, Daddy called me.*

*I am sorry to have to tell you this, but Daddy is
married and has three children. I don't know all the
details. He said something about a Mexican divorce.*

*He invited Brother and me—all of us children—to
visit him. Mama is urging us to go.*

Mama is going to be all right, Katie. Just pray.

> *Love,*
> *Jane*

Katie was reeling, her heart thumping. She couldn't
see the letter to read it again. *I could kill him! I could kill
him!*

People all around her stood up to sing. Someone
handed her an opened hymnbook; Katie struggled to
her feet. They were singing, "There's a Wideness In
God's Mercy," and the words pounded in her head as if
God wanted in.

They finished the hymn, prayed, and remained standing for another hymn—number 106. She did not turn
to it. The organist played the introduction and Katie
could not believe her ears! The congregation began
singing—"Will There Be Any Stars in My Crown?"
Katie's knees were weak and buckling under her; she
eased herself down in the seat. She sat through the
hymn, her chin trembling, and then she left.

She took the stairs to the dorm floor to avoid seeing
anyone. The fourth floor was deserted. Katie put on her
coat, slipped back downstairs, and stepped out onto the
street.

Traffic noises drowned out everything, insulating

her, closing her in to herself. Mechanically, she paused for the light, crossed the street, moved up Eighth Avenue. Snow swirled down from the leaden skies, clinging to her coat, wetting her face.

Crossing the circle and entering the park, Katie walked with head down, hands thrust deep inside her pockets. She was driven straight ahead, without aim or goal, one foot after the other, unseeing, unfeeling.

The winding path carried her away, around and up; over and down, all the way through the park.

On the other side, she walked onto the Avenue and followed the sidewalk to where it broadened and steps led up to the Museum. With the same dogged pace, her feet carried her up the steps and through the doors into the gallery. Moving from room to room, she was only vaguely aware of the vast hollowness amplifying every footfall, every sound.

Body and soul numb she came to a vacant room, its bench unoccupied. Katie stopped, sat down before a painting that dominated the room. Her eyes were resting on it long before she saw it, a woman and a boy—Hagar and blue-lipped Ishmael—forlorn, bewildered; the rejected wife and child. The bronze plaque boldly asked, "What aileth thee?"

Katie stared at the painting for some time and then her lips parted. "I know," she answered. "Oh, Hagar . . ." she whispered. "Did you ever forgive them?"

Katie stayed away from the Institute all day. When everyone was at supper, she slipped into the building and went to the deserted Admissions office. She sat at her desk in the darkness collecting her thoughts. "Lord, help me," she prayed, and lifted the receiver.

The switchboard operator placed the call. Katie held her breath as the phone rang once, twice . . . then Mama's voice.

"It's Katie, Mama." Her voice quavered.

"I'm all right, Katie," Mama said, her voice clear. "I'm all right now."

"Mama—" She couldn't talk.

"Please, Katie, you mustn't." But Katie couldn't say anything. "Jane called me after she talked with your father."

"Was anyone with you?"

"No, but I'm all right, Katie. I was on my way to church. I don't remember what Mr. Powell said but when I came home—when I walked into the house—I burst into tears. The dam broke, Katie. All the uncertainty, all the fears were swept away. All the vain hopes were stilled."

"Oh, Mama—"

"Release, Katie. After fifteen years, release."

After the call, Katie folded her arms on the desk and rested her head. "Thank you, Lord. Thank you."

In a few minutes, she called Nels.

"Nels, I must see you. I need to hear what we talked about on the beach."

He could not mistake the urgency in her voice. "Katie, what is it?"

"I need to know about forgiveness."

"Forgiveness?"

She could hardly get the words out. "We found my father."

Nels came as fast as he could. She met him in the lobby and handed him Jane's letter. People were everywhere. He took her by the arm. "Come on, we'll go up to the roof."

On the rooftop, he steered her to the shelter of the stairwell wall. He opened his overcoat and wrapped her close against the cold. She laid her head on his chest and looked beyond the roof to the Hudson. On the other side, the Jersey shore was strung with lights twinkling in the wintry night.

In bits and pieces, Katie told Nels all she could. When she was done, he told her simply, "Katie, you're not ready to deal with this. The time will come, and then you will know what is right." He kissed her hair and hugged her closer, rocking her in his arms.

The *Queen Mary* was moving out to sea, the tugboats

sounding their plaintive laments. The boats moved farther and farther away until Katie and Nels could no longer hear them. "Nels, you must go," she whispered. He pressed her closer to him.

When he could stay no longer, she made him go. Coming down in the elevator, Katie got off on the dorm floor, leaving him to descend alone.

It was very late. Katie tiptoed down the hall, slipped into the room silently, and undressed in the dark. Chris never stirred.

Katie could not sleep. She lay the whole night, thinking. Before dawn, the clanking of milk cans being rolled in the alley signaled that morning was on its way. Katie eased out of bed and slipped into her clothes. The chef should have the coffee made. She left the room quietly and went down the four flights of stairs. As she was turning to go down to the dining hall, someone at the desk called her. "Katie, Nels left a note for you."

She reached for it and went into the lobby to open the envelope.

"Katie, dear, I believe God gave me this for you," the note read. He had written a poem.

Scales removed,
   the light sears.
The Holiest of holies
   is truth.

Myths told over and over,
Believed:
Savored morsels
   nourishing the sinew of the will,
The dark side of Shekinah
   cloaking reality—
   admired as love in all its blindness.

Myths must die.
Close the lid on them.
Hush their voices echoing in the hollows
   of your mind;

Lower them gently into the grave
  as lies of love.

Light's pain is not relieved
  through glasses smoked by would-be truth;
Stare light in the face.
It will never die,
Never go away,
But neither will it blind.

CHRISTIAN HERALD ASSOCIATION AND ITS MINISTRIES

CHRISTIAN HERALD ASSOCIATION, founded in 1878, publishes The Christian Herald Magazine, one of the leading interdenominational religious monthlies in America. Through its wide circulation, it brings inspiring articles and the latest news of religious developments to many families. From the magazine's pages came the initiative for CHRISTIAN HERALD CHILDREN'S HOME and THE BOWERY MISSION, two individually supported not-for-profit corporations.

CHRISTIAN HERALD CHILDREN'S HOME, established in 1894, is the name for a unique and dynamic ministry to disadvantaged children, offering hope and opportunities which would not otherwise be available for reasons of poverty and neglect. The goal is to develop each child's potential and to demonstrate Christian compassion and understanding to children in need.

Mont Lawn is a permanent camp located in Bushkill, Pennsylvania. It is the focal point of a ministry which provides a healthful "vacation with a purpose" to children who without it would be confined to the streets of the city. Up to 1000 children between the ages of 7 and 11 come to Mont Lawn each year.

Christian Herald Children's Home maintains year-round contact with children by means of an *In-City Youth Ministry*. Central to its philosophy is the belief that only through sustained relationships and demonstrated concern can individual lives be truly enriched. Special emphasis is on individual guidance, spiritual and family counseling and tutoring. This follow-up ministry to inner-city children culminates for many in financial assistance toward higher education and career counseling.

THE BOWERY MISSION, located at 227 Bowery, New York City, has since 1879 been reaching out to the lost men on the Bowery, offering them what could be their last chance to rebuild their lives. Every man is fed, clothed and ministered to. Countless numbers have entered the 90-day residential rehabilitation program at the Bowery Mission. A concentrated ministry of counseling, medical care, nutrition therapy, Bible study and Gospel services awakens a man to spiritual renewal within himself.

These ministries are supported solely by the voluntary contributions of individuals and by legacies and bequests. Contributions are tax deductible. Checks should be made out either to CHRISTIAN HERALD CHILDREN'S HOME or to THE BOWERY MISSION.

Administrative Office: 40 Overlook Drive, Chappaqua, New York 10514
Telephone: (914) 769-9000